W9-CRV-208
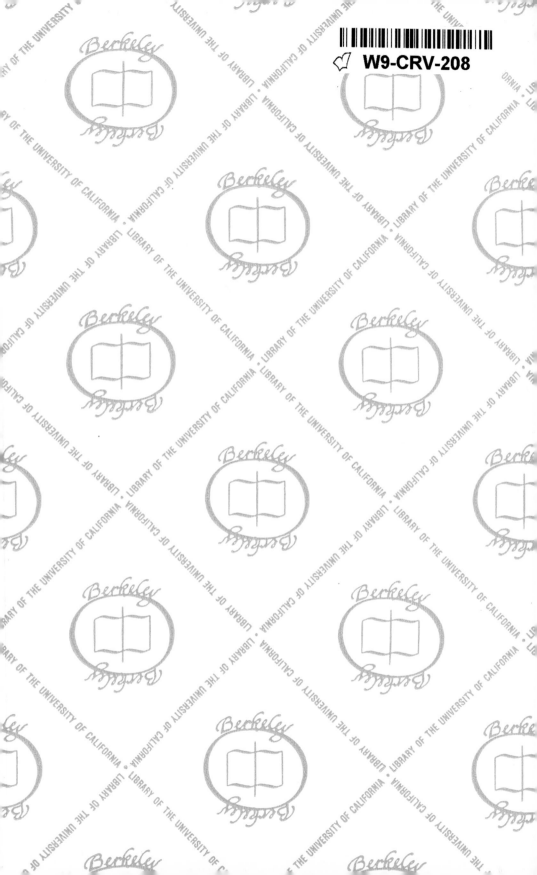

CHEMISORPTION:
AN EXPERIMENTAL APPROACH

Chemisorption:
An Experimental Approach

GERD WEDLER

Universität Erlangen-Nürnberg

Translated by

DEREK F. KLEMPERER

University of Bristol

BUTTERWORTHS

LONDON – BOSTON

Sydney – Wellington – Durban – Toronto

THE BUTTERWORTH GROUP

ENGLAND
Butterworth & Co (Publishers) Ltd
London: 88 Kingsway, WC2B 6AB

6308-319X ✓

CHEMISTRY

AUSTRALIA
Butterworths Pty Ltd
Sydney: 586 Pacific Highway, NSW 2067
Also at Melbourne, Brisbane, Adelaide and Perth

CANADA
Butterworth & Co (Canada) Ltd
Toronto: 2265 Midland Avenue, Scarborough, Ontario M1P 4S1

NEW ZEALAND
Butterworths of New Zealand Ltd
Wellington: 26-28 Waring Taylor Street, 1

SOUTH AFRICA
Butterworth & Co (South Africa) (Pty) Ltd
Durban: 152-154 Gale Street

USA
Butterworths (Publishers) Inc
Boston: 19 Cummings Park, Woburn, Mass. 01801

LIBRARY OF CONGRESS CATALOGING IN PUBLICATION DATA

Wedler, Gerd, 1929-
   Chemisorption: an experimental approach.

   Translation of Adsorption.
   Bibliography: p.
   Includes indexes.
   1. Adsorption.   2. Chemisorption.   I. Title.
QD547.W3813   541'.3453   76-9822
ISBN 0-408-10611-5

This revised English language edition first published 1976 and © 1976
Butterworth & Co (Publishers) Ltd

Original German language edition first published under the title *Adsorption* 1970
and ©   1970

Verlag Chemie GmbH, Weinheim/Bergstr.

All rights reserved. No part of this publication may be reproduced or transmitted in any form or by any means, including photocopying and recording, without the written permission of the copyright holder, application for which should be addressed to the publisher. Such written permission must also be obtained before any part of this publication is stored in a retrieval system of any nature.

This book is sold subject to the Standard Conditions of Sale of Net Books and may not be re-sold in the UK below the net price given by the Publishers in their current price list.

ISBN 0 408 10611 5

Printed in Great Britain by Chapel River Press, Andover, Hants.

QD547
W3813
CHEM

PREFACE

The field of adsorption has continued to develop vigorously since the appearance of the German edition in 1970 under the title 'Adsorption, Eine Einführung in die Physisorption und Chemisorption'. A complete revision of the book has therefore been required. A number of new chapters have been added, others have been made shorter or dropped. The chapter on the study of adsorption using low energy electrons, for instance, was substantially enlarged and new chapters were written on the use of energetic photons and the use of ion beams. Those sections on the thermodynamics of adsorption and the theory of adsorption were curtailed because they no longer gave a balanced picture of the current state of the subject within the context of this book. As a result, the book is now oriented even more towards presenting the experimental possibilities for studying adsorption than was the German edition; this is reflected in the new title 'Chemisorption: An Experimental Approach'.

I have adopted the policy of discussing major problems as they occur in relation to a number of selected adsorption systems. This approach enables one to illustrate how an insight may be obtained into the state of the bonding in an adsorption complex via the investigation of individual adsorption phenomena. On the other hand, the use of examples clarifies the way in which the physico-chemical properties of solid surfaces are influenced by the adsorption of foreign molecules. The pertinent literature has been covered until about the autumn of 1974.

I am much indebted to Dr D.F. Klemperer who not only undertook the task of translation, but also contributed to the present version by making many valuable comments and suggestions.

Erlangen   G. Wedler

636

CONTENTS

1

INTRODUCTION

Atoms or groups of atoms which lie in the surface of a phase differ fundamentally from those within the bulk of the phase. They cannot interact symmetrically with neighbouring atoms and their effect is unbalanced. For this reason they frequently exhibit unsaturated valencies which are capable of forming a bond with foreign atoms or molecules on the surface. This process, which is called adsorption, is of considerable interest for both fundamental and applied research.

Investigations into adsorption should provide information concerning the amount of a substance which can be adsorbed on a surface, the influence of pressure and temperature on this amount, and the strength of the adsorption bond. Investigation should also reveal the changes which the adsorbing surface and the adsorbed particles undergo as a result of adsorption, and a description should be given of the condition of the orbitals which take part in the adsorption bond. In this way one gains an insight into the specific properties of the surface, as influenced by its structure. At the same time various interactions come to be characterised between the individual adsorbed particles and between the two partners linked by an adsorption bond.

Adsorption influences all those phenomena which depend on the properties of surfaces. They include, for example, electron emission or electrical resistance at contacts. Adsorption constitutes the primary step in corrosion processes and it is a prerequisite for every catalytic reaction involving solid catalysts.

The high degree of technical relevance which adsorption enjoys has been particularly effective in providing a driving force for the intensive experimental and — latterly — theoretical work which has been undertaken.

In order to avoid any misunderstandings regarding the nomenclature adopted, we shall proceed at once to a description of some concepts. By adsorption is meant the pure surface effect; this means that we shall only consider those cases in which molecules or atoms of a gas become bound to the surface of a solid. If an additional uptake of gas occurs in the bulk of the solid, i.e. there is a volume effect, then one speaks of occlusion or absorption when the volume effect predominates. The term 'sorption' is employed where one cannot or does not wish to commit oneself to the relative proportions of surface and volume effects.

1

When a gas (the free adsorbate) is introduced to a solid (the adsorbent), an adsorbed phase consisting of bonded adsorbate and adsorbent molecules may form:

$$\text{adsorbent + free adsorbate} \rightarrow \text{adsorbed phase} \qquad (1.1)$$

The terms 'chemisorption' and 'physisorption' (or 'physical adsorption') have not, in the past, been clearly defined. The heat of adsorption which is associated with the adsorption process has frequently been used as a criterion with which these two types of adsorption may be distinguished. Thus, if the heat of adsorption exceeded 10 kcal mol^{-1}, then the process was deemed to be chemisorption; but if the heat fell short of 10 kcal mol^{-1}, then physisorption was occurring. This classification, however, is not without uncertainty.

A more definite way of distinguishing chemisorption and physisorption can be arrived at in the following way. Even at room temperature the interaction of very active gases and adsorbents leads to the formation of chemical compounds on the surface. The heat of adsorption is then made up entirely of the heat of formation and the sorption process is identical with a chemical reaction. An example is furnished by the action of oxygen on various metals.

On the other hand, the sorption of completely inactive gases leads to a very weak union between the adsorbed atoms or molecules and the adsorbing surface. The heats of sorption are of the same order of magnitude as enthalpies of condensation and the 'bonding' occurs solely as a result of dispersion forces. This process is called physisorption. The action of rare gases on most adsorbents serves to provide an example.

Formation of a chemical compound and physisorption represent the two limiting cases of interaction between a gas and an adsorbing surface.

In the majority of cases of sorption effects one measures heats of sorption which lie between the heat of condensation and the heat of formation of the corresponding chemical compound. A rise in temperature serves to break up these complexes with a varying degree of ease and the sorbed gases are re-evolved as such so long as they neither decompose at the higher temperatures nor react with other sorbed gases. In contrast to the case of a chemical compound, the bound adsorbate may, under certain circumstances, possess appreciable mobility on the adsorbing surface. Since this type of sorption exhibits properties which lie between those of physisorption and chemical compounds, one refers to it as chemisorption. Nevertheless it will be evident from the foregoing that the transition from physisorption to chemisorption is a continuous one.

The aim of this book will be to give a review of the experimental methods and the information which can be deduced from experimental results. For the sake of clarity we shall collect together related methods in the same chapter. We shall also, as far as possible, concentrate on the systems nickel/hydrogen and nickel/carbon monoxide, because these systems are of outstanding technical interest. It will be shown that certain conclusions can be drawn from the experimental results regarding the interaction between the adsorbent and the adsorbate, and a description will be given of how the adsorption process affects the properties of the solid surface. In addition to the two systems mentioned, extensive material will be included from other systems so that at the end of the book the various adsorption systems can be presented again in classified form.

GENERAL FUNDAMENTALS

2.1. Thermodynamics of adsorption

The thermodynamic description of an adsorption system requires a knowledge of certain 'reaction parameters', namely the enthalpy of adsorption and the entropy of adsorption. If it is possible to calculate these quantities for a specific model of adsorption using statistical thermodynamics, then the calculated values may be compared with the values obtained experimentally. Such a comparison enables conclusions to be drawn about the state of the adsorbate.

Space does not permit a detailed account of the thermodynamics of adsorption, for which there is a very extensive literature (see, for instance, references 332, 584, 737). The more recent developments are due particularly to the work of Everett [204-208] and Hill [328-332]. Here we shall only give a few relationships, keeping to those which are important for the discussion of experimental data. The basic adsorption system to which the relationships apply consists of a single one-component gas phase for the free adsorbate and a single one-component solid phase for the adsorbent.

In handling the problem one can proceed as in the treatment of liquid solutions and arrive at an equation which is the equivalent of the Clausius-Clapeyron equation:

$$\left(\frac{\partial \ln p}{\partial T}\right)_{\theta} = \frac{s_G - \bar{s}_S}{RT} = \frac{h_G - \bar{h}_S}{RT^2} = \frac{q_{st}}{RT^2} \tag{2.1}$$

In this equation p is the equilibrium pressure at a coverage θ; s_G and h_G are, respectively, the molar entropy and the molar heat of the free adsorbate; $\bar{s}_S$ and $\bar{h}_S$ are, respectively, the partial molar entropy and the partial molar enthalpy of the bound absorbate; and q_{st} is the so-called isosteric heat of adsorption. The term 'isoteric heat' is used because relationship (2.1) involves the temperature dependence of the equilibrium pressure at constant coverage. As will be shown in Section 3.2, it is possible to determine q_{st} calorimetrically as well. This means that the partial molar entropy of the bound adsorbate can also be obtained via equation (2.1) by direct experiment.

Statistical thermodynamics makes it possible to calculate the molar entropy of the bound adsorbate for a specific model. It is not possible, however, to calculate the partial molar entropy of the bound adsorbate, and for this reason little can be said about the state of the bound adsorbate by just considering values of the isosteric heat of adsorption. To get at the state of the bound adsorbate one has to ascertain the temperature dependence of the equilibrium pressure at constant surface pressure Φ; this gives us the so-called equilibrium heat of adsorption ΔH and equation (2.1) transforms into equation (2.2),

$$\left(\frac{\partial \ln p}{\partial T}\right)_{\Phi} = \frac{s_G - s_S}{RT} = \frac{h_G - h_S}{RT^2} = \frac{\Delta H}{RT^2} \qquad (2.2)$$

because the molar quantities s_S and h_S turn up in place of the partial molar quantities. The surface pressure cannot, of course, be measured directly. It is evaluated from equilibrium pressures measured at uptakes n according to the relationship

$$\Phi = RT \int_0^p n \, d \ln p \qquad (T = \text{const.}) \qquad (2.3)$$

Here n is expressed as the number of moles of bound adsorbate divided by the surface area.

The molar heat capacity is another quantity which serves to characterise the thermodynamic properties of the bound adsorbate. As in the case of a chemical reaction, Kirchhoff's equation holds, so that

$$\frac{\partial q_{\text{integr.}}}{\partial T} = c_S - c_G \qquad (2.4)$$

Since the molar heat capacity of the free adsorbate in its gaseous state c_G is generally known, it is possible to calculate the molar heat capacity of the bound adsorbate c_S from the temperature dependence of the integral heat of adsorption q_{integr}. For a detailed consideration of these relationships we refer to the literature [225,737]. The thermodynamic quantities of an adsorption system will also be examined more closely in Chapter 3.

In three dimensions the thermal equation of state can be described quite generally in terms of isotherms, isobars and isochores. The same situation obtains in the case of an adsorption equilibrium

$$n_S = f(p,T) \qquad (2.5)$$

which is also described by

adsorption isotherms: $\quad n_S = f(p) \qquad (T = \text{const.}) \qquad (2.6)$

adsorption isobars: $\quad n_S = f(T) \qquad (p = \text{const.}) \qquad (2.7)$

and

adsorption isosteres: $\quad p = f(T) \qquad (n_S = \text{const.}) \qquad (2.8)$

Of these, adsorption isotherms have special significance. This is because theoretical isotherms may be set up on the basis of certain models and then, if the isotherms check with experiment, it is possible to draw inferences regarding the state of the adsorption.

2.2.   Energetics of adsorption

The thermodynamic treatment of adsorption only enables one to obtain the magnitude of the bond strength in adsorption; one cannot also discover the nature of the forces involved in bonding. In the following we shall therefore develop a few plausible models for the interaction which occurs between a bound adsorbate atom or molecule and a solid surface or the adsorbent.

It will only be possible to present a rough outline here. For a detailed description reference is made to the specialised literature [72, 318,478,662,737].

A number of quite different types of force are responsible for the bonding which keeps the adsorbate and the adsorbent together. In principle, the forces are the same as those which operate between two atoms or molecules. But in the case of adsorption the theoretical treatment is made more difficult by the one partner being an atom which is incorporated in a solid. This partner, viz. the adsorbent, can equally well be a grouping of atoms belonging to the solid.

The following forces may be identified:

(1) Dispersion forces, which arise from fluctuations in the electron density clouds of two atoms. The time average of the charge distribution in these atoms may be symmetrical, yet the charge fluctuations are sufficient to induce resonance and cause an attraction. The resultant force has a relatively long range.
(2) The overlap or repulsive forces. They appear when the two partners approach very near to each other and their electron orbitals or eigenfunctions overlap.

If the free adsorbate and the adsorbent are composed of non-polar molecules, then the dispersion and repulsive forces are the only ones which must be taken into account in treating the interaction which takes place. If the molecules are polar, then other forces will be effective:

(3) Dipole interactions. These forces occur in addition to the above forces whenever a polar adsorbate is adsorbed on a non-polar or a polar adsorbent (ionic crystal), or whenever a non-polar adsorbate is adsorbed on a polar adsorbent. In the latter instance the action of the polar partner is also to induce an electric moment in the non-polar molecule.
(4) Valency forces, which are like the repulsive forces in that they occur at sufficiently close distances. They are due to the electron orbitals overlapping in a suitable way and they are responsible for chemisorption.
(5) Interaction forces between the atoms or molecules of the bound adsorbate themselves. These forces must be considered in both physisorption and chemisorption when the coverage of adsorbate

on the adsorbent reaches the stage at which the distance separating adsorbate molecules is small.

We shall consider physisorption first. Here one has to discuss chiefly the superposition of an attractive force and a repulsive force. Usually the Lennard-Jones expression for the interaction between two gas molecules can be applied:

$$E = -ar^{-m} + br^{-n} \tag{2.9}$$

In this expression E denotes the potential energy and r is the distance between the particles. The first term is the attractive energy and the second the repulsive energy. m is taken as 6 and n is 12.

It is already a matter of some difficulty to calculate the constants for the interaction between two gas molecules. To undertake a theoretical calculation for the problem of adsorption is hardly possible because it involves the superposition of several potential equations. This is because the adsorbate molecule usually interacts with many adsorbent atoms. The general form of the potential energy is, nevertheless, preserved.

Figure 2.1 shows the potential energy curve for the physisorption of a molecule S_2 on the surface of a solid A. The energy zero has been chosen for the situation in which the adsorbate is infinitely far away.

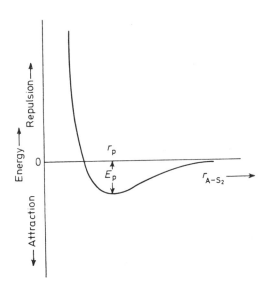

Figure 2.1   Potential energy for the physisorption of a molecule S_2 on the surface of a solid A: r_{A-S_2} = distance between S_2 and A; r_p = equilibrium separation; E_p = potential energy in the equilibrium condition

One recognises from the diagram that the depth of the minimum (E_p) with respect to $E_{r=\infty}$ must be the heat of adsorption. The calculation of such potential energy curves has occasionally been achieved. An example is afforded by the physisorption of non-polar substances on graphite [369].

A calculation for the case of chemisorption is far harder. The potential energy curves described in the literature have usually been determined in a semi-empirical manner.   Just as in physisorption, the equilibrium condition in chemisorption must be given by numerical equality of the attractive and the repulsive forces, and by a minimum in the potential energy.   In principle, therefore, the potential energy for chemisorption is given by a curve which is similar to that shown in *Figure 2.1*.

One frequently observes that a molecule decomposes on being chemisorbed on the surface of an adsorbent.   Hydrogen or oxygen, for instance, usually exists as atoms in the chemisorbed state.   In such a case, the chemisorbed phase can equally well be produced in either of two ways: molecules of the free adsorbate may be allowed to react

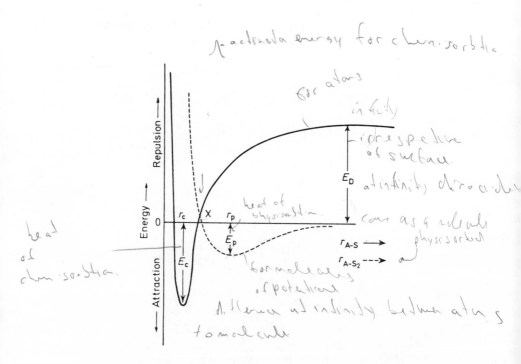

Figure 2.2   Potential energy for the physisorption and dissociative chemisorption of an adsorbate S_2 on an adsorbent A: E_p = heat of physisorption; E_c = heat of chemisorption; E_D = dissociation energy

directly with the adsorbent, in which case they transform via the physisorbed state into the chemisorbed state; alternatively the free adsorbate can first be dissociated (energy E_D) and then allowed to react as atoms with the adsorbent. Both of these routes are shown in *Figure 2.2*. The continuous potential energy curve has its minimum at r_c at a depth E_c. When the adsorbate atom S is infinitely far from the adsorbent, the curve lies above zero by an amount equal to the dissociation energy E_D. The dashed curve corresponds to the physisorption of S_2 molecules on A.

The two potential energy curves cross at X. The position of X with respect to the zero energy line is decisive in determining the rate of transfer of molecules S_2 into the chemisorbed state $A<{S \atop S}$. The height of X represents the magnitude of the activation energy for chemisorption. To desorb physisorbed molecules, one only has to supply the heat of physisorption, but desorption of chemisorbed atoms in the form of molecules S_2 is only possible if an activation energy is supplied which exceeds the heat of chemisorption E_c by an amount X.

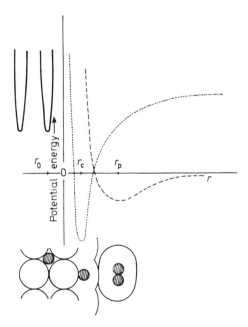

Figure 2.3 Potential energy of a chemisorption system in which occlusion of S atoms is possible. The surface of the adsorbent lies at $r = 0$. The lower part of the diagram indicates the location of the adsorbate [72]

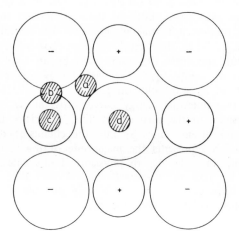

Figure 2.4 Energetically distinguishable sites for a bound adsorbate on a heterogeneous surface, e.g. on an ionic crystal

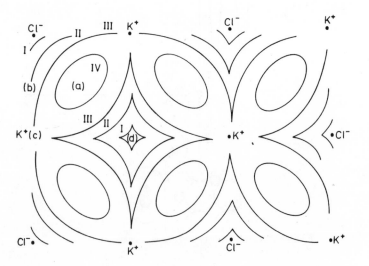

Figure 2.5 Physisorption of Ar on a KCl surface. The equipotential energy contours correspond to adsorption energies of I, 1.235 kcal mol⁻¹; II, 1.320 kcal mol⁻¹; III, 1.410 kcal mol⁻¹; IV, 1.495 kcal mol⁻¹ [278,525]

The potential energy diagram may be extended to allow for the possibility of chemisorbed molecules passing into an occluded condition, i.e. they can penetrate the adsorbent lattice. This is done in *Figure 2.3*, where the potential energy curves for occluded S-atoms have been added. As the figure shows, a large activation energy must generally be supplied to transfer molecules into the occluded state.

Our considerations so far have been based on the assumption that the surface of the adsorbent is entirely homogeneous. In actual fact, however, every surface is energetically heterogeneous, at least on an atomic scale. This becomes particularly evident if one looks at the surface of an ionic crystal, as depicted in *Figure 2.4*. Clearly there is a different environment in each of the four positions denoted by the letters a, b, c and d. These positions represent possible sites for bound adsorbate atoms on the surface of the adsorbent.

Orr [525] has calculated the adsorption energy for the physisorption of argon on KCl. The result is shown in *Figure 2.5* with the aid of equipotential energy contours (for the respective equilibrium distances r from the surface).

Energetically distinguishable adsorption sites must exist on every adsorbent; one only has to think of the variously indexed faces of a crystal to see that neighbourhood situations can differ widely from one part to another, even where the surface is constructed entirely from one type of atom. It is for this reason that an adsorbate can, in general, be adsorbed on an adsorbent in a number of different states. In such cases, one or more additional potential energy curves (E_{C2}, r_{C2}; E_{C3}, r_{C3}; ...) would be needed to supplement *Figure 2.2*. Corresponding to the point X there would be points Y, Z ... whose position determines the transition from one state of adsorption to another.

In the potential energy diagrams discussed so far, we have not allowed for the mutual interaction which occurs between bound adsorbate molecules, particularly at higher coverages. This effect alters the equilibrium distance r_C from the surface slightly as well as the depth of the potential energy well E_C to a much greater extent. One may take it that the heat of adsorption E_C invariably becomes smaller as the coverage θ rises. This is shown in *Figure 2.6*, which also reveals that the position of the cross-over point X for chemisorption has altered as a result of mutual interaction (compare *Figure 2.2*). The magnitude of the activation energy for chemisorption is altered accordingly.

2.3. Kinetics of adsorption and desorption

Investigation of the kinetics of an adsorption or a desorption process frequently enables interesting information to be obtained about the state of the bonding in the adsorbed phase.

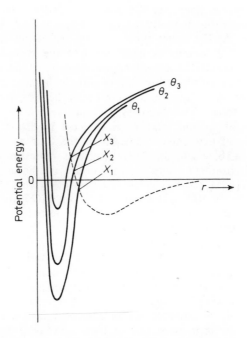

Figure 2.6   Influence of the coverage θ on the potential energy curves.
$\theta_3 > \theta_2 > \theta_1$.

For this reason very many investigations have been conducted on adsorption kinetics. In the following pages we can only offer some general reflections, keeping to those which will provide the basis for discussion of experimental data. For an exhaustive study of adsorption kinetics reference is made to the specialised literature [318].

According to the kinetic theory of gases, the number of molecules of mass m colliding on 1 cm^2 of a surface per second at a gas pressure p is given by

$$\frac{dN}{dt} = \frac{p}{(2\pi mkT)^{1/2}} \tag{2.10}$$

Let the probability that an impacting molecule is adsorbed be s. This so-called sticking probability will clearly influence the rate of adsorption r_a according to

$$r_a = s\frac{p}{(2\pi mkT)^{1/2}} \tag{2.11}$$

The sticking probability is influenced by a number of factors:

(1) If the adsorption is an activated process, then only those molecules which possess the requisite activation energy can be adsorbed.
(2) Even when the activation energy is available, steric considerations or the special configuration of an activated complex can still hinder adsorption.
(3) The arriving molecule possesses kinetic energy and, in addition, the heat of adsorption is liberated on adsorption. For this reason adsorption will only be effected if the energy can be dissipated sufficiently quickly; otherwise the molecule will immediately be desorbed again.
(4) Where adsorption occurs on a heterogeneous surface, s will have different values on the various adsorption sites.
(5) The arriving molecule has to chance upon a suitable adsorption site. This is particularly true of chemisorption, where the molecule can only be taken up at those sites which are not already occupied by adsorbed molecules. In the case of physisorption, however, a multimolecular layer is possible.

In general, therefore, it is going to be difficult to calculate the sticking probability directly and then obtain the rate of adsorption from it. For an activated adsorption we may say from the foregoing that s is given by

$$s = \kappa(\theta)\, f(\theta)\, \exp[-\Delta E(\theta)/RT] \qquad (2.12)$$

In this expression $\Delta E(\theta)$ is the activation energy and $f(\theta)$ takes into account the necessary available surface. $\kappa(\theta)$ may be regarded as a condensation coefficient. All these quantities depend on the coverage θ. The rate of adsorption is then

$$r_a = \frac{p}{(2\pi m k T)^{1/2}}\, \kappa(\theta)\, f(\theta)\, \exp[-\Delta E(\theta)/RT] \qquad (2.13)$$

$f(\theta)$ is the simplest term to discuss. If the adsorbate molecule is only adsorbed at one point, then the unoccupied part of the surface is $(1 - \theta)$ and the probability of the molecule striking an unoccupied site becomes

$$f(\theta) = 1 - \theta \qquad (2.14)$$

On the other hand, if dissociative adsorption takes place on two sites, then one has to distinguish whether the adsorbed layer is immobile or mobile, i.e. whether the adsorbate can wander over the surface of the adsorbent or not.
For mobile adsorption

$$f(\theta) = (1 - \theta)^2 \qquad (2.15)$$

For immobile adsorption the number of nearest neighbours z plays a role [475] because unoccupied sites must have an unoccupied neighbour for dissociative adsorption to occur:

$$f(\theta) \;=\; \frac{z}{z-\theta}\,(1-\theta)^2 \tag{2.16}$$

The way in which the activation energy depends on the coverage θ can vary a great deal. On homogeneous surfaces one may often assume a linear dependence of the activation energy on the coverage:

$$\Delta E \;=\; \Delta E_0 + a\theta \tag{2.17}$$

For surfaces which are energetically heterogeneous one has to integrate over the distribution of activation energies.

It is very difficult to calculate the condensation coefficient κ theoretically. The transition state theory has been used in an attempt to interpret κ. According to the theory, the free adsorbate molecule would have to pass through an activated complex (AS)$^{\#}$ before it could become the bound adsorbate molecule. This involves passing over the potential energy hump of height ΔE, as shown in *Figure 2.7*.

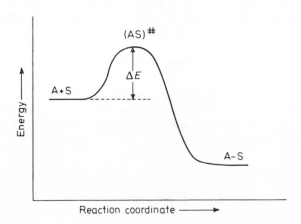

Figure 2.7 Passage of the system adsorbent A + free adsorbate S to the bound adsorbate A−S. (AS)$^{\#}$ characterises the transition state

The molecules of activated complex are in statistical equilibrium with both the reactants and the products. The reactants are the molecules S in the gas phase and the unoccupied adsorption sites A, while the product is the bound adsorbate. For the first equilibrium

$$A + S \rightleftharpoons (AS)^{\#} \qquad (2.18)$$

the rate of adsorption is given by

$$r_a = k^{\#} c_A c_S \qquad (2.19)$$

that is, by the rate of formation of the activated complex, assuming that an immobile adsorbed layer is formed. $k^{\#}$ stands for the velocity constant of the reaction which forms the activated complex. This constant is given by the transition state theory as (see, for instance, ref. 243)

$$k^{\#} = \frac{kT}{h} \frac{Z_{(AS)^{\#}}}{Z_A Z_S} \exp(-\Delta E / RT) \qquad (2.20)$$

In this expression k is the Boltzmann constant, h is Planck's constant, Z is the partition coefficient of a reacting molecule referred to its ground state as zero and ΔE is the activation energy (see *Figure 2.7*). The rate of adsorption accordingly becomes

$$r_a = c_A c_S \frac{kT}{h} \frac{Z_{(AS)^{\#}}}{Z_A Z_S} \exp(-\Delta E / RT) \qquad (2.21)$$

To ascertain the condensation coefficient, equation (2.13) is compared with equation (2.21). In doing this we note that the partition function for the transition complex is made up of the specific properties of the complex, namely vibration and rotation. Translation is not included because in setting up equation (2.19) the adsorbed layer was assumed to be immobile.

The general observations which have been made should suffice to indicate that the properties of the bound adsorbate are reflected in the kinetics of adsorption in innumerable ways. This becomes the clearer if the considerations are followed through in a detailed manner (see reference 318).

Considering the large number of factors which influence the sticking probability, it is not surprising that the experimentally determined values are subject to wide variations [313,314]. Kinetic measurements drawn from a wide range of methods have been applied to the determination of sticking probabilities, but one can only attach significance to those data which were obtained under extremely well-defined working conditions [299,302].

There is yet another significant limitation which must be pointed out, regarding the value of investigations of adsorption kinetics.

It is only the requirement of a finite activation energy which enables measurements to be made at all using conventional apparatus. This activation requirement is embodied in the exponential term in equations (2.12) and (2.13). Should adsorption occur without an appreciable activation energy – that is, the cross-over point X of the potential energy curves in *Figure 2.2* lies below the zero energy line – then practically instantaneous adsorption is observed. Transport processes in the gas phase are then responsible for any delays in uptake. There is as yet no complete theory for the treatment of non-activated adsorption.

These last-mentioned difficulties do not crop up in the study of desorption kinetics because an activation energy must always be associated with desorption (see *Figures 2.1-2.3*). The activation energy for desorption is either equal to the heat of adsorption E_c or E_p, or – where the adsorption was an activated process – equal to the sum of the heat of adsorption E_c and the activation energy ΔE.

The treatment of desorption kinetics corresponds in principle to the treatment which led us to equation (2.13) for the case of adsorption kinetics. The dissociated adsorbate is produced by desorption so that the rate of desorption will be proportional to the concentration of bound adsorbate. This, in turn, is proportional to the coverage θ or, in more general terms, to a function $f'(\theta)$. Furthermore, only those adsorbed complexes which possess the requisite activation energy can dissociate. As a result we write for the rate of desorption r_d

$$r_d = \delta(\theta) f'(\theta) \exp[-\Delta E(\theta)/RT] \tag{2.22}$$

All the indeterminate, special properties of the system under study are collected together in the desorption coefficient $\delta(\theta)$. As for the condensation coefficient, an explanation may be given for $\delta(\theta)$ which relies largely on the transition state theory.

Desorption spectra will be studied in Section 3.4, where it will be established that very special significance is to be attached to the term containing the activation energy. The expression $f'(\theta)$ is basically determined by whether or not desorption and recombination occur together; they do, for instance, when hydrogen atoms desorb as molecules.

2.4.   Theory of adsorption

The theory of chemisorption has only attracted considerable attention in the last few years. Originally, hypothetical models were developed and approximate techniques were applied, but nowadays exact, quantum mechanical treatments have taken over the forefront.

Levine and Gyftopoulos [417] investigated the chemisorption of metal atoms on metals using a quantum mechanical approximation. Moesta [478] has taken up their method in more detail and gives a comparison of experimental and calculated values for the bonding energy of alkali metal atoms on tungsten. Newer data are given in the more extensive works of Gadzuk, Hartman and Rhodin [244] and Wojciechowski [724].

Building upon the considerations of Goodenough [275], Dowden [156] developed a method which demonstrates clearly that face specificity is a property of adsorption and that differently adsorbed species are capable of co-existing side by side on the surface. The method, which actually does not permit bonding energies to be calculated, is based on molecular orbital theory and takes crystal field theory into account. In this connection, Bond's work [73,74] on adsorption has become particularly well known. Drawing on Dowden's method, he treated the adsorption of hydrogen, carbon monoxide and olefins on nickel. Andreev and co-workers [16,609] attempted to use the same model for making quantitative deductions. Further extensions on these lines have also been given by Weinberg and Merrill [710,711].

Work described in a series of papers has sought to simplify the quantum mechanical investigation of chemisorption on metals. The technique adopted consists of replacing the solid by a 'small metallic cluster' composed of only a small number of atoms. Such a procedure was used by, for example, both Blyholder and co-workers [67,68] and Dunken and co-workers [157,158,160,161,391,500,501].

A far-reaching theoretical treatment has been carried out by Grimley and co-workers [280,282-284,663], by Newns [514] and by Schrieffer and Gomer [596]. We should still single out for mention the articles by Grimley [279,281] and by Wojciechowski [723].

The work which has been cited above only represents a tiny selection taken from the body of the literature on the theory of chemisorption on metals. It would greatly exceed the scope of this book, however, if we were to go into the theoretical work any further.

2.5. Basic experimental matters

The aim in all investigations of adsorption is to obtain information about the interaction between an adsorbed gas and a well-defined adsorbent. Now, under normal circumstances, all surfaces are bound to be covered to a greater or lesser extent by a thick layer of adsorbed material. This layer exists as a direct result of the adsorptive capacity of surfaces, and, in the first instance, its nature is entirely unknown. Adsorption experiments therefore need clean, unadsorbed surfaces. Such a surface can only be prepared and maintained under extreme vacuum conditions. The high degree of vacuum which is necessary may readily be extracted from dN/dt, the number of gas molecules which strike 1 cm^2 of surface per second at room temperature. It follows from equation (2.10) that if the residual gas pressure is 10^{-6} Torr of oxygen, for instance, then 10^{15} molecules strike 1 cm^2 of surface per second. And since oxygen is generally adsorbed on metals with a sticking probability of unity, this means that a monomolecular layer of gas is adsorbed in 1 second. This emphasises that one has to work under extreme vacuum conditions and it is now commonplace to use ultrahigh vacuum systems which are capable of achieving pressures below 10^{-10} Torr.

An extensive literature exists on vacuum technique. The subject is concerned as much with the technique of achieving vacuum [57,148,197, 481,570] as with the technique of building vacuum systems [148,197-199,481]. Glass or metal apparatus is used; both can be heated to temperatures of 300-400 °C so as to free the walls of adsorbed gases. Glass apparatus has the advantage that it can be entirely blown together, thus obviating the need for any joints.

Various types of pumps are used to produce the vacuum. They include rotary mechanical pumps, diffusion pumps (with oil or mercury as the work fluid) and getter pumps, in which the high adsorptive capacity of suitable sorbents is exploited. In addition, it is usual to arrange for residual gases to be ionised by electron impact (ion getter pumping).

The pressure range which one wishes to cover determines the choice of instrument for measuring the pressure. The most commonly used instruments are the McLeod gauge (to 10^{-5} Torr), the Pirani gauge (to 10^{-6} Torr) and the ionisation gauge, which goes down to 10^{-11} Torr. Nowadays it is more and more usual to measure partial pressures [197] rather than the total pressure. The quadrupole mass spectrometer [543], the omegatron [252,623] and the time-of-flight mass spectrometer [48] are particularly well suited to this type of measurement in the pressure range between 10^{-6} and 10^{-12} Torr.

The extremely clean surfaces which are needed for investigations may be generated in a number of ways. The surface may either be prepared in ultrahigh vacuum by evaporation onto a substrate or by cleaving the solid. Alternatively, the surface of a solid can be cleaned using physical or chemical methods. Of these four methods, the first three are preferable.

The only forms of adsorbent which come in question are evaporated films, single crystals and powders. Of these, powders are only used in exceptional circumstances at the present time. Whether one uses films or single crystals depends on the problem to be tackled. For both types of adsorbent there are advantages and disadvantages which are capable of tipping the balance.

Adsorbents may be prepared in vacuum by heating the adsorbent material until it evaporates. This enables the highly purified form, which is needed, to be condensed on a suitable substrate [57,336]. Either ohmic or electron bombardment heating can be applied, and the adsorbent is generally obtained as a thin film.

The chief advantage of this procedure lies in the fact that not only the surface but also the bulk of the adsorbent is produced in a largely gas-free condition. This means that contamination of the surface cannot occur subsequently by diffusion of incorporated gases from the bulk to the surface.

The disadvantages of evaporation derive from the high degree of imperfection which is present in the crystal structure of films as compared with the normal bulk material. This can lead to atypical results using films [145]. The crystal imperfections can, however, be removed by annealing the film at elevated temperature and the properties of the film are then similar to those of the bulk material. It is often difficult to determine the film structure, especially if very thin films (*ca.* 100 Å) are being used. Furthermore, these films possess relatively little surface area, so that the accurate determination of amount adsorbed demands special precautions.

For all these problems the thin film technique [372] has enjoyed very widespread application, particularly in the investigation of adsorption on metals. This may be attributed to the intensive study of the properties of metal films [11,57,238,446,447,512,515,560] which the last few years has seen, particularly with regard to their structure [11,57,267,560,676-678,706-708,722].

If one is going to investigate single-crystal surfaces, then one is generally obliged to introduce a single crystal as such into the vacuum system. As yet the production of single-crystal films has only been possible in a few instances; see, for example, references 11,238,303, 502,503,629,722. The surface of a single crystal is rarely cleaned up by direct heating, especially in view of the fact that at elevated temperatures sorbed gases from the interior of the crystal diffuse continually to the surface. Electron or ion bombardment [357] is therefore used to clean the surface. In this process the adsorbed molecules or atoms are knocked off with electrons or rare gas ions [213,357]. Where one is dealing with extremely small single-crystal tips, such as those used in the field emission or the field ion microscope, then the application of a very high electric field will serve to clean the surface by field evaporation. The field has to be of the order of a few million V cm^{-1} (see Section 5.6).

The outstanding advantage to be gained by using single crystals is that the crystallographic nature of the surface is uniquely defined. The very small extent of the surface area, on the other hand, is a disadvantage.

Table 2.1 summarises the properties of adsorbents prepared by the various methods available.

The determination of the surface area of adsorbents is very important. It is usually done using physical adsorption measurements, and here the BET method plays a vital role, which will be discussed in more detail later. Chemisorption methods can also be used to establish the extent of the surface area (see Section 3.1).

Similar care must be devoted to the preparation of adsorbates, because even the slightest amount of contamination can lead to substantial errors in the results. Adsorbates are either admitted to the active surface from ampoules or prepared in the apparatus and admitted via a pipette. The thermal decomposition of solids is a convenient means of preparing the adsorbate — sodium azide for nitrogen, barium peroxide for oxygen and calcium oxalate for carbon monoxide. Pure hydrogen is conveniently leaked into the apparatus by diffusion through a heated palladium thimble.

Table 2.1   Preparation of adsorbents

	Evaporation in UHV	Physical cleaning of the surface	Chemical cleaning of the surface
Type of adsorbent used	film	compact crystal, single-crystal ribbon or wire	powder, supported catalyst
Examples	metals, alloys, semiconductors	metals, oxides, alloys	practically unlimited choice of materials
Advantages	very clean, even in the interior, low experimental costs	single crystals have a defined surface, usually very clean	large surface area, very versatile
Disadvantages	low extent of surface area, unknown make-up of the surface, structure frequently unknown, limited to certain materials	very low extent of surface area, partial limitation regarding choice of material, high experimental costs	low degree of cleanliness, undefined surface

One is generally interested in studying adsorption effects as a function of the coverage. Special significance is therefore attached to determining the amount of gas adsorbed. The following methods are available to this end:

(1) Volumetric methods – pressure fall on adsorption, pressure rise on sudden desorption (flash filament technique), pressure changes in flow systems.
(2) Gravimetric methods (direct weighing).
(3) Measurement of the changes in a physical property of the adsorbent (electrical conductivity, thermoelectric power, magnetic susceptibility, work function) where this property is proportional to coverage.

The amount adsorbed is usually determined by allowing gas from a storage space of known volume to react with the adsorbent. The amount of gas adsorbed is then determined from the pressure fall and a knowledge of the dead space volumes involved. It is, of course, necessary to ascertain that no significant adsorption occurs on the walls of the vessel. If various parts of the apparatus are maintained at different temperatures, then one must also take the effect of thermomolecular flow into account [47,162,418-421,737].

When the adsorbent is a wire or a ribbon, the total amount adsorbed can be determined as follows. After the adsorption equilibrium has been set up, the adsorbent is suddenly heated to temperatures which are so high that all the adsorbed gas is desorbed. The pressure rise which this causes is measured and, taken with the appropriate volume, gives a measure of the quantity of gas that was previously adsorbed [168].

Again, adsorbed amounts can be determined by a dynamic method. The adsorbate is allowed to diffuse from the largest possible storage volume into the measuring system via a capillary tube [589]. The diameter of the capillary is made small compared with the mean free path of the gas molecules, so that the amount of gas diffusing through per unit time is proportional to the difference in pressure between the ends of the capillary:

$$\frac{d(pV)}{dt} = f(p_{entry} - p_{exit}) \tag{2.23}$$

p_{entry} and p_{exit} are the respective pressures which obtain in the gas on entering and on leaving the capillary.

The total amount diffusing through the capillary is obtained by integrating equation (2.23). The amount adsorbed follows as the difference between the amount diffusing through and the amount still present in the gas phase.

The advantage of this method is that one observes the whole of the coverage range continuously. By simultaneously measuring p_{entry}, p_{exit} and the magnitude of a physical property of the adsorbent which is influenced by adsorption, one obtains an uninterrupted record of the coverage dependence of this property in one run.

Probably the surest and most accurate method of determining adsorbed quantities is to weigh them [318,737]. Very sensitive high-vacuum microbalances with electronic compensation permit weight changes to be measured to 10^{-8} g. Thus, provided the adsorbent has a sufficiently large surface area, the sensitivity of a balance is good enough to enable coverages which are well below the monomolecular layer to be measured accurately [451,579].

Sometimes all the techniques for measuring the amount adsorbed directly become inadequate. This occurs when one is working in metal apparatus with adsorbents of low area and the amount of gas taken up by the adsorbent only represents a fraction of the amount taken up on the metal walls. Another instance where this arises is field emission microscopy, where the area of the adsorbent is so low that the quantity of gas adsorbed defies detection by even the most sensitive methods. In such cases one turns to the effects which are brought about by adsorption and the effects themselves are used to establish the coverage. This is done by comparing measurements which have been made in the first instance on larger amounts of adsorbent. The adsorption effects which are particularly suitable for this procedure are the electrical, photoelectric and magnetic properties of adsorbents.

3

STUDY OF ADSORPTION USING THERMODYNAMIC AND KINETIC METHODS

3.1. Adsorption isotherms

A knowledge of the quantity adsorbed together with its associated equilibrium pressure enables the adsorption isotherm to be specified. An isotherm thus gives the dependence of the quantity adsorbed on the equilibrium pressure at constant temperature.

The measurement of equilibria is often very difficult because, particularly in the case of strong chemisorption, the equilibrium pressures are extremely low. Examples of this are the chemisorption of hydrogen and of carbon monoxide on transition metals [646,695]. Furthermore, decomposition of the adsorbed molecules frequently occurs as a consequence of chemisorption at higher temperatures. This occurs already at room temperature in the cases of chemisorption of water [644,645], methane [640] and benzene [643] on transition metals.

Nevertheless the investigation of adsorption isotherms is often a valuable aid in obtaining information concerning the nature of an adsorption process. Thus if one sets up a concrete model for the adsorption process, one also specifies a theoretically valid model for the adsorption isotherm. Comparison with the experimental data then enables one to decide whether the model attributed to the system is correct. Since the adsorption isotherms derived from various models often show little difference from one another, it is necessary to determine isotherms at a number of temperatures. In this way the assignment can be made with greater certainty. Having obtained the isotherm and its temperature dependence, one can evaluate thermodynamic quantities. These, in turn, provide the basis for further discussion.

In the following examination of models together with the adsorption isotherms that they entail, we shall only deal with a few fundamental cases. For a deeper study the reader is referred to the specialised literature [318,584,737].

In accordance with the concepts given in Chapter 1, one has to presuppose that there is direct interaction between the adsorbent and the adsorbed gas molecules. For this reason, chemisorption should only continue to occur so long as vacant sites are available on the surface of the adsorbent, and chemisorption may be expected to terminate with the completion of a monomolecular layer. Physisorption, on the other hand, is far more like a condensation process, and it will proceed to the formation of a multimolecular layer.

It is logical, therefore, to divide our models into those which are limited to monolayer adsorption and those which hold for the formation of multilayers. Furthermore, two limiting cases of mobility in the adsorbed phase can be distinguished — the adsorbed molecules may be freely mobile or they may be precisely located on the surface. In the first case the adsorbed molecules behave like a two-dimensional gas, and in the latter case a specific site for adsorption will be allocated to every molecule that is adsorbed on the adsorbent surface. The condition of the surface of the adsorbent also determines the type of adsorption isotherm that is obtained. One will obtain distinguishable results, for instance, if the surface is energetically homogeneous or heterogeneous. And it transpires that the way the enthalpy of adsorption depends on the gas coverage is of decisive significance in determining the shape of the isotherm.

The adsorption isotherm may be derived in various ways:

(1) From an examination of the kinetics [133].
(2) By consideration of the equilibrium.
(3) With the help of statistical thermodynamics [333].

Monomolecular adsorption that is ideally mobile is of special interest at very low coverages where the interactions between adsorbed molecules are excluded. In this case the adsorbed gas behaves like an ideal two-dimensional gas, for which

$$\Phi A \;=\; nRT \tag{3.1}$$

holds, where Φ denotes the surface pressure, A the area occupied by the adsorbed gas, n the number of moles, R the gas constant and T the absolute temperature. An isotherm can be derived [584,737] for this situation; it corresponds to Henry's Law for the solubility of gases in liquids and is called Henry's adsorption isotherm:

$$n \;=\; \text{const. } p \tag{3.2}$$

The quantity adsorbed n is thus proportional to the equilibrium pressure. Other adsorption isotherms reduce to equation (3.2) as limiting cases when the coverage is extremely low.

Of greater significance than Henry's adsorption isotherm is the isotherm derived by Langmuir [406] by considering the kinetics of adsorption. This isotherm holds for monomolecular adsorption that is ideally localised. According to the theory of the rate of adsorption (see Section 2.3), when every gas molecule is adsorbed on a fixed site, we have

$$r_a \;=\; \kappa \; \frac{p}{(2\pi mkT)^{1/2}} \; (1 - \theta) \exp\left(-\Delta E_a/RT\right) \tag{3.3}$$

κ is the condensation coefficient and ΔE_a is the activation energy for adsorption.   Since neither κ nor ΔE_a depends on the coverage, we may assume that the adsorption of a molecule is in no way influenced by the presence of another adsorbed molecule.   The corresponding equation for desorption is

$$r_d \;=\; \delta\theta \; \exp\left(-\Delta E_d / RT\right) \tag{3.4}$$

At equilibrium

$$r_a \;=\; r_d \tag{3.5}$$

so that

$$\kappa(1 \,-\, \theta) \,\frac{p}{(2\pi mkT)^{1/2}}\, \exp\left(-\Delta E_a/RT\right) = \delta\theta \; \exp\left(-\Delta E_d/RT\right) \tag{3.6}$$

or, setting

$$b \;=\; \frac{\kappa}{\delta(2\pi mkT)^{1/2}} \; \exp\left[-(\Delta E_a \,-\, \Delta E_d)/RT\right] \tag{3.7}$$

$$\theta \;=\; \frac{bp}{1 \,+\, bp} \tag{3.8}$$

Recalling that θ is the coverage, i.e. that

$$\theta \;=\; \frac{n}{n_m} \tag{3.9}$$

where n moles adsorbed corresponds to coverage θ and n_m to the monolayer coverage, one then obtains from equation (3.8)

$$n \;=\; \frac{n_m bp}{1 \,+\, bp} \tag{3.10}$$

or

$$n \;=\; \frac{n_m p}{(1/b) \,+\, p} \tag{3.11}$$

At very low pressures $1/b \gg p$, so that equation (3.11) simplifies to

$$n \;=\; n_m bp \tag{3.12}$$

i.e. the Langmuir isotherm becomes the Henry isotherm.   At high pressures, on the other hand, $1/b \ll p$, and it follows from equation (3.11) that

$$n \;=\; n_m \tag{3.13}$$

According to the Langmuir adsorption isotherm, the coverage approaches the monolayer asymptotically at high pressures and independently of the temperature.

The statistical derivation [235] yields more precise information about the constant b:

$$b = \frac{h^3}{(2\pi m)^{3/2}(kT)^{5/2}} \frac{Z_s(T)}{Z_g(T)} \exp(q/kT) \qquad (3.14)$$

$Z_s(T)$ and $Z_g(T)$ are the partition coefficients of a molecule in the adsorbed state and in the free gaseous state, respectively; the energy difference between these two states is the heat of adsorption q.

From equations (3.11)-(3.13) one immediately recognises the shape of the Langmuir adsorption isotherm (*Figure 3.1*).

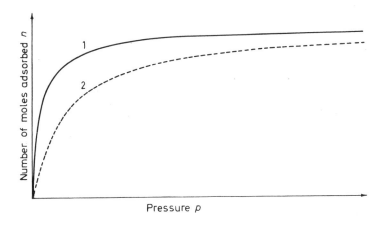

Figure 3.1   Adsorption isotherms of the Langmuir type

According to equations (3.12) and (3.14), the rate of rise of the Langmuir adsorption isotherm in the region of low equilibrium pressures is determined by the heat of adsorption and the temperature.   At constant temperature curve 1 in *Figure 3.1* corresponds to a strong chemisorption (q is large) and curve 2 to a weak one.   For any particular adsorption system the transition from 1 to 2 will occur as the temperature rises.

Frequently dissociative adsorption occurs; this means that a molecule is not chemisorbed in its molecular form but only after dissociation. An example of this is given by the chemisorption of hydrogen on transition metals.   In these cases the Langmuir adsorption isotherm (3.11) becomes[*]

[*]Equation (3.15) is obtained for mobile adsorption, following equation (2.15), although the Langmuir isotherm refers explicitly to immobile adsorption.   If the molecules move between definite sites and spend relatively little of their time moving, then the Langmuir isotherm is still applicable.   Of course for a two-dimensional gas the Langmuir isotherm does *not* hold.

$$n = \frac{n_m(bp)^{\frac{1}{2}}}{1 + (bp)^{\frac{1}{2}}} \tag{3.15}$$

This is because one has to take into account that two sites are involved both for the adsorption and for the desorption of one gas molecule. The terms $(1 - \theta)$ and θ therefore become $(1 - \theta)^2$ and θ^2, respectively, when the isotherm is set up by equating the right-hand sides of equations (3.3) and (3.4).

In order to check whether adsorption is described by a molecular or a dissociative form of the Langmuir adsorption isotherm, one rewrites equations (3.11) and (3.15) in a suitable form, viz. the equation of a straight line. Thus, for the case of molecular adsorption on single adsorption sites, equation (3.11) becomes

$$\frac{p}{n} = \frac{1}{n_m b} + \frac{p}{n_m} \tag{3.16}$$

and for the dissociative two-point adsorption

$$\frac{p^{\frac{1}{2}}}{n} = \frac{1}{n_m b^{\frac{1}{2}}} + \frac{p^{\frac{1}{2}}}{n_m} \tag{3.17}$$

In the first case the plot of p/n against p should give a straight line and in the second case the plot of $p^{\frac{1}{2}}/n$ against $p^{\frac{1}{2}}$ should be linear.

As will be shown later, more often than not adsorbates can be adsorbed in a number of different states. If the adsorption of each of these states can be individually described by the Langmuir adsorption isotherm, then for the general case of several molecular and dissociative states we may write

$$n = \sum_i \frac{n_{m_i} b_i \, p}{1 + b_i \, p} + \sum_j \frac{n_{m_j}(b_j \, p)^{\frac{1}{2}}}{1 + (b_j \, p)^{\frac{1}{2}}} \tag{3.18}$$

Here n_{m_i} and n_{m_j} are the quantities of the adsorbate in the states i and j, respectively, which altogether constitute the monolayer. b_i and b_j take into account that the different states display distinguishable heats of adsorption (compare equation 3.14).

As can be checked by many different methods of investigation, hydrogen in the Ni/H$_2$ system exists in various states. If one plots the quantity n moles adsorbed on a nickel film at 273 K against the square root of the equilibrium pressure p, then one finds that a linear relationship holds at low pressures ($p < 3 \times 10^{-3}$ Torr), as shown in *Figure 3.2* [650]. This result is to be expected if two or more atomic adsorption states with different heats of adsorption are taken up. In equation (3.18) the first summation on the right-hand side can then be omitted, while the first term or terms of the second summation are equal to the constants n_{m_j} because the heats of adsorption involved are large (large b_j). For a weakly bound state at low equilibrium pressures, this term takes the form $n_{m_j}(b_j \, p)^{\frac{1}{2}}$, so that altogether

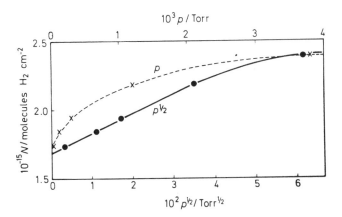

Figure 3.2   The adsorption isotherm for the Ni/H_2 system at 273 K

$$n = n_{m_1} + \ldots + n_{m_{j-1}} + n_{m_j}(b_j\,p)^{\frac{1}{2}} \qquad (3.19)$$

Evidently no molecular adsorption occurs in the range of pressure investigated, viz. the plot of quantity adsorbed against p (dashed curve in *Figure 3.2*) shows no linear section.

In the analysis which led to setting up equation (3.18) it was assumed that the surface of the adsorbent was not energetically homogeneous and that it consisted of regions that adsorb with different strengths. These individual regions should, nevertheless, have a constant heat of adsorption assigned to each of them.

The next step would now be to assume that the heat of adsorption varies continuously and so the constants b_i also vary. The summation in equation (3.18) would then be replaced by an integration. In addition, one also has to know how b varies with the coverage of adsorbed atoms.

By making the assumption that the heat of adsorption falls logarithmically with coverage, Zeldovich [739] was able to carry out the integration and obtained the expression

$$n = ap^{1/m} \qquad (3.20)$$

which had already been found empirically by Freundlich [240] at an earlier date. This isotherm has therefore entered the literature as the 'Freundlich adsorption isotherm'.

Of more frequent occurrence than the logarithmic fall of the heat of adsorption with coverage is a linear relationship between these two quantities:

$$q = q_0(1 - a\theta) \qquad (3.21)$$

If one puts this expression into equation (3.6) in place of $-(\Delta E_a - \Delta E_d)$ and abbreviates

$$b_0 = \frac{\kappa}{\delta(2\pi mkT)^{1/2}} \tag{3.22}$$

then one obtains

$$\frac{\theta}{1 - \theta} = b_0 \, p \, \exp[q_0(1 - a\theta)/RT] \tag{3.23}$$

By taking logarithms one obtains

$$\ln p = -\ln[b_0 \, \exp(q_0/RT)] + \frac{q_0 a\theta}{RT} + \ln \frac{\theta}{1 - \theta} \tag{3.24}$$

in which the middle term on the right-hand side is largest and the last term can scarcely be distinguished from zero at intermediate coverages ($\theta \sim 0.5$). If one abbreviates the bracketed part of the first term to A_0, one then obtains from equation (3.24) the familiar 'Temkin adsorption isotherm' [660]

$$n = n_m \frac{RT}{q_0 a} \ln (A_0 p) \tag{3.25}$$

which predicts a logarithmic relationship between the coverage and the equilibrium pressure.

Particularly in physisorption, one often observes that multimolecular adsorption occurs. In the adsorption isotherm this makes itself noticeable in that the plot of n against p first appears to approach a limiting value but subsequently rises again; there is thus a point of inflection. *Figure 3.3* reproduces the adsorption data for nitrogen on silica gel [103] as an example of this.

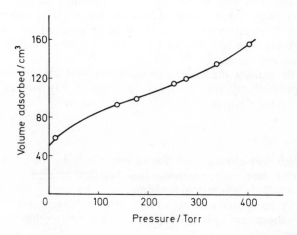

Figure 3.3   Adsorption of nitrogen on silica gel at 77 K

In 1938 Brunauer, Emmett and Teller [103] were the first to derive an adsorption isotherm for multilayer adsorption that could be applied practically. The special advantage of this 'BET isotherm' is that one can use it to determine the surface area of porous adsorbents.

In a way, the BET isotherm represents a generalisation of the ideal localised monolayer adsorption. The starting point for its derivation is again taken as the homogeneous adsorbent surface on which molecules can be adsorbed without there being any lateral interactions between them. The heat of adsorption E_1 is constant. Every molecule that is adsorbed in the first layer can itself serve as a site for adsorption of a molecule in the second layer, and so on. A column of adsorbed molecules is therefore built up over every adsorption site on the bare surface. The columns do not interact with one another and the heat of sorption E_2 in the second and higher layers of adsorbed molecules is simply taken as the heat of condensation.

The isotherm can be derived either from a kinetic point of view [133] or by the use of statistical methods. The end result obtained in each case is

$$\frac{p}{n(p_0 - p)} = \frac{1}{n_m c} + \frac{c - 1}{n_m c} \frac{p}{p_0} \qquad (3.26)$$

in which n is the number of moles adsorbed at an equilibrium pressure p, n_m is the number of moles adsorbed in the monolayer and p_0 is the saturated vapour pressure of the adsorbing gas at the temperature of the measurement. The constant c contains the difference between the heat of adsorption E_1 in the first layer and the heat of condensation E_2 of the adsorbate:

$$c = \exp[(E_1 - E_2)/RT] \qquad (3.27)$$

To compare experimental results with the BET theory, one plots $p/[n(p_0 - p)]$ against p/p_0. The resulting straight line enables one to obtain n_m and c.

In *Figure 3.4* the adsorption of nitrogen on silica gel (compare *Figure 3.3*) has been presented in accordance with equation (3.26). In place of the adsorbed quantity n, the adsorbed volume V has been plotted.

Undoubtedly the BET theory only represents a crude approximation of the real state of affairs that obtains in multimolecular adsorption. This is due to the simplifying assumptions that were made and, as a result, there has been no lack of attempts to arrive at an isotherm which does more justice to the experimental findings. This is particularly true of the last decade, the essential feature being the introduction of further constants into the equation. The physical basis of these equations, nevertheless, tends to be little better founded. In this connection we refer to the specialised literature [737].

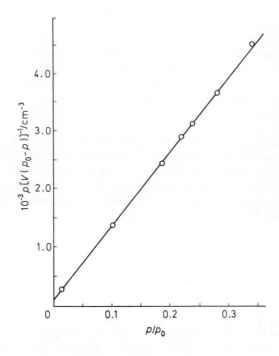

Figure 3.4   The adsorption of nitrogen on silica gel at 77 K, plotted according to the BET equation [103]

The theme of this section has so far been to show how markedly any analytical expression for the adsorption isotherm depends on the particular circumstances of the adsorption system.   As in kinetics, one can eliminate incorrect models for the system under study by investigating isotherms.   But proof for the correctness of a model should not be built up on the measurement of adsorption isotherms alone. It is vital to draw in other methods.

We turn now to consider the determination of surface areas of adsorbents by the measurement of adsorption isotherms.   Isotherms are particularly well suited for this important application.   Furthermore, there is frequently no other way of finding the surface area, especially where the surface geometry is unknown.

The BET method is of considerable value in determining the extent of the surface area of high-area, porous adsorbents.   The method rests on equation (3.26).   In general, it transpires that the BET plot is linear over the range $0.05 < p/p_0 < 0.3$.   To obtain the true extent of the surface area from the monolayer value n_m, one needs to know the area that is occupied by a molecule of adsorbed gas.   This is calculated assuming that the molecules in the adsorbed layer are hexagonal close packed and that the density of the adsorbed layer is the same as that of the solidified gas.

Table 3.1 shows a few examples to illustrate the reliability of surface area determinations by this method.

Table 3.1 Surface areas (in $m^2\ g^{-1}$) of porous glass and silica gel determined by the BET method with various adsorbates

Adsorbate	N_2	Ar	O_2	CO	CO_2	C_2H_2	NH_3	Ref.
Adsorbent at	77 K	77 K	90 K	90 K	195 K	195 K	240 K	
Porous glass	121	120	120	–	–	–	–	[184]
Porous glass	232	217	–	–	164	159	207	[183]
Silica gel	560	477	464	550	455	–	–	[103]

The differences that crop up can, at least in part, be traced back to uncertainty in the value that is taken for the area of an adsorbed molecule. In Section 5.6 we shall mention that the molecular area can sometimes show a substantial variation between different crystal faces of the adsorbent.

Formidable problems tend to appear when one attempts to use this method for the determination of small surface areas such as those met with in the case of evaporated metal films (total area of the order of 100 cm^2). One of the difficulties is to determine the quantity adsorbed exactly. This is because the quantity adsorbed is often comparable to the quantity of gas which unavoidably remains in the dead space. One can only avoid the larger corrections due to the gas remaining in the dead space by making the measurements with a gas which has a very low saturated vapour pressure at the temperature of adsorption (popularly 77 K). This means that the optimum values of p/p_0 for the BET analysis already obtain at low pressures. These requirements are fulfilled by xenon, which is therefore used pre-eminently in the determination of small surface areas [3,13,95,96,111,278,298,324,683].

The analysis of adsorption isotherms is undertaken not only on the basis of the BET equation but also using the Dubinin-Radushkevich equation [371,572]. Here, again, certain difficulties arise concerning the cross-sectional area of an adsorbed Xe atom. The most probable value is likely to be 24 $Å^2$.

Pritchard [561] showed that the surface area of evaporated films can be measured very conveniently by use of the variation of work function caused by xenon adsorption (see Section 5.1).

The methods referred to so far have been aimed at finding the total surface area of an adsorbent. Frequently, however, one wishes to know what proportion of the surface is made up of one particular component. This could arise, for instance, in the case of the metal in a supported catalyst where the metal often occupies less than 1 per cent of the total available surface. The procedure then consists of first measuring the total area by using the non-specific physisorption of nitrogen or xenon in conjunction with the BET method. This is followed by measuring the metal area by use of chemisorption of a gas which adsorbs well on the metal but badly on the supporting material. Oxygen, or better still hydrogen or carbon monoxide, is suited to this kind of 'surface titration'. A wide range of methods has been developed to obtain the amount of gas chemisorbed and the chemisorption isotherm [278,286]. These methods include volumetric techniques [285,392], gas chromatographic measurements [309] and calorimetric determinations [393].

The investigation of alloy surfaces has recently aroused a great deal of interest. As in the case of supported metals, it is often possible to obtain the surface composition of an alloy by chemisorption titration. One has to choose an adsorbate which chemisorbs well on the one component but is not chemisorbed by the other. An example is afforded by the use of hydrogen to study the surface composition of Pt-Au alloys [588]. Variations in the characteristics of physisorption have also been applied to the analysis of composite surfaces [373].

3.2.   Heat of adsorption

To discuss the bonding of the adsorbed phase, a knowledge of the strength of this bonding is especially important. The strength manifests itself in the magnitude of the heat of adsorption. Two methods are available for determining heats of adsorption: either the heat is calculated from the temperature dependence of the equilibrium pressure which is observed between the gas phase and the adsorbed phase, or one measures the heat calorimetrically. The term 'heat of adsorption' has often not been defined clearly. The amount of heat exchanged between a system and its surroundings depends on the conditions and the methods of conducting an experiment because heat is not a function of state. If one wishes to use the experimental results for thermodynamic calculations, then it is necessary to establish that one is dealing with equilibrium values. The adsorption process must therefore be conducted in a reversible fashion.

Of immediate concern is the distinction between integral and differential heats of adsorption. The integral heat $q_{integr.}$ is obtained in accordance with the First Law from the change of internal energy of the system and the work done; it is related to the differential heat according to

$$q_{diff.} = \frac{dq_{integr.}}{dn_S} \tag{3.28}$$

We stipulate here that in the adsorption process no volume work is done.

Distinguishable heats of adsorption are obtained according to whether adsorption is carried out isothermally or adiabatically. In the first case the heat of adsorption is evaluated from the amount of heat exchanged with the surroundings. In the second case one uses the thermal capacity of the entire calorimeter together with the rise of temperature it experiences.

The thermodynamic derivation of the relationships between the various heats of adsorption is fully covered in the literature [584,737]. We distinguish the following cases.

(a) The volumes of the gas phase V_G and of the adsorbed phase V_S remain constant, as does the area A of the adsorbent. The 'differential heat of adsorption' q_d is then

$$q_d = q_{V_G, V_S, A} = u_G - \left(\frac{\partial u_S}{\partial n_S}\right)_{V_S, A, T} \tag{3.29}$$

(b) The process is isothermal and isobaric:

$$q_{p,A,T} = T_{s_G} - T\bar{s}_S \tag{3.30}$$

The right-hand side of this equation may be identified in equation (2.1) – except for the RT^2 factor. The right-hand side of equation (3.30) is therefore identical with the isosteric heat of adsorption:

$$q_{st} = RT^2 \left(\frac{\partial \ln p}{\partial T}\right)_\theta = -R \left(\frac{\partial \ln p}{\partial 1/T}\right)_\theta \tag{3.31}$$

The connection between the differential and the isosteric heats of adsorption is finally obtained as

$$q_d = q_{st} - RT \tag{3.32}$$

(c) The differential adiabatic heat of adsorption is defined according to Kington and Aston [367] as

$$q_a = \sum_i n_i c_{p_i} \left(\frac{\partial T}{\partial n_S}\right)_{\text{adiab.}} \tag{3.33}$$

where i refers to all the components of the calorimeter and the adsorption system. q_a is related to the isosteric heat of adsorption in the following way:

$$q_a = q_{st} + V_g \left(\frac{\partial p}{\partial n_S}\right)_{T,A} + V_g \left(\frac{\partial p}{\partial T}\right)_\theta \left(\frac{\partial T}{\partial n_S}\right)_{\text{adiab.}} \tag{3.34}$$

In general, therefore, the adiabatic heat is larger than the isosteric heat of adsorption.

(d) The process is isothermal and occurs at constant surface pressure Φ. The equilibrium heat of adsorption ΔH then follows from equation (2.2):

$$\Delta H = RT^2 \left(\frac{\partial \ln p}{\partial T} \right)_\Phi = R \left(\frac{\partial \ln p}{\partial (1/T)} \right)_\Phi \qquad (3.35)$$

It is found [737] that this is connected with the isosteric heat of adsorption according to the equation

$$\Delta H = q_{st} - \frac{T}{\theta} \left(\frac{\partial \Phi}{\partial T} \right)_{p,\theta} \qquad (3.36)$$

In the determination of heats of adsorption from adsorption isotherms it is possible to decide exactly whether one is dealing with q_{st} or ΔH. But if the measurement is made with a calorimeter, then the isothermal and isobaric process is really more like an adiabatic process because of the experimental conditions. However, an adiabatic process is never quite reached. Frequently calorimeters function as 'surroundings calorimeters'. If small, successive quantities of gas are allowed to react with the surface, then chiefly volume work is evolved, although it is uncertain whether this work is given to the calorimeter as heat. One therefore measures effects which lie between q_d and q_{st}. The difference between these two quantities is RT according to equation (3.32), viz. *ca.* 150 cal mol^{-1} at 77 K and *ca.* 550 cal mol^{-1} at 273 K. In the case of heats of physisorption, such an uncertainty is enough to disturb the measurements; but in the case of chemisorption, the effect is smaller. For this reason one preferably determines heats of physisorption from the isosteres, while heats of chemisorption are frequently measured calorimetrically.

To determine isosteric heats of adsorption one must measure the adsorption isotherm at two temperatures on one and the same adsorbent. The temperatures should not be too far apart. *Figure 3.5* shows two such adsorption isotherms for the adsorption of carbon monoxide on copper powder at 77 K and 90 K, respectively [638]. We notice that at these temperatures readily measurable equilibrium pressures of between 10^{-4} and 10^{-1} Torr are obtained when the coverage lies between 6×10^{14} and 8×10^{14} molecules CO cm^{-2}. These coverages correspond to somewhat less than a monomolecular layer. As discussed in Section 3.1, the convenient pressure range at higher temperatures occurs at lower coverages. At 278 K, for example, the coverage is 0.5×10^{14} molecules CO cm^{-2}, which is as yet below one-tenth of the monomolecular coverage.

According to equation (2.1), the isosteric heat of adsorption at constant coverage is obtained from the horizontal separation of the two curves in *Figure 3.5* together with their temperature difference (in this case 13°). The accuracy of the measurements is usually good enough to enable one to determine heats of adsorption which are as small as the heat of condensation.

The dependence of the heat of adsorption on coverage may also be measured by this method, in that equation (2.1) can be applied at a number of uptakes N molecules cm^{-2}. This is, in fact, how

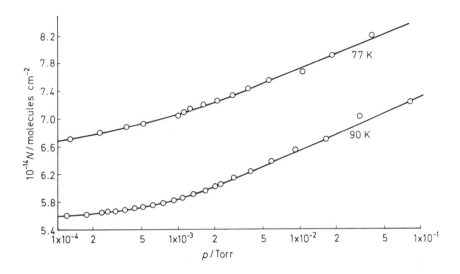

Figure 3.5   Adsorption isotherms at 77 K and 90 K for the system Cu powder/CO; after Strothenk [638]

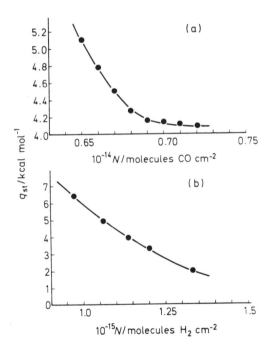

Figure 3.6   Isosteric heats of adsorption q_{st} as a function of uptake N: (a) for the adsorption of CO on copper powder at 83 K [638]; (b) for the adsorption of H_2 on nickel films at 283 K.   After Suhrmann et al. [650]

Figure 3.6 was obtained.   *Figure 3.6(a)* shows the result for carbon
monoxide adsorbed on copper powder at 83 K and *Figure 3.6(b)* refers
to hydrogen adsorbed on nickel films at 283 K (compare *Figure 3.2*).
At 278 K one finds in this manner that the heats of adsorption of
carbon monoxide on copper powder are 15 kcal mol^{-1} at coverages
of about one-tenth of a monomolecular layer.

Figure 3.6 reveals that the heat of adsorption falls to approach the
heat of condensation, and this is typical.   Usually the heat of condensation is reached near a monolayer coverage.

The direct determination of uptake is no longer possible if one is
working with specimens of very low area.   This occurs, for instance,
in LEED investigations on single crystals (see Section 6.1).   Nevertheless, it is often feasible to measure a physical quantity which — at least
at not too high a coverage — varies in proportion to the coverage.
A case in point, as will be shown in Section 5.1, is the work function
variation $\Delta(e_0\phi)$.   Thus if, as Ertl and Küppers [192] have done, $\Delta\phi$
or log $\Delta\phi$ is plotted against log p, then one can extract the isosteric
heats of adsorption from these diagrams in an entirely analogous
manner to that used with *Figure 3.5*.   This procedure has recently
proved to be particularly suitable for a number of adsorption systems
in which the equilibrium pressures lie between 5×10^{-9} and 5×10^{-6}
Torr.

Despite all the foregoing, the direct calorimetric determination of
heats of adsorption yields data which are almost as significant as
those obtained by measuring isosteric heats.   The first experimental
work in this direction dates back to Beebe [42] and Garner and Veal
[249], and a detailed review of the literature is given in [737].   We
should also mention Calvet's microcalorimeter [110].   To measure the
rise in temperature caused by the adsorption process it is usual to use
thermocouples or resistance thermometers.   If the adsorbent is a powder,
then difficulties may crop up over temperature equilibration in the
calorimeter and retardation of the adsorption process due to diffusion
processes.   If the adsorbent is an evaporated film, then the amount of
heat released is very small because of the small area available.

For measurements on evaporated films the adsorbing surface does
not usually amount to more than 100 cm^2, so that a complete monomolecular layer of adsorbed gas only consists of the order of 10^{17}
molecules or 1.6×10^{-7} mol.   Taking a typical heat of adsorption
as 20 kcal mol^{-1}, such an adsorption leads to the liberation of only
3×10^{-3} cal.   For this reason calorimeters have had to be built with
a small thermal capacity.   This development can be traced notably in
the work of Beeck, Cole and Wheeler [44], Bagg and Tompkins [28]
and Brennan, Hayward and Trapnell [99], who used very thin-walled
glass tubes as the calorimeter.   Bagg and Tompkins used 20 thermocouples to measure the temperature rise, but Beeck *et al.* and Brennan
et al. wound their tubes with a resistance thermometer.   *Figure 3.7*
shows Beeck's calorimeter.   That section of the inner tube which is

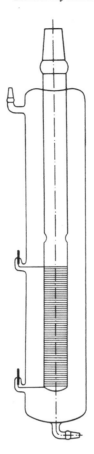

Figure 3.7 Adsorption calorimeter; after Beeck et al. *[44]*

wound with a resistance thermometer is covered on its inner surface
with the evaporated metal film adsorbent. The outer, evacuable jacket
serves as a thermostat. A disadvantage of this arrangement is posed by
the uneven coverage of the adsorbate during adsorption (see *Figure
5.19*).

A significant improvement in sensitivity was achieved by Wedler [684],
who built a spherical calorimeter and was the first to make measurements under ultrahigh vacuum conditions. Further development of this
calorimeter (*Figure 3.8*) was accompanied by the automatic recording
of all measurements [101,703]. The side arm A_1 serves to connect
the inner part of the calorimeter consisting of the calorimeter sphere S
to the ultrahigh vacuum apparatus. The other side arm A_2 connects
the outer part of the calorimeter consisting of the jacket J with the
apparatus. The metal film is evaporated from the coil E onto the
inner surface of the sphere. To determine the thermal capacity, one
passes electric current for a short time between the two platinum

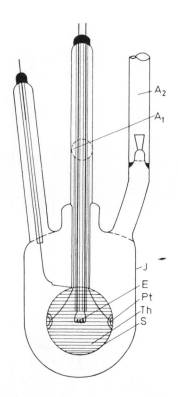

Figure 3.8. Spherical calorimeter; after Wedler and co-workers [101, 703]

contacts Pt. This current passes through the evaporated film and the temperature rise in the calorimeter is measured with the glass-covered tungsten resistance thermometer Th. The thermometer is fused directly to the outer surface of the glass sphere, which is only some 0.1 mm thick. Release of heat in the calibration process is in this way compared directly with the heat released during the adsorption process.

Such a calorimeter has a thermal capacity of 0.5 cal K^{-1} and the sensitivity reached in the installation amounts to 65 mm of recorder deflection for a temperature change of only 10^{-4} degrees. It is therefore possible to make very accurate measurements of the heat of adsorption for quantities of adsorbed gas which constitute less than one-twentieth of a monolayer even if the differential enthalpy of adsorption is only 5 kcal mol^{-1}. Measurements can be made at any temperature for which constant-temperature baths are currently available. This refers particularly to 77 K, 90 K, 178 K and 273 K. A further advantage of this calorimeter lies in its ability to be used for simultaneous measurements of heats and changes in electrical resistance of the evaporated film. The resistance technique will be covered in Section 5.2.

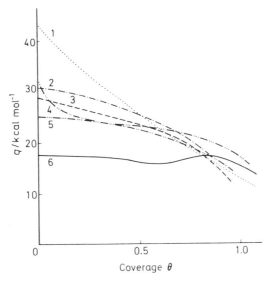

Figure 3.9 Heats of adsorption in the Ni/H₂ system at 273 K: 1, Klemperer and Stone [375]; 2, Beeck et al. [44]; 3, Whaba and Kemball [681]; 4, Rideal and Sweett [575]; 5, Brennan and Hayes [97]; 6, Bröcker and Wedler [101]

If one examines the calorimetric heats of adsorption reported in the literature, then one often finds that very substantial differences exist. This is particularly noticeable in the Ni/H_2 system. The values given by various authors as a function of the coverage are compared in *Figure 3.9*. There is unanimity over the value of 15 kcal mol^{-1} for the heat of adsorption at around monatomic coverage (1.5×10^{15} H atoms cm^{-2}). It is also agreed that the heat falls off relatively steeply at higher coverages. Comparison with *Figure 3.6(b)* shows that the isosteric heats of adsorption bear out the calorimetric determinations very well for uptakes which are higher than 0.9×10^{15} H_2 molecules cm^{-2} ($\theta \sim 1.3$). Marked differences exist, nevertheless, with respect to the heats of adsorption at low coverages. At the same time, there is also a variety of slopes for the fall-off of the heat of adsorption with coverage.

Consideration has been given to the possibility that the observed differences in values for the heats of adsorption arise from the method of measurement and the calibration of the calorimeter [94,113,686,687]. However, these sources of error can be largely discounted. The differences may invariably be attributed to variations in the vacuum conditions (ultrahigh vacuum conditions were only present for curve 6) and variable structural properties of the nickel films used.

The pattern of curve 6 in *Figure 3.9* has been verified during the course of many measurements on the Ni/H_2 system at 273 K. Other authors have also recently reported concordant values. Thus Ertl and Küppers [192] measured equilibrium pressures and changes in work function on nickel (110) crystal faces and found that the isosteric heat of adsorption remained at a steady value of 19.5 kcal mol[-1] up to half the monomolecular coverage. In more recent work, Ertl and co-workers [121] also report isosteric heats of adsorption for hydrogen which amount to 23 kcal mol[-1] on Ni(111) and Ni(100) and 21.5 kcal mol[-1] on Ni(110).

Lapujoulade and Neil have evaluated heats of adsorption by considering the kinetics of adsorption and desorption. At very low coverages they found values of 21.8 kcal mol[-1] [407] and 22.7 kcal mol[-1] [408] on Ni(111) crystal faces and 23.1 kcal mol[-1] [410] on Ni(100) crystal faces. On Ni(110) faces they found 20.3 kcal mol[-1], rising to 23 kcal mol[-1] [409].

Wedler and Fisch [692] investigated the way in which temperature influences the relationship between the differential heat of adsorption and the coverage of hydrogen. Using 100 Å thick nickel films, they obtained the results shown in *Figure 3.10*. Evidently the occurrence of a minimum and a maximum is connected with a change in the structure of the adsorbed phase (see Section 6.1). Such a structural change would confer a degree of mobility on the adsorbed particles and this could actually be picked up in isotope exchange experiments (see Section 3.5) which show that the minimum and the maximum in the curves of *Figure 3.10* can only be detected at temperatures at which the adsorbed phase is significantly mobile.

In a similar manner, the heats of adsorption of carbon monoxide on nickel films were formerly reported to be higher than recent measurements reveal. Brennan and Hayes [98] reported a value of 42 kcal mol[-1] and Beeck [43] found 35 kcal mol[-1], the latter value being independent of coverage over a wide coverage range.

The most recent calorimetric data are given in *Figure 3.11*. At low coverages the heat of adsorption amounts to 30 kcal mol[-1]. Then, after falling off, a marked plateau forms at 25 kcal mol[-1] and the heat finally falls to low values. This result agrees closely with the findings of other authors. On Ni(100) faces Tracy [667] obtained a value of 30 kcal mol[-1] which remained constant over a wide range of coverage. On Ni(100) faces Madden, Küppers and Ertl [435] observed 30 kcal mol[-1] at low coverages and a plateau at 25 kcal mol[-1] at higher coverages. Furthermore Klier, Zettlemoyer and Leidheiser [377] reported values of both 25.3 kcal mol[-1] on (110) faces and 26.1 kcal mol[-1] on (100) faces of a nickel crystal.

It is interesting to see that the crystallographic nature of the adsorbing face only has a slight effect on the value of the heat of adsorption. This is the case for both hydrogen adsorption and carbon monoxide adsorption on nickel.

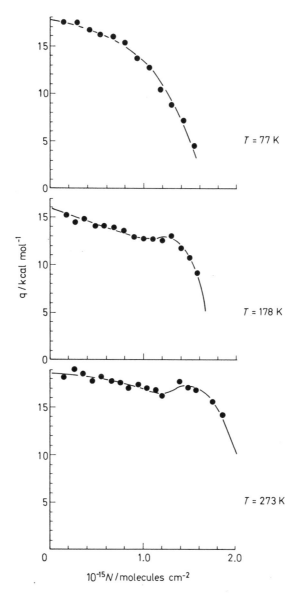

Figure 3.10 The effect of temperature on the relationship between the differential heat of adsorption and the coverage for hydrogen on nickel films; after Wedler and Fisch [692]

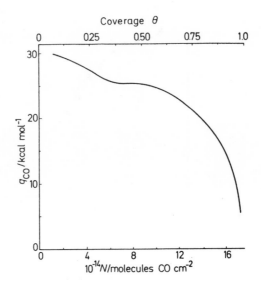

Figure 3.11   Coverage dependence of the differential heat of adsorption for carbon monoxide on nickel films at 273 K; after Wedler and Schroll [702]

In order to draw conclusions regarding the nature of the adsorbate binding, a specific model must be set up. The heats of adsorption are then calculated for this model and compared with the experimentally observed values.

For the calculation of heats of physisorption one must take into account whether the adsorbed phase is formed from non-polar or polar adsorbing gases and adsorbents. In Section 2.2 we have already gone into the various combinations which are possible. For the individual calculations, however, we refer to the specialised literature (see, for instance, reference 737).

As a first approximation in the evaluation of heats of chemisorption, the limiting cases of purely ionic and purely covalent bonding may be distinguished. The interaction between adsorbed molecules is also disregarded in the calculation, so that experimental values can only be compared at very low coverages. For the energy zero the condition is chosen in which the adsorbing gas and the adsorbent are infinitely far apart.

The formation of an ionic bond may be visualised as occurring in two steps: first, an electron passes from the gas molecule to the adsorbent, and then the gas ion approaches the adsorbent until the equilibrium separation is reached. The transfer of an electron from the gas molecule to the adsorbent involves an energy gain of $e_0\phi - e_0I$ ($e_0\phi$ is the work function and e_0I is the ionisation potential). The energy of attraction which is needed to bring the ion to within the ionic radius r_0 of the surface is given by the energy of formation $e_0{}^2/4r_0$. The heat of adsorption q_0 is therefore given by

$$q_0 \;=\; N_L\left(e_0\phi \;-\; e_0I \;+\; \frac{e_0{}^2}{4r_0}\right) \tag{3.37}$$

where N_L is Avogadro's number.

Table 3.2 Calculated and experimental heats of chemisorption for purely ionic bonding [318]

System	$N_L\ e_0\phi$ kcal mol^{-1}	$N_L\ e_0 I$ kcal mol^{-1}	$N_L\ e_0{}^2/4r_0$ kcal mol^{-1}	$q_{0,calc.}$ kcal mol^{-1}	$q_{0,exp.}$ kcal mol^{-1}
W/Na	104.0	118.0	44.5	30.5	32.0
W/K	104.0	99.6	35.9	40.3	–
W/Cs	104.0	89.4	31.1	45.7	64.0

As *Table 3.2* shows, the values calculated in this way are comparable throughout with the experimental values if one considers the adsorption of alkali metal atoms on metallic surfaces such as tungsten, molybdenum and the like. Such systems have been treated particularly by Moesta [478].

Nevertheless equation (3.37) leads to results which are in no way useful when one comes to handle the adsorption of gases such as hydrogen or oxygen on metallic surfaces. Here the other limiting case must be considered, viz. that of purely covalent bonding. To depict the hydrogen adsorption process as

$$2Me + H_2 \longrightarrow 2Me - H \tag{3.38}$$

does not represent the state of affairs correctly. This is because no metal-metal bonds have to be broken during adsorption, the adsorbent remaining essentially unchanged. The heat of adsorption is therefore made up of

$$q_0 \;=\; 2E_{Me-H} \;-\; E_{H-H} \tag{3.39}$$

where E_{Me-H} and E_{H-H} are the bond energies for the adsorbed phase and for hydrogen, respectively. Although E_{Me-H} is not available, it may be evaluated by means of the Pauling relationship [544,545]:

$$E_{Me-H} \;=\; \tfrac{1}{2}(E_{Me-Me} + E_{H-H}) \;+\; 23.06(X_{Me} - X_H)^2 \tag{3.40}$$

The last term, containing the electronegativities X, allows for the ionic part of the bond. E_{Me-Me} is obtained from the heat of sublimation of the metal $\Delta_{sub}.U$ by applying

$$E_{Me-Me} \;=\; \frac{2}{12}\ \Delta_{sub}.U \tag{3.41}$$

in the case, for example, of a face centred cubic metal with 12 nearest neighbours. The heat of adsorption is then given by combining equations (3.39) and (3.40) to give

$$q_0 = E_{Me-Me} + 46.12(X_{Me} - X_H)^2 \tag{3.42}$$

It is difficult to obtain a value for the difference of electronegativities. However, two approximate methods of arriving at this have been proposed.

(1) According to Eley [179,180], the difference of electronegativities may be taken as the dipole moment M of the Me–H bond. M can be evaluated from measurements of the surface potential (see Section 5.1), although there are a number of problems concerning the determination of M.

(2) According to Stevenson [635], the electronegativity of the metal is given by $X_{Me} = 0.355e_0\phi$ (that is, in terms of the work function), while Pauling's value [545] of 2.1 is used for the electronegativity X_H.

Experimental heats of adsorption for a number of chemisorption systems have been collected together in *Table 3.3*, which also gives the values calculated by Eley and by Stevenson. Clearly the calculated values are of the correct order of magnitude and we may conclude that in these systems the bonding has a predominantly covalent character.

Many attempts have been made [442] to improve the agreement between calculated and experimental values. Special attention has been paid to allowing for the ionic part of the bond (see, for instance, reference 318). Nevertheless such detailed comparisons would appear to be premature in view of the uncertainty which is associated with the experimental values (see Ni/H$_2$).

Table 3.3 Measured and calculated heats of chemisorption [318]

System	$q_{0,exp.}$	Eley $q_{0,calc.}$	Stevenson $q_{0,calc.}$
	kcal mol⁻¹	kcal mol⁻¹	kcal mol⁻¹
Ta/H$_2$	45	33.5	50
W/H$_2$	45	36.7	46
Cr/H$_2$	45	16.2	24
Ni/H$_2$	18...42	18.6	29
Fe/H$_2$	32	19.0	32

The heat of adsorption has also been calculated for other gases – CO, N_2, O_2, CO_2, C_2H_4, NH_3 – and compared with the experimentally determined values. The calculations are similar to those for adsorption of hydrogen. In this way it has again been shown that the bonding in the adsorbed phase must have a predominantly covalent character.

As already mentioned in Section 2.5, the heat evolved during adsorption can be used as a measure of the amount adsorbed. Such 'thermal titration' is useful for determining the amount of metallic constituent in a supported catalyst. A flow calorimeter is applied to this end [393, 394].

3.3. Molar heat capacity and entropy of adsorption

For the complete thermodynamic description of an adsorption system one must have data on the molar heat capacity and the entropy of the system. These data are primarily of interest in the case of physisorption systems and have been obtained chiefly on such systems as a result. The significance of these quantities lies in the fact that they are determined directly by the state of the bound adsorbate. An exhaustive treatment of these problems is to be found, for instance, in Young and Crowell [737], Ross and Oliver [584] or Flood [225,226]. Here we shall only mention this extensive field briefly.

Morrison and Los [486] have described a precision calorimeter which is suitable for the measurement of the molar heat capacity of the bound adsorbate. The instrument operates adiabatically. One either makes a direct measurement of the molar heat capacity or determines it from the temperature dependence of the heat of adsorption according to

$$c_S = c_G + \left(\frac{\partial q}{\partial T}\right)_\theta \tag{3.43}$$

where c_S is the molar heat capacity of the bound adsorbate and c_G that of the free adsorbate. Again, the temperature dependence of the molar heat capacity is of interest because it may be used to calculate entropy (see, for instance, reference 528) and especially the zero-point entropy. We also note that phase changes in the adsorbed layer are shown up in the temperature dependence of the molar heat capacity of the bound adsorbate. This method was used, for instance, by Morrison, Drain and Dugdale [485] to reveal phase changes in nitrogen physisorbed on rutile.

According to equation (2.2), the entropy of the bound adsorbate s_S may be calculated from the equilibrium values of the heat of adsorption ΔH if the surface pressure Φ is known, as in equation (2.2). s_S may also be calculated from the isosteric heats of adsorption. Both methods require that measurements of the equilibrium pressure are made.

The experimental values of entropy which have been obtained in one of these ways are then compared with theoretical values obtained on the basis of certain adsorption models. For this purpose entropies are calculated from the partition functions according to the rules of statistical thermodynamics. The model adopted is decisive in determining the entropy value because degrees of translational, rotational and vibrational freedom are lost in passing from the gaseous to the adsorbed state and the extent to which this occurs depends on the state of sorption. On the other hand, an entropy of configuration makes its appearance in the case of localised immobile adsorption. It enables differing ways of arranging the adsorbate on the adsorbent to be taken into account. In this connection, special significance is also associated with the zero-point entropy [124,340,528,632]. A study of the entropy of the bound adsorbate thus yields additional information on the mobility of the adsorbate on the adsorbent. Intensive investigations along these lines have been pursued, particularly by Everett [207], Kemball [363] and de Boer and Kruyer [134-139].

The adsorption of hydrogen on annealed nickel films was subjected to such an investigation by Rideal and Sweett [575]. They determined the isosteric heats of adsorption from adsorption isosteres, plotted as log $p_{H_2} = f(1/T)$. These isosteric heats $q_{st} = h_G - \bar{h}_S$ (see curve 4 in *Figure 3.9*) were integrated graphically to give the molar heat of adsorption according to the integral

$$h_{S,\theta} - h_G = \frac{1}{\theta} \int_0^\theta (\bar{h}_{S,\theta} - h_G) d\theta \tag{3.44}$$

As we have explained in Section 2.1, a knowledge of the molar entropy of the bound adsorbate s_S is needed if we are to compare the calculated entropy values. The isosteric heats of adsorption only give us the partial molar entropy $\bar{s}_S$, the two entropies being related according to the equation

$$\bar{s}_{S,\theta} = \left(\frac{\partial S_{S,\theta}}{\partial (n\theta)} \right)_T = \left(\frac{\partial (n\theta s)_{S,\theta}}{\partial (n\theta)} \right)_T = \theta \left(\frac{\partial s_{S,\theta}}{\partial \theta} \right)_T + s_{S,\theta} \tag{3.45}$$

or

$$s_{S,\theta} = \frac{1}{\theta} \int_0^\theta \bar{s}_{S,\theta} \, d\theta \tag{3.46}$$

Consider the change in free energy ΔG which occurs when an infinitely small amount of gas standing at temperature T under a pressure of 1 atm passes isothermally into the adsorbed state (equilibrium pressure p). ΔG is then given by

$$\Delta G = (\bar{h}_{S,\theta} - h_G) - T(\bar{s}_{S,\theta} - s_G) \tag{3.47}$$

and also by

$$\Delta G = RT \ln p \tag{3.48}$$

We may therefore write

$$\bar{s}_{S,\theta} = s_G - R \ln p + \frac{1}{T}(h_{S,\theta} - h_G) \tag{3.49}$$

If this is substituted in equation (3.46) and the result combined with equation (3.44), we obtain for the molar entropy of the bound adsorbate

$$s_{S,\theta} = s_G - \frac{R}{\theta}\int_0^\theta \ln p \, d\theta + \frac{1}{T}(h_{S,\theta} - h_G) \tag{3.50}$$

Curve 1 in *Figure 3.12* shows the molar entropies for adsorbed hydrogen which were obtained in this way by Rideal and Sweett.

In order to set up a model for the adsorption process, we may assume that hydrogen is dissociated on the nickel surface and then adsorbed as localised atoms. As such, the bound adsorbate possesses neither translational nor rotational nor vibrational degrees of freedom. Only the configurational entropy then comes into question. According to Everett [207], it is given in this case by

$$s_{S,\text{conf.}} = -2R \ln \theta - 2R\left(\frac{1}{\theta} - 1\right)\ln(1 - \theta) \text{ cal K}^{-1} \text{ mol}^{-1} \tag{3.51}$$

This function is shown as curve 2 in *Figure 3.12*. If no dissociation of hydrogen occurs, then the configurational entropies are halved.

If, however, the adsorbed phase is mobile, then the translational entropy of the two-dimensional gas must be taken into account. According to Kemball [363], this is given by

$$s_{S,\text{trans.}} = R \ln(MTa) + 65.8 \text{ cal K}^{-1} \text{ mol}^{-1} \tag{3.52}$$

where M is the molecular weight of the adsorbate and a is the area in square centimetres which is available per adsorbed molecule. Taking the case of nickel with an average value of $a = 6.5 \times 10^{-16}$ cm^2 per adsorption site, we evaluate $s_{S,\text{trans.}}$ at 25 °C from equation (3.52) for a number of adsorbed states:

for H atoms which occupy one site at $\theta = 1$

$$s_{S,\text{trans.}} = 15.1 - 9.16 \log \theta \tag{3.53}$$

for H atoms which occupy two sites at $\theta = 1$

$$s_{S,\text{trans.}} = 17.9 - 9.16 \log \theta \tag{3.54}$$

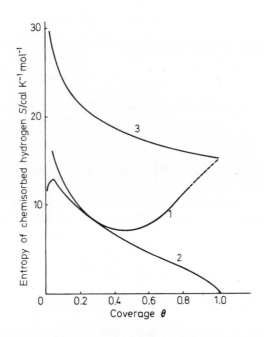

Figure 3.12   Entropy of hydrogen adsorbed on nickel at 25 °C after Rideal and Sweett [575]:   curve 1, experimental values of the molar entropy $s_{S,\theta}$ evaluated by use of equation (3.50); curve 2, configurational entropy for localised adsorption of hydrogen atoms obtained from equation (3.51); curve 3, translational entropy obtained from equation (3.53)

for H_2 molecules which occupy one site at $\theta = 1$

$$s_{S,trans.} = 8.9 - 4.58 \log \theta \tag{3.55}$$

and

for H_2 molecules which occupy two sites at $\theta = 1$

$$s_{S,trans.} = 10.3 - 4.58 \log \theta \tag{3.56}$$

The transitional entropy corresponding to equation (3.53) is shown as curve 3 in *Figure 3.12*.

We see that curve 2 is much the same as the experimentally determined curve 1 up to a coverage of about $\theta = 0.4$. This means that hydrogen is atomically bound and immobile at 278 K. At higher coverages the experimentally determined entropy is significantly higher than the configurational entropy. This means that the adsorbed layer becomes more mobile as the coverage rises. As θ rises to 1, the experimental values of $s_{S,conf.}$ approach 15 cal K^{-1} mol^{-1}. According to equation (3.53), this would indicate that the adsorption continues to be atomic. In any event we must take translational as well as configurational entropy into account in the region $0.4 < \theta < 1$.

In the general case it would be necessary to make additional checks to see whether a contribution from rotation or vibration should be included in the entropy.

The example we have given shows that the discussion of entropy enables valuable information about the state of the bonding and the mobility to be obtained. The reliability of the conclusions should, nevertheless, not be overestimated, especially as it is rare to find a limiting case which is easily explained. One should therefore give preference to direct methods of attack as far as possible. Mobility can, for instance, be investigated by field emission microscopy (see Section 5.6). But one should always try to draw in additional indirect methods for the investigation of mobility.

3.4. Thermal desorption spectra and the flash filament technique

Our examination of the way in which the heat of adsorption depends on coverage has revealed that the heat of adsorption usually falls with rising coverage. This could be due to two things: either the adsorbed molecules interact mutually (induced heterogeneity) or distinguishable binding states occur on various regions of differing energy on the adsorbent surface (*a priori* heterogeneity). A study of thermal desorption spectra is one of the methods by which these two possibilities may be distinguished.

According to the energetics and the kinetics of adsorption and desorption (Sections 2.2 and 2.3), the activation energy for desorption ΔE_d is given by

$$\Delta E_d = q_0 + \Delta E_a \tag{3.57}$$

viz. by the sum of the heat of adsorption q_0 and the activation energy for adsorption ΔE_a.

If an adsorption system at low temperature is warmed, then the adsorbed gas is partially desorbed. The temperature at which this occurs is a direct measure of ΔE_d and this, in turn, is invariably a measure of the binding strength. As a result of stepwise desorption, pressure rises occur during warming or, if the gas phase is pumped continuously, pressure maxima occur. Moreover, the height of each maximum is a measure of the quantity of gas desorbed under the particular conditions employed.

The methods of recording thermal desorption spectra may be divided into three groups:

   (1) The flash filament method, in which the adsorbent is a wire or a metal ribbon.

(2) The general method of heating to desorb, in which evaporated metal films can also be used as the adsorbent.

(3) Desorption from porous powder adsorbents.

In the flash filament method [167-170,565] the wire or ribbon which acts as the adsorbent is electrically heated at a convenient rate. The temperature of the adsorbent can be found from its electrical resistance at any time and the gas pressure can be measured with an ionisation gauge. Depending on the rate at which the adsorbent is heated, an XY recorder or an oscilloscope is used to record the spectra, temperature being fed on to the X input and pressure on to the Y input.

Desorption spectra observed by Redhead are typical of the results to be obtained in this manner. His spectra for the W/CO system are reproduced in *Figure 3.13*.

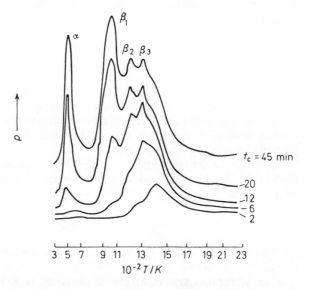

Figure 3.13   Desorption spectra of carbon monoxide adsorbed on tungsten at 300 K; after Redhead [565]. Rate of heating 35 K s^{-1}. For the sake of clarity, the curves have been displaced vertically with respect to each other. (Pressures were measured as a function of time. Since the temperature did not vary linearly with time, the abscissa scale is also not linear)

The number attached to each curve refers to the time of adsorption — that is, the time during which a low pressure of carbon monoxide was allowed to flow from a gas reservoir on to the tungsten wire at 300 K. These times are a measure of the total amount adsorbed, the top curve corresponding approximately to saturation. The equilibrium pressure during adsorption was about 5×10^{-9} Torr. The pressure maxima which occur during desorption can clearly be divided into two groups.

Thus there is an α-maximum which occurs at a temperature of around 500 K and there are several maxima designated as β which appear at temperatures between 900 and 1400 K.

At low coverage the β_3-maximum is invariably the only peak to be observed. This peak occurs at the highest temperature. Hand in hand with increasing coverage, the β_2-, β_1- and α-peaks then appear at respectively lower temperatures. These curves therefore reveal very clearly that carbon monoxide is adsorbed on tungsten with a bond strength which varies. Furthermore, adsorption at low coverage occurs first at those centres which can form the strongest bond.

If we know the rate of desorption and the temperature at which the desorption maximum occurs, it is possible to evaluate the activation energy for desorption from equation (2.22). This, in turn, enables an approximate value for the enthalpy of adsorption to be deduced. In this way Redhead calculated the following activation energies from *Figure 3.13*. α-maximum: 29 kcal mol^{-1}; β_1-maximum: 61 kcal mol^{-1}; β_2-maximum: 69 kcal mol^{-1}; β_3-maximum: 74 kcal mol^{-1}.

It is also possible to deduce the order of the reaction in addition to the activation energy for desorption if the time dependence of the temperature change is known (preferably a linear rate of heating). This was done, for instance, by Redhead [565,566], using the position and the shape of his desorption peaks, and it enables an even deeper insight to be obtained into the mechanism of desorption. Thermal desorption data may be processed for linear, hyperbolic and exponential heating regimes by use of tables and charts [622]. The significance and evaluation of experimental data have also been the subject of a very critical review by Pétermann [549].

If the adsorbent is an evaporated film or a single crystal, such as is used in LEED investigations, then it is not possible to achieve very rapid temperature rises. Furthermore, compared with the flash filament method the upper limit for the temperature is limited by the apparatus to considerably lower values (600 K for films; 800 to 900 K for single crystals). On the other hand, one can use simple heating desorption to investigate the low-temperature region particularly well.

Slow heating of the adsorbent does, however, lead to a possible complication, as discussed by Hayward, Taylor and Tompkins [317]. Thus under certain circumstances it is no longer possible to ascribe a particular state of adsorption to every maximum in the desorption spectrum. This situation arises when rearrangements can occur within the adsorption system, as occasioned by the ability of the adsorbed phase to diffuse to sites which were inaccessible during adsorption from the gas phase at lower temperature. The effect therefore occurs as soon as the temperature reaches a value at which the adsorbed phase is mobile. The resulting redistribution on the surface then leads to a transient fall in the pressure.

By taking into account the possibility of these disturbances, one can still use desorption spectra to find out how the adsorbed phase is distributed among the individual adsorption energies. King's [364]

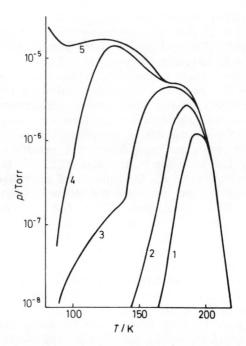

Figure 3.14   Desorption spectra for nitrogen adsorbed at 78 K on an annealed nickel film; after King [364].   The uptake for each curve was: (1) 0.17 × 10¹⁴, (2) 0.5 × 10¹⁴, (3) 1.3 × 10¹⁴, (4) 3.5 × 10¹⁴, (5) 5.4 × 10¹⁴ molecules cm⁻²

investigation of the Ni/N_2 system serves as an example. *Figure 3.14* shows how sites of lower adsorption energy are increasingly occupied as the coverage rises. The energy distribution which was calculated from these desorption spectra is shown in *Figure 3.15*. The numbers 3, 4 and 5 refer to the corresponding desorption curves in *Figure 3.14*.

By taking into account the influence which annealing or the crystallographic make-up of nickel films had on the desorption spectra, King [364] was able to assign the individual states of adsorption to specific crystal planes of nickel: the most weakly bound γ_1-state with a binding energy of <7 kcal mol⁻¹ is located on the (111) plane; the γ_2-state (6-10 kcal mol⁻¹) on the (100) plane; and the most strongly held γ_3-state (9-14 kcal mol⁻¹) on the (100) and higher index planes.

While nitrogen is only weakly adsorbed on nickel, the majority of the uptake probably being physisorbed, the systems nickel/hydrogen and nickel/carbon monoxide show an additional strong chemisorption. This is shown up by comparing *Figure 3.14* with *Figure 3.16*, which reproduces desorption spectra recorded by Wedler and co-workers [693, 697] for hydrogen and for carbon monoxide on nickel films. The desorption maximum associated with the most strongly bound nitrogen

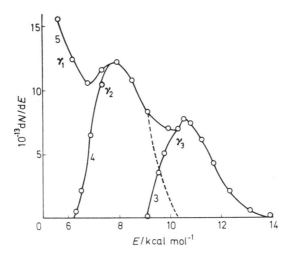

Figure 3.15 Distribution of the adsorption energies of nitrogen on a nickel film, after King [364], calculated from the desorption spectra shown in Figure 3.14

(γ_3) occurs at 195 K; that for the most strongly bound hydrogen at 380 K; and that for the most strongly bound carbon monoxide at 490 K. This order is reflected in the order for the heats of adsorption at low coverages (see also Section 3.2): $q_{Ni/N_2} \sim 10$ kcal mol^{-1}, $q_{Ni/H_2} = 18$ kcal mol^{-1} and $q_{Ni/CO} = 30$ kcal mol^{-1}.

The study of the desorption spectrum of hydrogen on nickel has shown in particular just how important it is to use a partial pressure gauge, such as a quadrupole mass spectrometer [693], to measure the pressure. Thus in earlier work on the desorption of hydrogen on nickel [576,577,591] in which only the total pressure was monitored, it had been found that further peaks existed at 170 and 200 K. Later [693] these peaks could be identified with desorbed contaminants (Ar, N_2, CH_4).

As *Figure 3.16* shows, the two adsorption systems Ni/H$_2$ and Ni/CO behave qualitatively in a very similar way as regards their desorption spectra. At coverages which are less than half a monolayer of molecules, one only observes a single pressure maximum. This is ascribed to the desorption of a β_2-state. If the coverage exceeds half a monolayer, then, as Völter and co-workers [576,577,675] have already shown, a further peak begins to build up. This peak is ascribed to a second state of chemisorption (β_1). Only at above monolayer coverage does one find a third species (γ), which is adsorbed particularly weakly and is probably physisorbed. The γ-species desorbs at the lowest temperature.

Recent efforts have been directed at fitting theoretically calculated desorption curves to the experimentally derived ones. This leads to

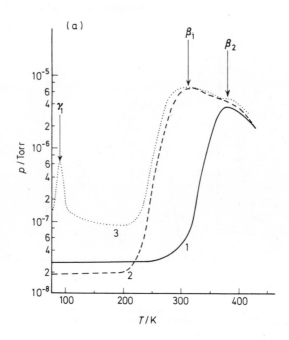

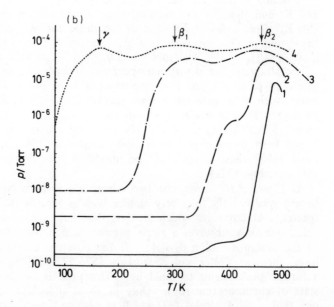

Figure 3.16 (a) Desorption spectra for hydrogen adsorbed on nickel films at 77 K; after Wedler et al. [693]. The coverages corresponding to the curves are (1) θ = 0.4, (2) θ = 1.0, (3) θ = 1.1. (b) Desorption spectra for carbon monoxide adsorbed on nickel films at 77 K; after Wedler and Papp [697]. The coverages corresponding to the curves are (1) θ = 0.2, (2) θ = 0.5, (3) θ = 1.05, (4) θ = 1.36

values for the activation energy for desorption, the interaction energy between adsorbed particles and the reaction order for desorption. Such an evaluation necessitates the condition that the temperature during the desorption process changes with time in a strictly linear matter. This condition has not been assured, however, in most of the work that has been published to date. Using the correct conditions, Benndorf and Thieme [46] were able to show that chemisorbed hydrogen desorbs according to second order kinetics. It follows from this that hydrogen in the chemisorbed state must be atomically adsorbed.

Recently desorption spectra for hydrogen on nickel single crystals have also been recorded [121,408-410]. The desorption spectra show far-reaching agreement with those reproduced in *Figure 3.16(a)*, although they were only taken above 258 K. While the behaviour of hydrogen on the (100) and (111) faces is much the same, hydrogen on the (110) face shows distinct differences. Christmann *et al.* [121] find that the desorption kinetics in the first two cases are second order but they think the third case is first order. The activation energies for desorption were determined as 23 ± 1 kcal mol^{-1} for desorption from the (100) and the (111) faces, and 20.3 kcal mol^{-1}, rising to 23 kcal mol^{-1}, for desorption from the (110) face. A review of some desorption spectra on single crystals has been published by Schmidt [592].

Turning to technical catalysts which consist of finely divided powders, we note that the entire desorption process is diffusion-controlled, so that attempts to produce desorption spectra of the type considered only lead to pressure maxima that are very blurred. Amenomiya and Cvetanovic [5-8,130] overcame these difficulties in the following way. The adsorbent was first charged with adsorbate (generally a hydrocarbon), the gas phase was pumped out and then a constant flow of an inert carrier gas (helium) was passed through the powdered catalyst. When the temperature is now raised, the hydrocarbons are desorbed and carried by the helium into a suitable detector, where they are quantitatively determined. The desorption spectra produced by this technique are very similar to the ones obtained by the flash filament or the thermal desorption method considered previously.

Frequently, however, it is not established at the outset whether the desorbed gas is chemically identical with the adsorbate. Thus, under certain circumstances, chemisorption can lead to decomposition reactions and conversions. Both for this reason and for the one mentioned earlier, the pressure in all the methods we have covered is appropriately measured with a partial pressure gauge. Moore and Unterwald [484] used a mass spectrometer; Ricca and co-workers [573,574], as well as Yates and Madey [734], used an omegatron; and McCarroll [429] used a time-of-flight mass spectrometer.

Using the flash filament technique, Yates and Madey [734] investigated the adsorption of nitrogen on tungsten. They used an equimolar mixture of $^{14}N_2$ and $^{15}N_2$ and monitored the partial pressure of masses 28, 29 and 30. The experiments showed that at 77 K the adsorption was mainly molecular because the nitrogen which was desorbed at 200 K contained no mass 29 component. On the other hand, gas which was desorbed at about 1300 K did contain mass 29 in such quantities as to indicate that the majority of the adsorption was fully atomic. The same approach was taken by Wedler, Borgmann and Geuss [690] to decide whether nitrogen is adsorbed dissociatively or as molecules on polycrystalline iron films. The mass spectrometric analysis revealed that in this case there was no isotopic equilibration among gas molecules taken up at temperatures up to 400 K. By using an iron wire as the catalyst, it could be shown that isotopic equilibration did not even occur at red heat. The gas must therefore be adsorbed as molecules.

Recording desorption spectra thus not only enables differing binding states to be identified, but also permits conclusions to be drawn concerning the nature of these binding states. It is worth noting that in the last few years evidence has been accumulating which suggests that desorption spectra are unable to resolve the fine structure in binding states. For instance, calorimetric measurements using the calorimeter shown in *Figure 3.8* have been applied to the iron/hydrogen system and it turns out that the β_2-state, which corresponds to the β_2-state in *Figure 3.16(a)*, really consists of two states. These states, which have heats of adsorption differing by barely 2 kcal mol^{-1} [696], are responsible for the shift from 450 to 430 K which is observed for the desorption maximum as the coverage rises [688]. Yates *et al.* [732] were also able to prove by means of IR spectroscopic investigations that the a-state for CO on W shown in *Figure 3.13* is, in fact, made up of two distinguishable states, a_1 and a_2.

Completely new possibilities should be afforded by laser-induced desorption. In this technique, which was introduced by Ertl and Neumann [194], the surface region of the adsorbent is strongly heated by a laser flash for a few microseconds. This leads to a momentary desorption, but since the whole of the adsorbent, including the heated part, returns to its starting temperature within a few microseconds, the adsorption equilibrium is rapidly re-established. The re-establishment can be followed by measuring any parameter which depends on the coverage yet is virtually free of lag. Such a parameter is the surface potential (see Section 5.1). In this way it should be possible to apply a relaxation method to the investigation of the kinetics of adsorption-desorption processes.

3.5.   Isotope exchange

The previous section has shown us that adsorbed molecules can be bound to the adsorbent in various energy states at the same time. The explanation for this is to be sought in terms of the energetic and structural heterogeneity of the surface. Hayward, Taylor and Tompkins [317] were able to conclude from their desorption spectra that under certain circumstances an equilibrium must exist between the various states. The equilibrium will be set up as soon as the adsorbate possesses sufficient surface mobility. Desorption spectra cannot tell us, however, whether all the adsorbed states contribute to the equilibrium at any particular temperature or in which order the different states are occupied during adsorption.

Measurements using isotopes enable these matters to be clarified. In addition, such measurements permit conclusions to be drawn concerning the path of the surface reaction. We shall begin by discussing those investigations which concern heterogeneity and mobility of the adsorbate.

The surface is partially or entirely covered with molecules marked with an isotope and exchange is then followed with molecules marked with another isotope. The evaluation of data is particularly simple if no isotope effect is to be expected on grounds of small mass differences — as, for example, with the variously marked carbon monoxide molecules. Should the marked molecules differ substantially in their masses, as in the case of water, deuterium and tritium, then isotope effects must be taken into account.

Toya [666] has criticised the 'differential isotope method' developed by Keier and Roginskii [362]. He points out that complete coverage of the surface must be established during exchange measurements in order to draw meaningful conclusions regarding the presence or absence of any heterogeneity.

Suhrmann, Heyne and Wedler [647] have studied the adsorption of carbon monoxide on evaporated nickel films, taking this requirement into account. They used $^{12}C^{16}O$ (mass 28), $^{13}C^{16}O$ (mass 29) and $^{12}C^{18}O$ (mass 30). Their films were first covered with $^{12}C^{18}O$ up to $\theta = 0.15$, then with $^{13}C^{16}O$ up to $\theta = 0.5$ and finally with $^{12}C^{16}O$, until there was an equilibrium pressure of 8×10^{-3} Torr. Two series of experiments (A and B) were conducted, the difference between them being that in A the entire coverage was taken up at 77 K, whereas in B $^{12}C^{18}O$, $^{13}C^{16}O$ and $^{12}C^{16}O$ were taken up at 273 K, but only to an equilibrium pressure of about 10^{-7} Torr; B films were then cooled to 77 K and more $^{12}C^{16}O$ was adsorbed up to an equilibrium pressure of 8×10^{-3} Torr.

The gas phase above the surface was now analysed continuously in both series with a mass spectrometer (Atlas CH3). It seemed worth establishing to what extent the adsorption equilibrium for the various types of molecules set itself up. Since there was a large excess of $^{12}C^{16}O$ molecules in the gas phase, it is evident that the establishment of equilibrium would involve displacement of both $^{12}C^{18}O$ and $^{13}C^{16}O$ from the adsorbed phase.

It is convenient to describe the observations in terms of a ratio $x = (N_a/N_g)_M$, where N_a and N_g are the numbers of molecules of gas of mass M in the adsorbed phase and in the gas phase, respectively. In series A, x increased in the order $x_{30} < x_{29} < x_{28}$. Clearly adsorption equilibrium was not established, otherwise the x-values for all masses would have been the same. Similar x-values for x_{30} and x_{29} were, in fact, observed in series B.

Equilib..ium only set in for all masses when the nickel films were warmed slowly from 77 K to 195 K, i.e. at 195 K $x_{30} = x_{29} = x_{28}$. The results obtained during warming in both series of experiments are given in *Figures 3.17* and *3.18*. The ratio $(N_T/N_{195})_M$ has been plotted against temperature, where N_T and N_{195} are the numbers of molecules of mass M in the gas phase at temperature T and 195 K, respectively; these quantities were measured after the establishment of equilibrium. Notice that in series A (adsorption temperature 77 K) the adsorption equilibrium for the first-adsorbed $^{12}C^{18}O$ molecules sets in at higher temperatures than the equilibrium for the $^{13}C^{16}O$ molecules that were adsorbed between $\theta = 0.15$ and $\theta = 0.5$. The molecules adsorbed at low coverage must therefore be bound to the adsorbent more tightly than the molecules adsorbed at higher coverage. This result speaks unequivocally for the existence of energetic heterogeneity.

The results for an adsorption temperature of 273 K are shown in *Figure 3.18*. Here we notice that the equilibrium for masses 30 and 29 sets in to just the same extent. The difference between those molecules adsorbed at $\theta < 0.15$ and those adsorbed at $0.15 \leqslant \theta \leqslant 0.5$ cannot be recognised any more. Since the difference that was clearly proved at 77 K no longer exists at 273 K, we may conclude that place exchange between $^{12}C^{18}O$ and $^{13}C^{16}O$ occurs at the higher temperature, i.e. at 273 K the adsorbed layer is mobile, but according to the results obtained, the layer is immobile at 77 K.

Mass 31, as in $^{13}C^{18}O$, was never found in any experiment. This proves that below 273 K carbon monoxide must always be bound to nickel as a molecule. Decomposition into oxygen and carbon atoms is no more in evidence than isotope exchange among the adsorbed molecules.

These rather qualitative results regarding the extent of the heterogeneity were supplemented by the further work of Fricke [241]. He investigated the kinetics of exchange between $^{12}C^{16}O$ and $^{12}C^{18}O$ or $^{13}C^{16}O$ on nickel and iron films at temperatures between 90 and 195 K. A relationship was discovered linking the activation energy for establishing equilibrium and the enthalpy of adsorption to the coverage, and quantitative statements could be made about the heterogeneity of nickel films as far as the adsorption of carbon monoxide was concerned. The conclusions were essentially in agreement with those deduced for the nickel/hydrogen system by Gundry [287].

Hydrogen/deuterium exchange has been drawn into the study of heterogeneity in a number of ways. The nickel/hydrogen system has been investigated by Schuit and co-workers [598-600], Gundry [287] and Wedler and Santelmann [701], while the palladium/hydrogen system was investigated by Suhrmann, Schumicki and Wedler [652]. The platinum/hydrogen system has also been studied by Gentsch [252] as well as Boreskov and Vassilevich [81,82]. The method of Schuit, Gundry, Gentsch and Boreskov employed the principle we have described for investigating the nickel/carbon monoxide system: at a

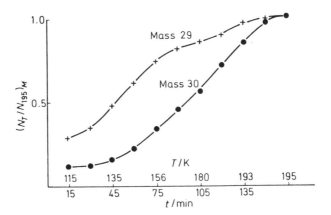

Figure 3.17 Increase of the ratio N_T/N_{195} for CO molecules in the gas phase as a function of T. Temperature of adsorption, 77 K [647]. The adsorbent is a nickel film

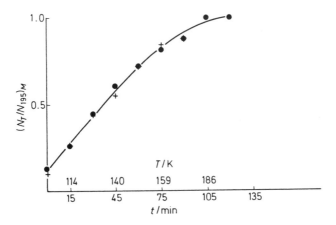

Figure 3.18 Increase of the ratio N_T/N_{195} for CO molecules in the gas phase as a function of T. +, mass 29; •, mass 30. Temperature of adsorption, 273 K [647]. The adsorbent is a nickel film

certain temperature, adsorbents in the form of films or supported catalysts were precovered to an arbitrary extent with hydrogen or deuterium. Adsorbed gas was then exchanged with the other unadsorbed isotope.

Both activation energies for exchange and any isotope effects occurring could be specified after studying the kinetics and the equilibrium conditions attained. Gasser, Roberts and Stevens [251] have specially concerned themselves with the mechanism of hydrogen/deuterium exchange on nickel.

In contrast, an elution technique was employed by Suhrmann, Wedler and co-workers [652,701]. They first covered their adsorbents with an amount of one isotope, say deuterium, which varied from film to film. If there was a residual gas pressure, the gas was pumped off before the elution experiment was started. About 5×10^{-3} Torr of the other isotope – hydrogen in this case – was then repeatedly admitted and the gas phase was pumped off again. On each occasion the gas phase was allowed to stand over the film for a while. If adsorption equilibrium is established during each cycle, then the concentration of deuterium on the film is bound to fall, i.e. deuterium will be progressively eluted. On the other hand, if deuterium is held on the adsorbent in markedly differing states, then one might expect that the activation energy for exchange of at least one of these states would not be available. In this case an unexchangeable residue would finally be left on the film after many elution steps; during each individual step the deuterium taking part in equilibration would only be that decreasing amount left surrounding the unexchangeable fraction. Both types of behaviour are actually observed in the palladium/deuterium system at 295 K, as evidenced in *Figure 3.19*. No unexchangeable residue can be detected when the film has 0.38×10^{15} (curve 1) or 0.98×10^{15} molecules cm^{-2} (curve 2) preadsorbed. These uptakes correspond to $\theta = 0.15$ and $\theta = 0.4$, respectively. However, if the preadsorbed quantity is 2.37×10^{15} molecules cm^{-2} or almost the monolayer coverage, then an unexchangeable residue of 0.74×10^{15} molecules cm^{-2} remains on the film after numerous elution steps. Calculations confirm [652] that this residue has not taken part in any of the equilibration steps.

One may conclude from this result that the deuterium taken up initially to about $\theta = 0.5$ must be more loosely bound than that taken up at higher coverage. There is, therefore, in the palladium/deuterium system – the same holds for the palladium/hydrogen system – a certain coverage above which the adsorbed phase must exist in a new state. This new state can only be wrested from the surface with a very high activation energy. An explanation for this unexpected result could be that after the chemisorbed layer has been built up, there is bulk uptake [655] in the palladium/hydrogen system. The unexchangeable residue would thus represent the transition from chemisorption to absorption. According to Section 2.2 and *Figure 2.3*, one should, in fact, expect to find a high activation energy for penetration

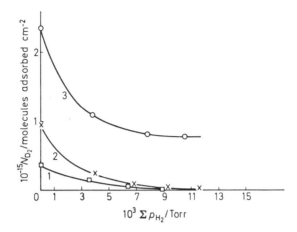

Figure 3.19   Elution of deuterium from a palladium film by repeatedly adsorbing hydrogen at 295 K [652]. Σp_{H_2}, the cumulative total pressure of hydrogen used for elution, is plotted as abscissa.   The preadsorbed quantities of deuterium are as follows: curve (1) 0.38 × 10¹⁵, curve (2) 0.98 × 10¹⁵, curve (3) 2.37 × 10¹⁵ molecules cm⁻²

of the adsorbed phase through the surface of the adsorbent.   This barrier causes absorption to be kinetically disfavoured in comparison with chemisorption, and absorption will only play a role at higher coverage.

A different picture emerges for the nickel/hydrogen system.   In agreement with Gundry [287], Wedler and Santelmann [701] found that there was complete exchange at 195 K and 273 K, but practically no exchange of hydrogen with deuterium or vice versa at 77 K (*Figure 3.20*).   While the results for adsorption and exchange obtained at 195 K are similar to the results at 273 K, one observes an unexchangeable residue at 150 K (*Figure 3.21*).   In contrast to the palladium/hydrogen system, however, the unexchangeable residue does not appear after reaching a certain coverage but instead it is present already at low coverage.   Furthermore, the amount which does not take part in the exchange equilibrium is proportional to the total amount chemisorbed: 0.30 × 10¹⁴ molecules cm⁻² for a preadsorption of 1.35 × 10¹⁵ molecules cm⁻² and 0.13 × 10¹⁴ molecules cm⁻² for a preadsorption of 0.7 × 10¹⁵ molecules cm⁻².   This means that at every stage during adsorption some 20 per cent of the adsorbed phase must be bound in a manner that is energetically particularly favoured.   Gundry [287] mentions that about 10 per cent of the surface is heterogeneous and specially active.

Since the exchange temperature, but not the adsorption temperature, exerts an influence on the results of the exchange experiments, we may infer from the results given above that at 77 K hydrogen is

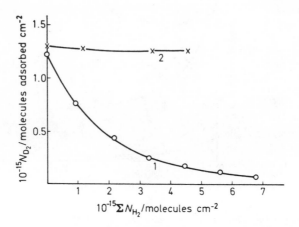

Figure 3.20 Elution of deuterium adsorbed on a nickel film by repeatedly adsorbing hydrogen at 273 K (curve 1) and at 77 K (curve 2). The ordinates are the amounts of deuterium left on the film and the abscissae are a cumulative measure of the hydrogen quantities admitted

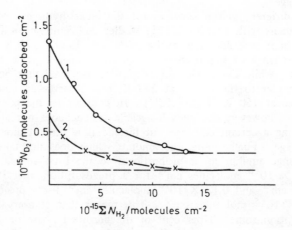

Figure 3.21 Elution of deuterium adsorbed on a nickel film by repeatedly adsorbing hydrogen at 150 K. The preadsorbed quantities of deuterium are 1.35 × 10^{15} (curve 1) and 0.70 × 10^{15} molecules cm^{-2} (curve 2)

immobile on the nickel films, that at 150 K it is partially mobile and that at temperatures of 195 K or above it is fully mobile. By partial mobility we mean that some of the variously adsorbed species are mobile and others are immobile.

As has been mentioned in Section 3.4, the use of isotopes may also be turned to distinguishing between molecular and dissociative adsorption.

When isotope exchange measurements are applied to the study of chemisorption on oxides, one has an important additional advantage. This is the insight which can be gained into the binding situation in the adsorbed phase [718]. Thus more often than not one observes that the oxygen atom in carbon monoxide exchanges with oxygen from the adsorbent without there being any indication that carbon monoxide is dissociating. Clearly a complex must be formed in the adsorbed phase and, in the complex, oxygen formed from the carbon monoxide is indistinguishable from oxygen of the adsorbent.

Isotope exchange experiments are therefore seen to provide us with a valuable supplement to other methods of investigating the heterogeneity of adsorbents. They enable the amount of a strongly adsorbed species to be assessed quantitatively and they also allow the nature of the adsorbed phase to be investigated.

3.6. Sticking probabilities

We have seen that characteristic properties of adsorption systems manifest themselves in adsorption isotherms and enthalpies of adsorption, in the entropy of the bound adsorbate and in thermal desorption spectra. The properties should also — at least partly — be reflected in the kinetics of adsorption. The sticking probability s has been introduced in equation (2.11), and in Section 2.3 the case has been presented for this quantity being a centralised depository for all the data which have bearing on the kinetics of an adsorption system. It is for this reason that there has been no shortage of experiments whose purpose was to investigate adsorption systems via measurements of the sticking probability.

Equation (2.11) shows that the sticking probability may be expressed as a quotient. The numerator corresponds to the number of collisions gas molecules make with the surface of the adsorbent, counting only those collisions which result in adsorption. The denominator, on the other hand, gives the total number of collisions in the same time interval, regardless of whether they lead to adsorption or not. Sticking probabilities were, in fact, originally calculated by direct application of equation (2.11):

$$s = \frac{\begin{array}{c}\text{(total no. of} \\ \text{collisions)}\end{array} - \begin{array}{c}\text{(no. of collisions} \\ \text{which do not lead} \\ \text{to adsorption)}\end{array}}{\text{total no. of collisions}} = \frac{dN_{ads.}/dt}{p/(2\pi mkT)^{1/2}} \qquad (3.58)$$

$dN_{ads.}/dt$ is the rate of adsorption, taken for 1 cm² of surface.

Many sources of experimental error are encountered in the measurement of sticking probabilities and credit must be given to the Tompkins, Hayward, King and Taylor group for the identification of these errors [313] and the formulation of concrete proposals to avoid them. The more important points concern improvements to the apparatus and more exact calculations [312,315]. Correct sticking probabilities will only be obtained if pressures are determined properly, desorption is taken into account, geometric issues are observed and the adsorbate is distributed as evenly as possible on to the film. There is a wide range of experimental possibilities which contorms with these requirements for measuring sticking probabilities.

A particularly clear procedure has been set down by Taylor and co-workers [315,659]. Gas leaves a constant-pressure gas reservoir (pressure p_1) of suitably large dimensions to flow through a capillary (conductance F) and enter the spherical reaction vessel (see *Figure 3.22*). The inner wall of the reaction vessel bears an evaporated metal film and the dimensions of the capillary are chosen so that it takes 10-1000 min for the amount of gas needed to form the monolayer to enter the vessel. The gas inlet tube terminates in a sphere which is full of holes. This ensures that the gas is distributed evenly over the film. A second ionisation gauge is attached to the reaction vessel in such a way that gas which flows into the vessel cannot immediately enter the gauge. The gauge serves to measure the gas pressure in the reaction vessel (pressure p_2).

The quantity of gas which flows into the vessel in unit time $(^A\dot{N}_e)$ follows directly from the pressure difference across the capillary and its conductance:

$$^A\dot{N}_e = F(p_1 - p_2) \tag{3.59}$$

If desorption is not playing any part and p_2 is sufficiently low, then $^A\dot{N}_e$ is identical with the rate of adsorption $A[(dN_{ads.})/dt]$. This is because the mean free path is large and every adsorbate molecule which enters strikes the film. In addition to the molecules which flow through the capillary, however, the film is also struck by molecules which were not adsorbed at first impact. The number of these molecules per unit time is $^A\dot{N}_r$. They, and only they, are responsible for the pressure p_2 which is recorded in the ionisation gauge attached to the vessel. Taking A as the area of the film, the expression corresponding to equation (2.11) becomes

$$^A\dot{N}_r = p_2 A(2\pi mkT)^{-\frac{1}{2}} \tag{3.60}$$

An expression for the sticking probability can now be obtained by combining equations (3.59) and (3.60):

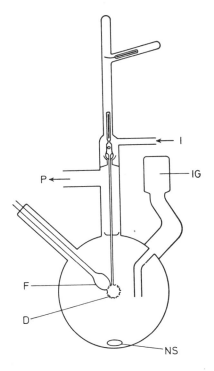

Figure 3.22 Reaction vessel for measuring sticking probabilities; after Taylor and Creasy [659]. I = gas entry; P = to pumps; D = diffuser; F = metal wire for evaporation of the film; IG = ionisation gauge; NS = magnetically operated nickel shield

$$s = \frac{A_{\dot{N}_e}}{A_{\dot{N}_e} + A_{\dot{N}_r}} = \frac{A_{\dot{N}_e}}{A_{\dot{N}_e} + p_2 A(2\pi mkT)^{-\frac{1}{2}}} \tag{3.61}$$

The sticking probability may thus be evaluated from pressure measurements.

For more refined calculations, particularly those which take desorption into account, we refer to the literature [315,316].

In addition to the technique described here, there is, as mentioned above, a range of other methods for measuring the sticking probability. These methods all conform to the given experimental requirements. One of the reasons for these variations is that the measurement of sticking probabilities is frequently combined with other experimental techniques which necessitate working in an all-metal apparatus.

Madey [436,437], for instance, joined up sticking probability determinations and investigations of electron stimulated desorption (see Section 6.5). He observed the fall in the 'steady state' pressure which occurred when he placed his adsorbent in the beam of inflowing molecules, and used this pressure fall to determine the sticking probability directly.

Sticking probabilities are often found at the same time as desorption spectra are recorded (see Section 3.4). To do this, one has to know the pumping speed afforded by the apparatus. A mass balance is set up and the sticking probability can be obtained from pressure measurements [21,365,565,658]. The technique even enables sticking probabilities to be obtained for the different states of adsorption.

Taylor and Creasy [659] investigated the nickel/hydrogen system using the reaction vessel shown in *Figure 3.22* in conjunction with the first method described in this section. They found:

(1) The sticking probability depends on the temperature.
(2) The sticking probability depends on the concentration of the adsorbed phase.
(3) The curve relating sticking probability to coverage shows distinct kinks.
(4) There is evidence of a redistribution of the adsorbate on the adsorbent.

At low coverages the sticking probability at 77 K turns out to be about 0.5, but the value falls as the temperature rises and only amounts to 0.37 at 273 K. As the coverage rises, the sticking probability falls off linearly, which indicates that there is a very small sticking probability on those adsorption sites which are already occupied by hydrogen. Isosteric heats of adsorption can be recorded simultaneously, and it is instructive to compare the way in which sticking probabilities and heats vary with coverage. The comparison shows that the kinks in the sticking probability curve lie at those coverages at which the heat of adsorption begins to fall off sharply. Two regions which differ from each other may therefore be identified in the curve relating sticking probability and coverage.

Using the same method and a very similar reaction vessel, Horgan and King [343] obtained sticking probabilities in the Ni/H_2 system which were like those of Taylor and Creasy at low coverages. One can, however, detect noticeable differences in detail between the two sets of results. This may be attributed to the general difficulty of reproducing measurements of the sticking probability; alternatively, it may be due to the way in which measurements are inordinately sensitive to slight structural differences in the adsorbent.

This last suggestion is nevertheless incapable of explaining the entirely different results of Gasser, Roberts and Stevens [250], who measured the sticking probability of hydrogen on nickel wire using the desorption method. Their sticking probabilities are as much as two orders of magnitude lower than those obtained by Taylor and by King, while no dependence on the coverage was found provided 80 per cent of the maximum uptake was not exceeded.

For the Ni/CO system, Horgan and King [343] measured sticking probabilities which were close to unity at low coverage, being independent of the temperature. The lower the temperature, the larger was the range of coverage over which the sticking probability remained constant, but it always started to fall relatively steeply on reaching a certain coverage. There was, however, a shoulder which developed on the side of the fall-off and which became more marked as the temperature rose. This testifies to the existence of three different species in the Ni/CO system and it agrees with the desorption spectra discussed in Section 3.4.

Measurement of the sticking probability is also a suitable means of investigating rearrangement processes in the adsorbed phase [312,659]. In general, these processes are likely to involve the diffusion of adsorbate molecules to adsorption sites which are not directly accessible from the gas phase. Thus if, instead of adding gas continuously in the usual manner, one interrupts the gas flow for a while, then the sticking probability may be significantly higher on renewing the gas flow. To demonstrate this, one interrupts the experiment at a point at which the sticking probability is clearly falling with rising coverage. The effect must be due to redistribution processes on the adsorbent which free adsorption sites that are accessible from the gas phase.

4

STUDY OF ADSORPTION USING SPECTROSCOPIC AND OPTICAL METHODS

Although the evaluation of thermodynamic quantities has been very helpful in developing an understanding of adsorption processes, these measurements have, nevertheless, been unable to produce satisfactory information concerning the type of bond which exists between the adsorbent and the adsorbate. For this reason it is desirable to make direct measurements or to render visible the changes in physical properties of the adsorbing species and of the adsorbent caused by the adsorption process. Methods of investigation have been drawn from an ever-widening compass. Spectroscopic methods invariably enable changes in the adsorbate to be recognised, while ellipsometry shows up changes in the optical properties of a reflecting surface.

4.1. Infra-red spectra

Special significance can be attached to infra-red spectroscopy. The basic investigations were made by Eischens and co-workers [173,174, 176-178], and since the mid-1950s very many papers have appeared concerning the IR absorption of chemisorbed molecules. The results have been thoroughly discussed in monographs [297,424] and other summary articles [173,177,318,416,425,662].

In general, it is not possible to measure bands corresponding to the adsorbent-adsorbate bond. Changes in spectra, however, characterise the adsorbed molecule as compared with the free adsorbate, and these changes give us valuable information about the state of the bonding in the adsorption complex. In addition, infra-red spectroscopy may often prove to be a suitable tool for distinguishing between physisorption and chemisorption. There may be an absence of new absorption bands when the adsorbate becomes adsorbed but this does not constitute proof of physisorption. On the other hand, the appearance of new bands unequivocally establishes that chemisorption has occurred.

Many difficulties are met in investigations employing infra-red spectroscopy. Initially, the limited absorption in the infra-red obliged investigators to send the beam through many adsorbed layers. Studies on metals were accordingly carried out using supported specimens. This introduced uncertainties with regard to absorption of the supporting material itself, scattering by the supporting material, undefined effects of surface contaminants, etc. As a result, doubt was expressed for a long time as to whether the measured bands actually corresponded to the adsorption complex which would form on an absolutely clean surface.

Attempts were made to avoid these difficulties by evaporating films in an atmosphere of the gas being investigated. In this manner films were obtained which were built up of many layers of the adsorption complex. A further advance occurred in investigations in which measurements were made on evaporated films using multiple transmission or multiple reflection. Only quite recently has it become possible to record infra-red spectra by use of the transmission of a single metal film.

Further problems of technique cropped up when attempts were made to extend the adsorption investigations to include work carried out under ultrahigh vacuum conditions. It is hardly permissible to cement an infra-red-transmitting window (NaCl,KBr) on to a high-vacuum cell, quite apart from the fact that such a cell cannot be baked out. A solution to this problem was first devised by using magnesium oxide as the window material [524]. Magnesium oxide seals directly to soda glass, but the use of intermediate seals to Pyrex borosilicate glass can be avoided by sealing silicon windows directly to Pyrex [541].

Despite our comments, far-reaching agreement has now been obtained under the most varying circumstances for the majority of adsorption systems and the results may be viewed with certainty.

The investigations which are described in the literature may be arranged according to the method of measurement as follows:

(1) Investigations on finely divided or supported adsorbents.
(2) Investigations on pressed pellets.
(3) Investigations on films with multiple transmission.
(4) Investigations on films with multiple reflection.
(5) Investigations on films with a single transmission.

Eischens and co-workers [174,177] carried out their earliest work on supported catalysts. For the support they used a non-porous silica such as Carbosil or Aerosil, which are both available commercially. The small particle size (150-200 Å) of this material acts favourably in so far as the scattering losses are very small. γ-alumina (Alon-C) of similar particle size is less suitable because it is not inert towards gases such as CO and CO_2. The metals (<10 per cent by weight) are brought on to the support in the form of their salts and these are reduced in the measuring cell itself. The absorption of metal particles of only 50-100 Å diameter is so small that it does not affect the measurements.

The cell used by Eischens is reproduced in *Figure 4.1*. It consists of a quartz or Pyrex glass body bearing calcium fluoride windows which are cemented on. An inner tube is wound with a heating wire and serves to heat the calcium fluoride sample-holder, which is mounted inside, to 500 °C. This temperature must be reached if the samples are to be reduced in hydrogen.

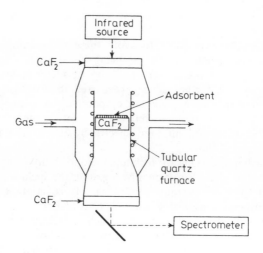

Figure 4.1 Cell for the measurement of infra-red spectra of adsorbed gases; after Eischens and Pliskin [177]

Various other cell constructions [69,380,548,618,729] have served to fit the geometric conditions imposed by infra-red spectrometers and to improve the working conditions.

Nash and De Sieno [510] avoided the disturbing influence of the support and the necessity of reducing a metal salt by fabricating their adsorbent from the explosion of a metal wire in an atmosphere of argon. This technique gave particles of about 200 Å diameter.

Blyholder [63] produced a support-free adsorbent by evaporating iron from a wire in an atmosphere of helium and allowing the metal to condense on an oil film. In this way he obtained an iron emulsion on which he carried out the investigation.

The use of pressed pellets for investigations of the infra-red spectra of adsorption systems has been described by Pliskin and Eischens [552] and by Erkelens and Liefkens [185].

Very much cleaner conditions are provided if one undertakes to make measurements on evaporated metal films. Garland, Lord and Troiano [248] evaporated a metal film in an atmosphere of adsorbate gas. In this way they obtained a support-free adsorbent which was also covered with adsorbate on its internal surfaces. Better conditions are provided, nevertheless, if the metal film is produced in ultrahigh vacuum and is only then covered with gas. Sufficient absorption is obtained by simultaneously placing several substrate plates, one after another, in the beam path, each substrate plate bearing evaporated metal [306].

Pritchard and co-workers [92,117,563] have particularly concerned themselves with recording IR spectra by means of multiple reflection. *Figure 4.2* shows the cell used by them. Two glass plates P,

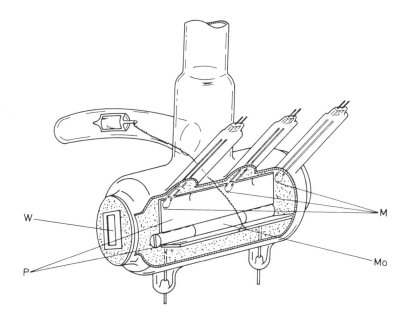

Figure 4.2 Reflection cell for recording IR spectra of adsorbed gases on metal films; after Pritchard and Sims [563]. Mo = molybdenum hinge; M = filament for evaporation of film; W = mica window; P = substrate plate

6 cm × 2 cm, are attached to a molybdenum hinge Mo. One of the plates is fixed and the other can be moved magnetically. In the open position the glass plates are covered with metal film evaporated from three coils M, and in the closed position the plates lie parallel to each other with a separation of 0.9 mm. The IR beam enters through the mica window W at such an angle that eight or nine reflections are obtained — this works for copper, which has an unusually high IR reflectivity [665]. Absorption per reflection is also enhanced by choosing the optimum angle for beam impingement [277]. Plane polarised radiation was used for the measurements.

Further studies using multiple reflection may be found in the literature [237,390,551,665,732,733]. Internal reflection has also found application [41,305,521].

Pritchard and Bradshaw and co-workers [29,90,91,93] were the first to obtain infra-red spectra by passing the beam through a single, adsorbate-covered film. *Figure 4.3* shows a cell which is suitable for this purpose. P is the film substrate, C is the refrigerator with which the substrate can be cooled to 113 K and M is the filament for evaporation of films.

The system nickel/carbon monoxide is one of the systems most intensively investigated by infra-red spectroscopy [29,90,91,93,174,178, 248,548,551]. The absorption spectrum of carbon monoxide on a

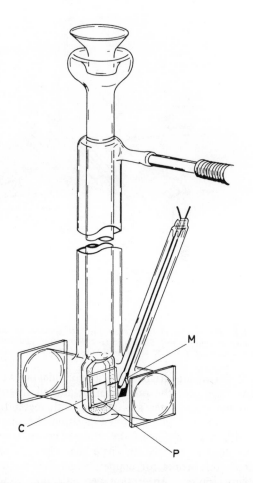

Figure 4.3   Bakeable cell for recording IR transmission spectra of adsorbed gases on metal films; after Bradshaw and Pritchard [90].   C = cold stage; P = substrate plate; M = filament for evaporation of film

Ni-SiO$_2$ adsorbent is shown at various surface coverages in *Figure 4.4*. Curve 1 was obtained at 298 K for a carbon monoxide pressure of 0.1 Torr, curve 2 after the pressure had been lowered to 10^{-4} Torr for 12 min and curve 3 after pumping at 10^{-4} Torr for nearly 2½ h.   To encourage further desorption, pumping was continued at 100 °C (curve 4) and then at 150 °C (curve 5).   The absorption bands shown in *Figure 4.4* may be assigned to the C–O vibration.   In the free, gaseous CO molecule an absorption maximum (transmission minimum) at 4.67 μm is assigned to the pure vibration, but because of superimposed rotation this appears as a doublet at 4.60 and 4.72 μm.   Evidently

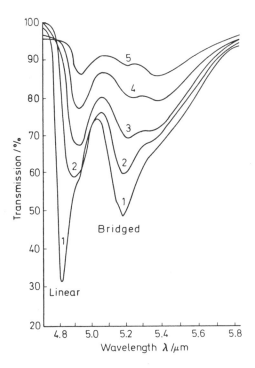

Figure 4.4 Absorption spectrum of the system Ni-SiO₂/CO as a function of coverage; after Eischens et al. *[174]*

bands appear at longer wavelengths in the case of adsorbed CO. This is to be expected because the formation of a bond between adsorbed CO and the adsorbent should lead to a weakening of the C–O bond and thus to a displacement of the absorption bands to longer wavelengths. Two regions may be distinguished, the one below and the other above 5 μm. By analogy with the spectra of the metal carbonyls, the first region may be assigned to a bond between CO and a single metal atom, the second to a bond between CO and two metal atoms. For this reason it has become common to talk about 'linear' and 'bridged' CO in the bound state:

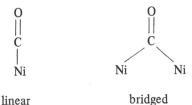

The occurrence of several absorption bands is *a priori* evidence for the existence of differently bound adsorbate molecules on adjacent sites. This finding agrees with desorption spectra and measurements of isotope exchange. We also notice that the coverage dependence of the absorption spectrum shows that the proportion of CO which is bound in the linear and in the bridged forms depends on the coverage θ. This dependence is in the sense that with increasing θ the linearly bound amount grows. Furthermore, the occurrence of several maxima and shoulders shows that the heterogeneity of the adsorbent surface is evidently so large that various species of linear and bridged CO exist on the surface. Even the bonding of a particular species depends on the coverage: as θ rises, the lateral interaction between bound adsorbate molecules increases and so the bond to the adsorbent becomes weaker. This displaces the bands to shorter wavelengths.

Comparisons have frequently been made of the absorption spectrum of CO adsorbed on nickel films, unsupported nickel and variously supported nickel specimens. By and large, the curves shown in *Figure 4.4* are always obtained. This is so even if the bands are shifted [247,548] as a result of the influence of the support [248] or the presence of contaminants or catalytic poisons.

The more recent investigations on evaporated films [29,90,91,93] have nevertheless yielded significantly more information than the work on supported catalysts. This is because they have enabled a distinct influence of the film structure on the IR spectrum to be recognised. It also appears from the film work that the assignment of the bands to linear- and bridge-bonded species is not definite, especially if the considerations of Blyholder [64] are taken into account. In addition, one must not overlook the possibility of absorption by any nickel carbonyl that is formed.

A similar situation to that on nickel is found on rhodium [729], palladium [122,174,358], cobalt [361] and iridium [306].

CO adsorbed on iron only shows one C–O band and this occurs at 1950 cm^{-1}. By extending the range of measurement from 270 to 5000 cm^{-1}, Blyholder [63] was able to find an additional band at 580 cm^{-1} which may be assigned to the Fe–C vibration. Both the C–O and the Fe–C bonds are likely to be double bonds, so that the structure

has been proposed for the adsorbed phase [63]. In this structure the iron atom is part of the metal lattice, just as it was prior to CO adsorption.

In the same way one only finds linearly bound CO species on platinum [178,306], copper [178,359,618], silver and gold [360].

A summary of the absorption spectra which have been obtained for various metal/CO systems is presented in *Figure 4.5*.

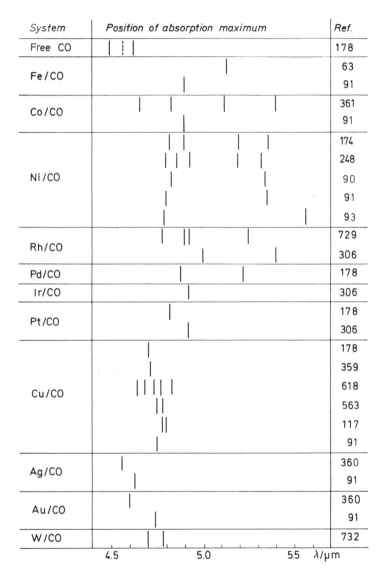

Figure 4.5 Summary of the absorption spectra obtained for various metal/CO systems

Despite much effort, it was not possible for a long time to obtain infra-red spectra for chemisorbed hydrogen. It was accordingly believed that hydrogen did not exhibit a covalently bound structure. Pliskin and Eischens [554], however, became the first to obtain a spectrum. They worked with the systems Pt/H_2 and Pt/D_2, the platinum being carried on Alon-C. As shown in *Figure 4.6*, two bands may be observed, one at 4.74 μm and the other at 4.86 μm. In the case of deuterium the bands lie at 6.60 μm and 6.76 μm. The deuterium result establishes for certain that the bands observed for the Pt/H_2 system are not due to small amounts of CO impurity.

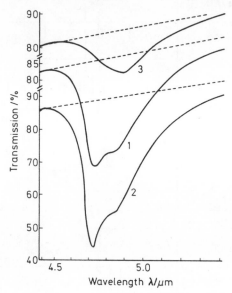

Figure 4.6 Infra-red spectrum for hydrogen adsorbed on platinum: curve (1) 35°C, p_{H_2} = 700 Torr; curve (2) −50°C, p_{H_2} = 700 Torr; curve (3) −50°C, after evacuation [554]

The Pt–H band at 4.74 μm disappears when hydrogen is pumped off and the band at 4.86 μm then shows up very clearly. The former must therefore be assigned to a species of hydrogen H_W whose bonding is significantly weaker than that of the latter (H_S). On the strength of various findings, the authors reach the conclusion that the weakly bonded form is localised on one platinum atom and the strongly bonded form lies between platinum atoms:

Eley, Moran and Rochester [181] were able to show that the appearance of these bands does actually depend to a marked extent on the pretreatment with oxygen.

It is interesting to note that no infra-red bands could be obtained for the system Ni/H_2 under similar circumstances. The bonding of hydrogen to nickel must therefore be significantly different from the bonding on platinum.

Infra-red bands have been observed on rhodium for chemisorbed hydrogen by Pickering and Eckstrom [551] and for chemisorbed deuterium by Smith, Eckstrom and Bär [621]. The interpretation of the unusually large number of bands observed is still a source of difficulty. Infra-red spectroscopic investigations have been extended to numerous other systems, such as Ni/N_2 [175,304,509], Cr/NO [661], Fe/NO, Ni/NO [66,661], Pd/NO, Pt/NO [159], Fe/CO_2, Fe/O_2, Fe/H_2O [69], Ni/C_2H_4 [177,185,427] and Ni/C_2H_2 [553].

Yates *et al.* [732] employed a combination of flash desorption and reflection absorption IR spectroscopy. With this approach, they were able to resolve the a-state of carbon monoxide chemisorbed on tungsten into two states, viz. a_1, which absorbs at 4.70 μm, and a_2, which absorbs at 4.78 μm (see Section 3.4). Work on the adsorption of formic acid on nickel [210,334] leads us on to infra-red spectroscopic investigations of reactions in the adsorbed phase [65,176,325].

In the case of metallic adsorbents, uncertainties may indeed exist concerning their structural properties – particularly at the surface. Their chemical properties, nevertheless, should generally be well defined. In the case of oxide adsorbents the circumstances are different. Here the conditions of preparation and handling can also cause variations in the chemical nature of the surface. In the first instance, therefore, the properties of the surface must be evaluated when one is concerned with investigations of adsorption on such adsorbents. This involves, *inter alia*, examining how the concentration and distribution of residual hydroxyl groups on the surface depend on the sintering, outgassing and bake-out conditions. For this purpose infra-red spectroscopic investigations themselves are particularly suitable.

Much work has been concerned with adsorption on silica. Folman and Yates and co-workers investigated the physisorption of ammonia, acetone and methyl chloride [228,230], water and methanol [228,229] on porous Vycor glass; Zecchina and co-workers investigated both the physisorption [80] and chemisorption [79] of methanol and the adsorption of benzene [738] on Aerosil. Alumina has also been frequently used as adsorbent. Yates and co-workers studied the chemisorption of ethylene [428] and acetylene [730] on alumina, and showed that distinguishable adsorption sites exist on this adsorbent. These sites, which differ in their properties, are probably independent of each other. The adsorption of various gases on iron oxide was studied by Blyholder and Richardson [70,71].

Investigations using oxide adsorbents are also important, of course, because these substances, particularly silica and alumina, are widely used as supports for metallic adsorbents. Should the support fail to be inert towards an adsorbate gas, then it is capable of falsifying the properties which one has ascribed to the metallic adsorbent. The location of the band for CO adsorption on platinum, for instance, depends on whether the platinum is supported by silica or by alumina [177].

The material in this section has enabled us to show that infra-red spectroscopic investigations confirm ideas which have been developed with the aid of other methods. The most widely varying adsorption systems may be examined and much new knowledge has been acquired, particularly in connection with the bonding structure.

4.2. Visible and ultra-violet spectra

When molecules pass from the gas phase to the adsorbed phase, a displacement of their infra-red spectral lines occurs, and information concerning the changes that occur in the binding of molecules can be drawn from this displacement. In a few cases (e.g. Pt/H_2) it is possible to identify a band which corresponds to the bond between the adsorbent and the adsorbate. In general, nevertheless, investigations of infra-red spectra have been confined to simpler molecules. To characterise complicated organic molecules that may be formed on the surface during adsorption processes, it is more appropriate to use ultra-violet spectroscopy. On occasions it is useful to combine both types of spectroscopy.

Only a small number of ultra-violet investigations have been made to date, despite their importance and fruitfulness. They are, of course, predominantly devoted to identifying adsorbed intermediates in a catalytic reaction. The lack of number of these investigations might be due, in part, to the experimental difficulties involved in preparing suitable, transparent samples: the problems of sample preparation are even greater than in the case of infra-red spectroscopy. The first survey of published work was given by Leftin and Hobson [416].

Leftin [415] has described an adsorption cell that is equally suitable for ultra-violet and infra-red measurements. This cell, which is shown in *Figure 4.7(a)*, allows an adsorbent consisting of a sliding slab to be heated, reduced and evacuated. When the cell is inverted, the sample slides out of the section containing the quartz windows and into the section fitted with NaCl windows. The outstanding advantage of this arrangement is that measurements can be carried out on one and the same sample in both spectral regions. In this way one avoids the difficulties associated with lack of reproducibility of the sample.

Ron, Folman and Schnepp [582] used a cell (*Figure 4.7b*) in which the adsorbent — in their case Vycor glass — is pressed against a copper block labelled Cu. In the centre of the block is an opening that allows the light beam to pass through. The block is connected to the inner tube D of the insert via a Kovar glass seal S. D acts as a Dewar

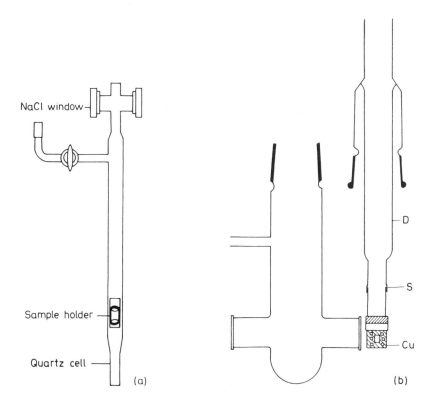

NaCl window

Sample holder

Quartz cell

(a)

D

S

Cu

(b)

Figure 4.7 Adsorption cells for recording UV spectra of adsorbed molecules: (a) cell suitable for additional measurements of the IR spectrum (after Leftin [415]); (b) cell for measuring the effect of temperature (after Ron et al. [582])

vessel into which liquids can be placed to maintain the sample-holder at a certain temperature.

In addition to measurements of transmission absorption, the examination of diffuse reflectance spectra [376] has been a rich source of information, particularly in the hands of workers such as Kortüm and associates [385-388]. The powdered adsorbent is filled into a round quartz cell of 6 mm width attached to a high-vacuum apparatus. The powder is then baked out and adsorbate is taken up prior to measurements using a spectrophotometer fitted with a reflectance attachment.

One measures the relative reflectance R'_∞ — that is, the reflectance referred to the clean surface as a standard. The Kubelka-Munk function

$$F(R'_\infty) \equiv \frac{(1 - R'_\infty)^2}{2R'_\infty} = \frac{k}{s} \tag{4.1}$$

gives us a relationship that enables the absorption coefficient k and the extinction coefficient ϵ

$$k \sim \epsilon c \qquad (4.2)$$

as well as the scattering coefficient s to be evaluated. If variations in s are assumed to be negligible, then

$$F(R'_\infty) = \frac{k}{s} = \text{const. } \epsilon c = ac \qquad (4.3)$$

where a is the absorption factor. An optical parameter that is proportional to the concentration is therefore provided by the Kubelka-Munk function. Since any absorption due to the adsorbent is eliminated by measuring the relative reflectance, one is only concerned with light absorption in the adsorbed phase.

The interpretation of an absorption spectrum for the adsorbed phase is often made by comparison with a known UV spectrum. As an example we shall take Leftin's [414] investigation of the adsorption of triphenylmethane on cracking catalysts. Curve 1 in *Figure 4.8* shows the absorption spectrum due to triphenylmethane adsorbed on a silica-alumina catalyst. It coincides closely with the spectrum of the triphenylcarbonium ion (curve 2) that is obtained when triphenylcarbinol is dissolved in concentrated sulphuric acid; it does not tie up with the spectrum of the triphenylmethyl radical (curve 3) or the triphenylmethide ion (curve 4). In this way Leftin was able to show that triphenylmethane was chemisorbed on silica-alumina as carbonium ions.

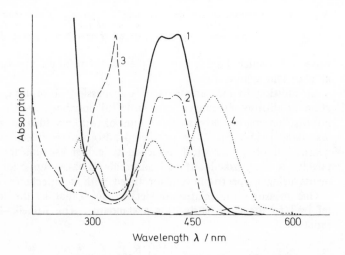

Figure 4.8   Absorption spectrum of triphenylmethane, $(C_6H_5)_3CH$, adsorbed on silica-alumina (1); $(C_6H_5)_3COH$ in conc. H_2SO_4 (2); $(C_6H_5)_3C$ in ether (3); $(C_6H_5)_3C^-$ (4).   After Leftin [414]

It should also be stated that UV spectra of adsorbed molecules are even more suitable than IR spectra for distinguishing between physisorption and chemisorption. In physisorption the spectrum is generally the same with and without adsorbent present. One only has to take into account the possibility that sometimes forbidden transitions can occur after adsorption. On the other hand, the major changes which the adsorbate undergoes upon chemisorption are liable to lead to a large alteration in the spectrum of the adsorbate.

4.3. Spin resonance

Two spectroscopic methods which have been developed over the last two decades utilise the interaction of spin and a magnetic field. These methods are nuclear spin resonance (or nuclear magnetic resonance, NMR) [227,426,580,617,637] and electron spin resonance (ESR; or electron paramagnetic resonance, EPR) [58,60,261]. Both techniques call for a considerable apparatus outlay and they have only recently been turned to investigations in the field of adsorption [22,550].

4.3.1. NUCLEAR MAGNETIC RESONANCE

Atomic nuclei with an intrinsic angular momentum can only take up certain spin directions with respect to an external magnetic field (direction z). The z-components of angular momentum are defined by the values

$$p_z = m_I \hbar \tag{4.4}$$

where m_I takes the values

$$I, I - 1, I - 2, ..., - I \tag{4.5}$$

I is the nuclear spin quantum number. As a result of angular momentum a nucleus possesses a magnetic moment μ, for which the z-component is given by

$$\mu_z = g_n \beta_n m_z \tag{4.6}$$

g_n is the nuclear g-factor and β_n is the nuclear magneton.

In an external magnetic field H_z the energy of the nuclear magneton is

$$E = -\mu_z H_z \tag{4.7}$$

A nucleus can therefore only take up discrete energies which are determined by equations (4.5) and (4.6) and separated by

$$\Delta E = g_n \beta_n H_z \tag{4.8}$$

If the nucleus is to undergo an energy transition to its next level, up or down, then it must absorb or emit electromagnetic radiation of a frequency $\omega_{res.}$ governed by the resonance condition

$$\hbar\omega_{res.} = g_n\beta_nH_z \tag{4.9}$$

For this purpose one produces a radiofrequency electromagnetic field in the *x*-direction, perpendicular to the *z*-axis. Nuclear transitions are induced by the magnetic part of this oscillating field rather than the electric part.

For reasons of technical expediency the frequency of oscillation is maintained at a fixed value and the magnetic field is varied to search for resonance.

The field strength to be inserted in equation (4.9) is that which is effective in the region of the nucleus. This field differs slightly from the applied field because of the influence of the electrons which surround the nucleus. Since the electron density around the nucleus is determined by chemical bonding, one observes a resonance shift (chemical shift) which depends on the nature of the bond.

The probability W that a nucleus will jump up is the same as the probability that it will drop down to an adjacent energy level. As a result, the energy L absorbed by interaction with the electromagnetic radiation is given by

$$L = g_n\beta_nH_zW(N_{+\frac{1}{2}} - N_{-\frac{1}{2}}) \tag{4.10}$$

where $N_{+\frac{1}{2}}$ and $N_{-\frac{1}{2}}$ are the numbers of nuclei in the lower (parallel orientation) and the upper (antiparallel orientation) energy states, respectively, and we have confined ourselves to nuclei with spin quantum number ½. According to the Boltzmann distribution, the populations at thermal equilibrium are given by

$$\left(\frac{N_{+\frac{1}{2}}}{N_{-\frac{1}{2}}}\right)_{\text{therm. equilib.}} = \exp[(g_n\beta_nH_z)/kT] \tag{4.11}$$

The difference in energy between the two states is so small that the quotient in equation (4.11) is, for example, 1.000 007 for the case of protons in a field of 10 000 G. All nuclear magnetic resonance phenomena are due to this minute excess in the population of the lower state. The macroscopic nuclear magnetisation observed in resonance experiments is thus simply the minute excess of nuclear spin moments that point in the direction of the constant, strong magnetic field H_z. At the thermal equilibrium concentration of states the macroscopic magnetisation becomes

$$M_0 = \chi_0 H_z \qquad (4.12)$$

where

$$\chi_0 = \frac{N\mu_z{}^2}{3kT}$$

denotes the static nuclear susceptibility.

If the equilibrium (equation 4.11) is disturbed through, for instance, the absorption of energy from an oscillating electromagnetic field applied in the x-direction, then equilibrium is not immediately re-established. The process is more commonly governed by an exponential function with a time constant T_1. T_1 is called the longitudinal, thermal or spin lattice relaxation time. For the difference between the z-component of the magnetisation $M_z(t)$ and the value at thermal equilibrium we may therefore write

$$M_z(t) - M_0 = -2M_0 \exp\left(-t/T_1\right) \qquad (4.13)$$

Notice that nuclei are unable to convert their energy to energy of vibration, rotation or translation in a straightforward manner because they do not undergo any collisions. It is only possible for energy to be exchanged via a coupling of those magnetic (or electric) fields of strength featured in equation (4.9). The energy exchange occurs as follows. If we focus attention on one nucleus, then it will be surrounded by the nuclei of neighbouring atoms (i.e. the atoms or molecules of the 'lattice') which are in thermal motion. As a result of this random Brownian motion to which the atoms are subjected, neighbouring nuclei can, by chance, produce alternating magnetic fields of the requisite frequency in the region of our nucleus. Longitudinal relaxation therefore depends on an interaction between the spin and the lattice, which leads to conversion of the magnetic energy of the nuclear spins to thermal energy of the surrounding molecules. Indeed, were it not for this process, it would be impossible to develop any magnetisation in the direction of the constant magnetic field.

According to the velocity of the molecular motion (determined, for instance, by the temperature or the viscosity of the 'lattice'), the Fourier component of $\omega_{res.}$ will be large or small. This causes energy transfer from the spin to the lattice system to be promoted to a greater or lesser extent, and this, in turn, means T_1 will be short or long.

So long as only the constant magnetic field is applied, the macroscopic magnetisation vector precesses about the z-direction. If we now introduce an electromagnetic field in the x-direction, its frequency being the resonant frequency of the nuclear moments (see equation 4.9), then the vector simultaneously carries out a slower nutation about the x-direction. For sufficiently short durations of the high-frequency field (so-called $90°$ pulses) it is possible to produce a 'transverse' magnetisation which is rotating in the xy-plane. During the application of pulses of the high-frequency field all precessing nuclear moments possess the same phase. But this phase relationship does not persist after the field has been switched off. As a result of Brownian molecular motion of neighbouring nuclei, the magnetic field which acts on the individual nuclei varies a little from nucleus to nucleus. The result is a gradual decay of the rotating magnetisation with a time constant T_2. This time is called the spin-spin or entropy relaxation time, because the degree of order in the transverse magnetisation falls through this process and the entropy of the system is raised. In this case, therefore, one has for the transverse magnetisation $M_\perp(t)$

$$M_\perp(t) = M_0 \exp(-t/T_2) \tag{4.14}$$

and the relaxation time is again dependent on the state of motion of the environment of a particular nucleus. In general, the relaxation rates $1/T_1$ and $1/T_2$ are made up of a linear combination of terms, each relaxation rate having the same general form:

$$\frac{1}{T_1} \propto \Sigma \left\{ \kappa^{\overline{12}} f(\omega_{res.}, \tau_c) \right\} \tag{4.15}$$

The functions $f(\omega_{res}, \tau_c)$ are strongly dependent on the stochastic molecular motion, the velocity of this motion being characterised by correlation times τ_c. $\omega_{res.}$ again denotes the resonant frequency of the system. $\kappa^{\overline{12}}$ represents the quadratic mean value of the interaction energy κ'. Sometimes it is possible to make the product $\omega_{res.}\tau_c$ equal to the order of unity by choosing suitable experimental conditions (the resonant frequency can be varied by altering the magnetic field strength H_z; the correlation time can be varied by altering the temperature). In these cases the interaction energy and the correlation time can be determined separately.

Common methods by which energy is exchanged during nuclear spin relaxation are the dipole-dipole interaction of the nuclear moments or magnetic coupling between nuclear spin and electron spin moments. The models used for the random molecular motion are taken, typically, from isotropically or anisotropically statistical rotation or statistical translation of molecules (see Chapter VIII in reference 1).

The line width of a nuclear resonance signal is influenced by T_1 and T_2 and can be used to find relaxation times provided there is no broadening of the lines due to inhomogeneity of the applied field. In general, the line profile is also determined by time-dependent phenomena such as rapidly completed chemical exchange processes or rotations of molecular groups.

If one is concerned with the measurement of line width, line profile or chemical shift, then a high-resolution nuclear magnetic resonance spectrometer must be utilised. This usually operates on the Purcell bridge principle or the Bloch induction method [580,637]. On the other hand, if one's main interest is in determining relaxation times, then it is expedient to use the spin echo method [637]. This method is preferable because, unlike the static method (investigation of line widths), it enables relaxation times to be measured directly. Under certain circumstances one can also extract self-diffusion coefficients from the time-dependent fall of transverse magnetisation.

Turning to adsorption investigations which involve working with very small amounts of substance, one is especially interested in the sensitivity of the method. In general, it is necessary to have at least 10^{17} spins in the measuring cell. Although this value depends on a number of parameters, it can be taken as approximately correct for a spin echo spectrometer at $\omega_{res}/2\pi = 16$ MHz with signal averaging [216].

The many possibilities of applying nuclear magnetic resonance to adsorption problems will already be evident from our introductory survey of the theory of nuclear spin resonance.

The bonding of the adsorbate to the adsorbent is responsible for a shift in the resonant frequency relative to the frequency of the free adsorbate, and the type and strength of the bond are reflected in the magnitude of this shift. If we compare the systems SiO_2/H_2O and SiO_2/cyclohexane [262], for instance, then the relative shift of proton resonance is larger in the first case. This is in agreement with the model in which the specific interaction of water molecules with the OH groups of the adsorbent is substantially stronger than the interaction between the non-polar cyclohexane molecules and the adsorbent. Any weakening of bond strength which occurs in the adsorbed phase as the coverage increases manifests itself in a fall of the relative shift of resonant frequency.

The line width of the nuclear magnetic resonance signal is increased by interaction with the adsorbent. The extent of this effect goes up with the extent to which the movement of adsorbed molecules is hindered and the strength of the magnetic interaction with paramagnetic impurities of the adsorbent. For molecules containing non-equivalent nuclei it should therefore be possible to establish through which chemical group adsorption occurs. Thus in these molecules the proton resonance signals of individual groups (−OH, −CH₃, etc.) are separated as a result of chemical shift. One would also, of course, be able to investigate the orientation of adsorbed molecules. Actually the line broadening for adsorbed molecules is often so large that a single wide line is observed instead of the individual resonance lines separated by chemical shift. Despite this, it is possible to carry out the required signal analysis in cases where sufficient structuring of the line occurs [264] or when it is experimentally possible to remove the dipolar coupling [19a,442a, 551a].

There are two other sources of information for the detailed investigation of the adsorbed state by proton resonance. These are longitudinal relaxation and the line shape function or its Fourier transform — that is, transverse relaxation function. This is because so much of the other information in proton resonance spectra is obscured by the large line broadening; in liquids this information can normally be extracted from the position of the various components of the multiplet in the spectrum.

The adsorbed phase does not usually constitute a homogeneous system, preferring to exist as two or more forms of differing mobilities. The resulting relaxation functions therefore generally tend to be superpositions of several exponential curves. The time constants of these curves are influenced by the average residence times and the proportions of the molecules in the individual mobility regimes.

Nevertheless, in such systems one often finds relaxation functions which are pure exponential decays. A whole range of unknown parameters may then operate in determining the two effective relaxation times T_1 and T_2 as well as the self-diffusion coefficients which one measures. The parameters include:

(1) The different magnetic interaction energies.
(2) The correlation times (with their activation enthalpies and entropies).
(3) The relative sizes and the average residence times of the adsorbed molecules in the individual regimes.

It is therefore necessary to make further measurements if the relaxation processes are to be characterised. The required data may be obtained by investigating the dependence of the rates of relaxation on the resonant frequency, the temperature and the surface charge; deuterated substances may also be utilised. As Michel [468,469] showed, minute quantities of paramagnetic impurities in the surface of the adsorbent can have a marked influence on the nuclear spin relaxation process; under certain circumstances they may even dominate the process.

A method for analysing relaxation has been worked out [550] which takes into account all the possible mechanisms of interaction of the adsorbed molecules — intra- and intermolecular magnetic dipole-dipole interactions, interactions between nuclei of the adsorbed material and paramagnetic impurities, magnetic interaction of the adsorbed molecules with protons (e.g. OH groups) of the adsorbent.

Both Beckert [40] and Haul and Boddenberg [308] have applied nuclear magnetic resonance to investigating surface diffusion.

Recently Geschke [263] has drawn attention to the advantages of measuring ^{13}C nuclear spin resonance for adsorbed molecules as opposed to investigating proton resonance signals. Essentially the advantages gained are substantially larger chemical shifts and narrower resonance lines. These differences are due to the lowered magnetic interaction energy caused by the smaller magnetic moment of ^{13}C nuclei. Despite the significant improvement one obtains, there are also serious disadvantages. The natural abundance of ^{13}C is very small, so that the signal strength is almost four orders of magnitude less than the proton resonance signal. Furthermore, the long-term stability of conventional apparatus is insufficient to permit the requisite spectral accumulation. For these reasons high resolution ^{13}C spectra of adsorbed molecules were first obtained by applying Fourier transformation to nuclear magnetic resonance spectroscopy (FT-NMR) [141].

Michel's work [471] reveals that the resolution of ^{13}C NMR spectra is incomparably better than that of ^1H NMR spectra for the same adsorbate on the same adsorbent. Thanks to this new technique, detailed information has been obtained about the adsorption of hydrocarbons, especially olefins and aromatics, on zeolites [140,141,470-472].

4.3.2. ELECTRON SPIN RESONANCE

In sub-section 4.3.1 we considered the energy of an atomic nucleus possessing intrinsic angular momentum when placed in a magnetic field. Essentially these ideas are also applicable to the behaviour of unpaired electrons in a magnetic field.

In an external magnetic field H_z the energy of an electron is

$$E = g_e \beta_e m_s H_z \tag{4.16}$$

where g_e denotes the g-factor for electrons, β_e the Bohr magneton and the spin quantum number m_s is $\pm\frac{1}{2}$. The energy of an electron in a magnetic field thus amounts to $\pm\frac{1}{2}g_e\beta_e H_z$ and the energy difference between two neighbouring levels is

$$\Delta E = g_e \beta_e H_z \tag{4.17}$$

As in the case of nuclear magnetic resonance, electromagnetic radiation can cause a transition between the two states of the electron to occur if their quanta fulfil the resonance condition

$$\hbar\omega_{res.} = g_e \beta_e H_z \tag{4.18}$$

ESR is about 2 000 times more sensitive than NMR. However, the number of materials which can give an ESR signal is limited because the required transitions are forbidden in accordance with the Pauli principle whenever electrons are paired. Only materials containing unpaired electrons – that is, paramagnetic substances – can be used for ESR investigations; examples of such substances are free radicals, transition metal ions, metals, O_2 and NO.

As in nuclear magnetic resonance, one observes two relaxation times, viz. the spin-lattice relaxation time T_1 (also called the 'longitudinal' relaxation time) and the spin-spin relaxation time T_2. T_1 is conveniently determined by using a sufficiently high intensity of electromagnetic radiation to bring about saturation (both levels populated to an equal extent). The radiation intensity is then suddenly lowered to a value which does not noticeably disturb the thermal equilibrium distribution, as given in equation (4.11). The time dependence of energy absorption then gives T_1 directly. The longitudinal electron spin relaxation time can also be found directly using an ESR spin echo spectrometer. T_2 is obtained from the line width of the ESR signal [58].

Numerous possibilities exist of applying electron spin resonance to adsorption problems [22]. The immediate possibility is to study the properties of the surface of the adsorbent and especially to check for the presence of radicals in the surface.

Radicals (such as hydrogen atoms) which are formed from the adsorbate can also be formed on the adsorbent, either spontaneously as a result of adsorption, or after exposure to energetic radiation. Since the intensity of the ESR signal is proportional to the amount of radical, one can follow chemical reactions involving radicals in the adsorbed phase by measuring the variation of intensity with time [534].

The ESR method can also be applied if radical-like charge transfer complexes are formed during adsorption or if paramagnetic ions are adsorbed.

Further possibilities unfold when adsorption occurs on a para- or a ferromagnetic adsorbent such as nickel. The adsorbent particles must, of course, be small enough to avoid having a low ratio of surface to bulk atoms. A particle radius of about 50 Å should not be exceeded. In these cases chemisorption should lead to a definite change in the ESR signal, whereas physisorption should have no noticeable effect. This is because chemisorption involves the formation of a covalent bond between the adsorbent and the adsorbate.

Figure 4.9 shows the ESR signal from a $Ni-SiO_2$ catalyst as a continuous line. The signals obtained after taking up hydrogen or nitrogen have been added as broken lines. We notice that hydrogen, unlike nitrogen, leads to a clear effect. The former is, in fact, a chemisorption, the latter a physisorption. Andreev and Selwood [18,19] have shown how such measurements can be quantitatively evaluated in the Ni/H_2 system.

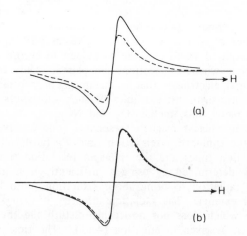

Figure 4.9   ESR signal obtained from a $Ni-SiO_2$ catalyst at 25 °C [17]: (a) in a hydrogen pressure of 450 Torr (broken line); (b) in a nitrogen pressure of 350 Torr (broken line).   The continuous lines are signals obtained after evacuation

Looking to the future, one can confidently expect that investigations using spin resonance methods will yield many fruitful results.

4.4. Ellipsometry

The previous three sections have been concerned with spectroscopic methods in which electromagnetic radiation is absorbed by the adsorbed phase. In general, these methods enable information to be obtained about the state of bonding in the adsorbate. In recent years a further optical method has been increasingly applied to surface and adsorption problems. This method, which is called ellipsometry, depends on changes in the state of polarisation of light after reflection at the adsorbent surface. It is possible to deduce the optical constants of the adsorbent and the variations in these constants as a result of adsorption. If the reflecting surface bears a thin film of another material, then ellipsometry enables the film thickness and its refractive index to be determined. The sensitivity amounts to less than one monolayer. Ellipsometry is also of special significance for the study of thin metal films such as those which are commonly prepared for use as adsorbents. The method can, in fact, be applied whenever it is possible to reflect coherent radiation, so that one can equally well study single-crystal surfaces, metal films evaporated on to flat substrates or polished polycrystalline materials. It is immaterial whether the substances absorb the light or not, and the wavelength can lie anywhere between the ultra-violet and the infra-red.

A difficulty which is frequently met in studying the theory and practice of ellipsometry concerns the large number of conventions and definitions which are used. Some of the most commonly used relationships have been reviewed by Muller [504,505]. For detailed information see references 26, 446, 542. Adequate information concerning the fundamentals of electromagnetic light theory can be obtained from pertinent textbooks [83,84,555].

Linearly polarised light is commonly employed for ellipsometric measurements, and the plane of vibration is usually tilted at $\theta = 45°$ to the incident plane. The vibration may be regarded as consisting of two components, one parallel and the other perpendicular to the incident plane. These components are of equal amplitude and show no phase difference. The light is allowed to impinge on the specimen with an angle of incidence ϕ (preferably equal to the optimum angle of incidence). Upon reflection, the ratio of the amplitudes of the two components changes and a phase difference occurs. As a result the light becomes elliptically polarised. Analysis of the elliptically polarised light is accomplished with the aid of a compensator and an analyser. The compensator (in the simplest case a quarter-wave plate, more accurately a Soleit compensator) removes the phase difference between the two components so that the light is linearly polarised again. The compensator and the analyser are rotated simultaneously until the intensity of the light getting through is at a minimum, this being established with a photomultiplier. The complete ellipsometric measurement thus consists of measuring two angles Δ and ψ, these being obtained from the settings of the compensator and the analyser, respectively. A suitable arrangement is shown in *Figure 4.10*.

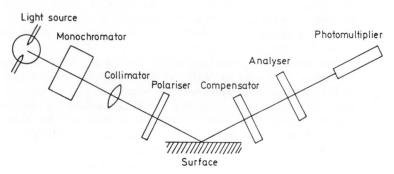

Figure 4.10   Experimental arrangement for obtaining Δ and ψ by use of linearly polarised light impinging with an azimuth of 45° (angle between plane of vibration and the incident plane)

Basically the Fresnel formulae are used to obtain the equations relating Δ and ψ on the one hand with the optical constants (refractive index n and absorption index κ) on the other. The details of these relationships depend on the particular system being investigated. Thus reflection may occur at the clean surface of a bulk metal ($\Delta \neq 0$) or dielectric ($\Delta = 0$), or it may occur after the adsorption of one or more layers on the surface of these materials. Again, reflection may occur on the clean or the adsorbate-covered surface of a thin metal film. For detailed information, especially concerning the various approximations, we refer to the specialised literature [26,84,446,673].

Very much work has been published concerning the theoretical and experimental background of ellipsometry, the possible sources of error and certain specialised arrangements. Good reviews of this work will be found in reference 26, and also more recent articles such as references 107, 396.

It is usual to assume that the optical properties of a clean adsorbent are precisely known when it comes to discussing the changes in properties due to adsorption or the formation of a surface film. Great care should be exercised here if older data are being used, because adequate vacuum techniques were rarely employed and the data may not be representative of clean surfaces. Furthermore, one has to watch whether the values were obtained for bulk material or for thin films, on which anomalies occur, especially on very thin films [220-224]. The optical constants have been measured as a function of wavelength for bulk silver by Steiger *et al.* [634], bulk copper, silver and gold by Otter [527], bulk nickel and iron by Menzel and Gebhart [463] and bulk potassium, rubidium and caesium by Mayer and co-workers [443,448-450, 633]. Regarding the determination of optical data for thin films, we also refer to the summaries of Mayer [446] and Heavens [319].

The chief difficulty which crops up with thin films is that an ellipsometric measurement is only capable of giving us two quantities, yet, in addition to the two optical constants of the film, the film thickness d is unknown. In general, therefore, a further technique must be used so that all three quantities can be established. Sometimes the film thickness is determined independently of the ellipsometric measurement by measuring the transmission as well as the reflection [727] in a combined intensity and polarisation experiment. Alternatively, the ellipsometric measurement can be repeated under different conditions, such as at various angles of incidence.

In this connection, there has been a whole series of suggestions for the mathematical exploitation of ellipsometric data [23,109,214,382,430, 522,529,597,608,664,682,727,728]. We may note that nowadays, thanks to the availability of computers, one is no longer dependent to such an extent on approximate formulae for the evaluation of data.

While the optical data for thick films correspond to those of the bulk material [449], the data for very thin films can show large deviations. In general, these deviations are structure-dependent [220-224,728].

Ellipsometric investigations of adsorption systems have embraced the entire field, from physisorption through chemisorption to the formation of protective films, the coverage ranging from sub-monomolecular to multimolecular. The only parameters which are of interest tend to be the film thickness and its refractive index. This is because films generally absorb little or no light.

Outstanding in the application of ellipsometry to adsorption is the work of Bootsma and associates. These workers have devoted particular attention to adsorption in the sub-monolayer region. Keeping to this coverage region, Bootsma and Meyer [77] have reviewed the various theories which existed in 1969 for interpreting ellipsometric measurements.

(1) *The extrapolated macroscopic theory.* Using the Lorentz-Lorenz equation, a relationship is set up between the macroscopic quantity refractive index n and the microscopic quantities polarisability a and atomic volume a^3. This equation is then extrapolated to the monolayer, to which the following parameters are formally assigned: refractive index n_m, cross-sectional area c_m and diameter d_m of the adsorbed atoms or molecules.

$$\frac{n_m^2 - 1}{n_m^2 + 2} = \frac{4\pi}{3} \frac{a}{c_m d_m} \tag{4.19}$$

There are two possibilities for discussing the transition to the sub-monomolecular region ($\theta < 1$). Either one takes a constant refractive index n_m and a variable film thickness $d_m\theta$, or one takes a constant film thickness d_m and allows the refractive index n_θ to vary.

(2) *The quasi-microscopic theory.* This is based on a model due to Strachan [636] according to which the sub-monomolecular layer consists of a two-dimensional array of Hertzian oscillators.

(3) *The microscopic theory.* Sivukhin's model [614-616] is taken as the basis of this theory, which characterises the adsorbed layer by means of parameters which are represented as the quotient of the dipole moment per unit surface area induced in the adsorbed layer and the polarisation vector of the homogeneous substrate.

All three theories lead to specific relationships between the ellipsometric quantities and the coverage θ. The relevant details will be found in the cited literature and the theoretical works of Dignam and Moskovits [150-152].

Bootsma and Meyer [77] have experimentally investigated both the physisorption of rare gases at low temperatures and also the chemisorption of active gases on silicon and germanium single crystals. They found that their results showed good agreement with values calculated on the basis of the extrapolated macroscopic theory and the microscopic theory. In the case of chemisorption, a change in the optical properties of the adsorbent was clearly discernible.

Very thin non-absorbing layers of physisorbed gas on silicon single crystals only cause the angle Δ to vary. However, since one has to find the two unknowns, refractive index and film thickness, progress can only be made if the refractive index is obtained independently of the ellipsometric measurement. One way of doing this is by calculation from the polarisability a and the diameter of the adsorbed molecule or atom. Using this method, Bootsma and Meyer [76,77,464] were able to show that the changes in Δ were generally proportional to the coverage θ. They ascribed the anomalous effects which occurred in chemisorption to the removal of a strongly disordered transition layer which lies on the surface of pure silicon or germanium [465]. In this manner it has been possible [466,467] to obtain further information concerning the adsorbed state. Bootsma and Meyer [78] even see a possibility of distinguishing between physisorption and chemisorption by means of the sign of the change observed in the angle ψ. In the adsorption of oxygen on a silicon (111) plane, Dorn, Luth and Ibach [155] were able to distinguish ellipsometrically between chemisorption of oxygen and oxidation.

In these studies it is evident that ellipsometry may be directly and advantageously combined with other methods of investigation, the information obtained being then substantially supplemented. One can, for instance, run Auger electron spectra, infra-red spectra or low energy electron diffraction simultaneously with ellipsometry. An 'optical film thickness' θd_m was determined ellipsometrically by Steiger *et al.* [634] and then used to obtain adsorption isotherms for the physisorption of various gases on silver single crystals. Enthalpies of adsorption were obtained from these isotherms.

Ellipsometry has been applied with profit to the study of oxide film growth [352]. Badia [27] has even shown that the formation of an island structure can be followed.

5

STUDY OF ADSORPTION USING WORK FUNCTION, ELECTRICAL AND MAGNETIC MEASUREMENTS

The spectroscopic methods discussed in previous chapters enable the bonding of the adsorbed phase to be clarified. This is possible because spectral changes occur when the free adsorbate turns into an adsorbed layer. In the adsorption process, however, the adsorbent undergoes changes as well as the adsorbate, and we shall now turn to a discussion of methods which make use of the physical properties of the adsorbent. In general, this will involve discussing the effect adsorption has on the electrical properties of the adsorbent. The measurements concerned are those of work function, electrical conductivity, thermoelectric e.m.f., Hall voltage, magnetisation and field emission.

5.1. Work function and surface potential

If neutral particles in phases 1 and 2 are in thermal equilibrium with each other, then their chemical potential μ in both phases is the same:

$$\mu_1 = \mu_2 \qquad (5.1)$$

If, on the other hand, we want to describe thermal equilibrium between charge carriers in the presence of electrical fields, then the electrochemical potential η must be considered. In this case the appropriate equilibrium condition corresponding to equation (5.1) becomes

$$\eta_1 = \eta_2 \qquad (5.2)$$

The electrochemical potential η consists of the sum of the chemical potential μ and the electrical potential:

$$\eta = \mu - e_0\varphi \qquad (5.3)$$

$-e_0\varphi$ is called the inner potential, and it is defined as the electrical work needed to bring an elementary charge from infinity into the interior of the adsorbent.

In general, the inner potential consists of two parts, the outer potential of the adsorbent $e_0\psi$ and the surface potential $e_0\chi$:

$$e_0\varphi = e_0\psi + e_0\chi \qquad (5.4)$$

The outer potential is simply the result of any excess electrical charge which exists on the surface. Such charge can be produced, for instance, by connection to a voltage supply, and the outer potential is defined as the electrical work needed to bring an elementary charge from infinity up to about 10^{-4} cm in front of the surface; 10^{-4} cm is chosen because this is the distance in front of the surface at which the image force becomes negligible.

The surface potential arises because electrons in the surface region are not uniformly distributed. Furthermore, any molecules adsorbed on the surface are polarised and build up an electrical double layer. If the adsorbent is electrically neutral, then the inner potential is determined by the surface potential alone.

To bring an electron from inside an adsorbent to 10^{-4} cm outside the surface needs an amount of work which is given by the chemical potential of the electrons μ together with the energy needed to surmount the surface potential barrier:

$$e_0\phi \; = \; \mu - e_0\chi \qquad\qquad (5.5)$$

$e_0\phi$ is the work function.

The relationships are shown in *Figure 5.1* with the aid of the potential well model. Here we bear in mind that the chemical potential of the electrons μ is identical with the Fermi energy E_F, both being the energy of the most energetic electrons measured above the bottom edge of the band at a temperature of $T = 0$ K. In the example chosen, the metal is positively charged. Accordingly, an electron which approaches the metal from infinity possesses an energy $e_0\psi$ when it is 10^{-4} cm in front of the surface.

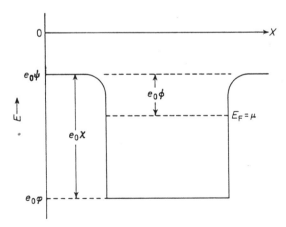

Figure 5.1   Potential well model for the electrons in a metal (positive charge on the metal)

The chemical potential μ is a property of the bulk, and as such it is independent of the properties of the surface. The surface potential, on the other hand, depends very much on the surface properties. As a result the work function of one and the same adsorbent differs for the variously indexed crystal planes. Furthermore, the work function must alter when the dipole layer on the surface is modified by adsorption processes. In this case the change in work function $\Delta(e_0\phi)$ brought about by adsorption is equal and opposite in sign to the surface potential:

$$\Delta(e_0\phi) = - \Delta(e_0\chi) \tag{5.6}$$

Consider two electrically conducting adsorbents 1 and 2 such as, for example, two metal plates which are facing each other and connect them electrically. Then if thermal equilibrium prevails, the electrochemical potential of the electrons in both adsorbents must have the same value according to equation (5.2). This is achieved by the transfer of electrons from one adsorbent into the other. From equation (5.3) we then have

$$\mu_1 - \mu_2 = e_0(\varphi_1 - \varphi_2) \tag{5.7}$$

and taking into account equation (5.4)

$$(\mu_1 - e_0\chi_1) - (\mu_2 - e_0\chi_2) = e_0(\psi_1 - \psi_2) \tag{5.8}$$

This equation can be written as

$$e_0(\phi_1 - \phi_2) = e_0(\psi_1 - \psi_2) \tag{5.9}$$

by substituting equation (5.5).

Equation (5.9) tells us that an electrostatic voltage difference $\psi_1 - \psi_2$ will be set up between the surfaces of two electrically connected adsorbents of different work functions $e_0\phi$. This voltage difference is given by the difference of the work functions divided by e_0, and it is called the Volta potential or the contact potential difference. (The term 'potential' is often loosely used to denote voltages φ, ϕ as well as potential energies $e_0\varphi$, $e_0\phi$.)

The significance of work function measurements for investigations of adsorption follows from equation (5.6). This shows that the change in work function during adsorption is due only to the formation of a dipole layer consisting of adsorbate molecules. Depending on the way the molecules are polarised, a double layer may be expected with either positive or negative towards the vacuum.

For the limiting cases of physisorption and ionic or covalent chemisorption the situations may be described as shown in *Figure 5.2* [129]. In physisorption the adsorbed molecules are only polarised by the surface field. In ionic chemisorption, on the other hand, there is transfer

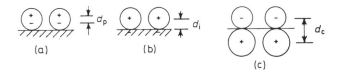

Figure 5.2   Dipoles arising in (a) physisorption, (b) ionic chemisorption and (c) covalent chemisorption on the surface of an adsorbent [129].   d is the distance between the charge centres of gravity.   The subscripts p, i and c denote physisorption, ionic and covalent bonding

of electrons from the adsorbate to the adsorbent.   This is observed, for example, in the system W/Cs.   And in covalent adsorption both the adsorbate and the adsorbent furnish a 'bonding partner'.   The resulting dipole is determined by the electronegativities of the bonding partners.

It is a problem to calculate the dipole moment if measurements have not been made on single-crystal surfaces   [478].   Nevertheless the dipole moment M may be calculated to a first approximation [132] from

$$M = \frac{\Delta(e_0\phi)}{300 \times 4\pi N} \quad \text{e.s.u.} \tag{5.10}$$

In this formula the dipole moment is in electrostatic units, the change of work function is in electron volts and the uptake N is in molecules per square centimetre of actual surface.

A number of methods are available for determining the change of the work function (see also references 129, 166, 357, 378, 478).   The methods depend either on direct measurement of the work function before and after adsorption or on applying equation (5.6) – that is, measuring the change in contact potential difference.

In the direct determination of work function one measures the energy which is needed to remove electrons from the metal.   Of course we are only concerned here with those electrons which are lost with relative ease, namely those coming from the highest energy band.   The energy required may be provided thermally or by irradiation with light quanta.   In the former case the metal must be heated to a certain extent; one then speaks of thermionic electron emission.

The work function for thermionic emission may be evaluated by use of Richardson's equation

$$i_s = CT^2 \exp(-e_0\phi/kT) \tag{5.11}$$

In this equation i_s is the saturation current of thermionic electrons, T is the absolute temperature and

$$C = \frac{4\pi m_e k^2 e_0}{h^3} = 120 \frac{A}{cm^2 K^2} \tag{5.12}$$

Suitable experimental apparatus is described by Becker [39], Smith [620] and Moore and Allison [483]. The current of thermionic electrons is measured as a function of temperature and the work function is obtained directly from the slope of the linear plot of log (i_s/T^2) against $1/T$.

When the electrons are given light energy, one speaks of photoemission or the photoelectric effect. The incident light must be of a frequency ν such that $h\nu \geqslant e_0\phi$. It is then a matter of measuring the photoelectric sensitivity curve – that is, the way in which the photoelectric current varies with the frequency. The work function may be calculated by use of Fowler's theory [234,613], according to which

$$I = M'T^2 f\left(\frac{h\nu - e_0\phi}{kT}\right) \tag{5.13}$$

In the region which is not too close to the threshold frequency ν_0 this expression approximates to

$$I = \frac{M'h^2}{2k^2}(\nu - \nu_0)^2 \tag{5.14}$$

I is the quantum yield (photoelectrons per light quantum absorbed), ν_0 is defined by

$$h\nu_0 = e_0\phi \tag{5.15}$$

and M' is a quantity constant which depends on the interaction probability.

To apply equation (5.13) the equation is rearranged to give

$$\log\left(\frac{I}{T^2}\right) = F(\delta) + \log M' \tag{5.16}$$

The function $F(\delta)$, where

$$\delta = \frac{h\nu - e_0\phi}{kT} \tag{5.17}$$

has been tabulated. Two plots, $F(\delta)$ against δ and $\log(I/T^2)$ against $h\nu/kT$, are now constructed. The horizontal displacement which is necessary to superimpose these plots is $e_0\phi/kT$ and the vertical displacement is $\log M'$ [613].

It is more convenient and, in general, no less accurate to apply equation (5.14) [14]. This analysis consists of plotting $I^{1/2}$ against ν to equally well obtain M' and ν_0. Crowell *et al.* [126] describe a further possibility for evaluating data.

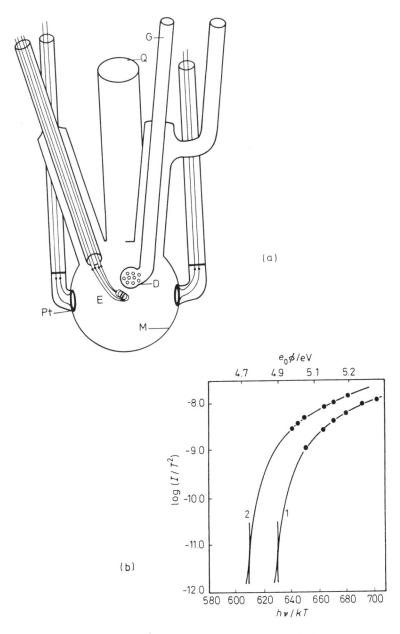

Figure 5.3 (a) Reaction vessel for the measurement of work function changes during adsorption on metal films. Q = quartz window; E = evaporator coil which also serves as anode; M = metal film cathode; Pt = platinum foil contacts; D = end of the gas inlet tube G bearing holes for the even distribution of adsorbate. (b) 'Fowler curves' corresponding to equation (5.16) for a clean Cu film before (1) and after (2) taking up 1.6×10^{14} molecules CO cm^{-2} at 90 K. The work function is given by the position of the vertical lines [651]

Photoelectric measurements have been pursued extensively. For the specific details we refer to the specialised literature [478,613]. A reaction vessel which is suitable for photoelectric investigations is shown in *Figure 5.3(a)*, and *Figure 5.3(b)* gives typical results plotted according to the Fowler theory.

The work function can also be determined with the aid of field emission of electrons. This method is described in Section 5.6.

Various methods are available to obtain the work function from measurements of the contact potential difference. We shall only mention two of these methods, choosing those which are especially important for investigations involving adsorption. In all cases a know-ledge of the work function of one of the electrodes is needed as a reference point.

One of these methods is the vibrating condenser method which was introduced in the main by Mignolet [474] for adsorption work. It utilises the displacement current which flows between two electrically connected plates when the capacity of the condenser they comprise is altered. *Figure 5.4* illustrates the principle. In *Figure 5.4(a)* the potential energy relationship is illustrated for electrons in two isolated metal plates. If the plates are electrically connected together (*Figure 5.4b*), then the Fermi levels of both plates set up a common level. This occurs through a flow of electrons from electrode II to electrode I. As a result, electrode I becomes negatively charged, it assumes an outer potential of $e_0\psi_1$ and its voltage rises to ψ_1. Simultaneously electrode II becomes positive and its voltage falls to ψ_2 so that a contact potential difference of $\psi_1 - \psi_2 = \phi_1 - \phi_2$ is set up between the two electrodes. The contact potential difference may be precisely

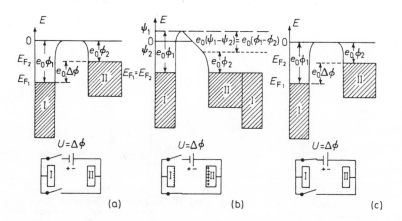

Figure 5.4   Potential energy relationships for electrons in two metal plates. (a) charge free, plates isolated; (b) plates connected electrically; (c) a voltage source is placed in the connecting wire and it just balances the contact potential difference

balanced by inserting a source of voltage U in the connecting wire.
A field-free region then exists between the plates (*Figure 5.4c*).
A current in the connecting wire is only generated in case (b) if a
periodical variation is applied to the distance between the plates. The
value of the contact potential difference is thus given by the balancing
voltage, which must be chosen so that the displacement current just
disappears.

The reaction vessel devised by Mignolet is shown in *Figure 5.5*. A
more modern vessel, and one which is better suited to ultrahigh vacuum
techniques, is that of Alexander and Pritchard [4].

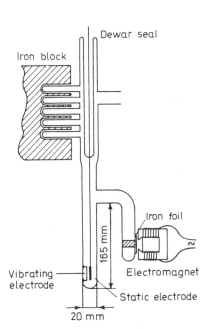

Figure 5.5   Vibrating condenser; after Mignolet [474]

In this method one obtains the contact potential difference $\Delta\psi$
between two electrodes; if the work function of one condenser plate
is known, then one can also obtain the work function of the other
plate by applying equation (5.9). Changes in the work function during gas adsorption may be determined if the work function of one of
the electrodes remains uninfluenced by adsorption.

Delchar and Ehrlich [143] were able to apply the vibrating condenser to the investigation of adsorption on single crystals. A variation
of this technique, in which a static condenser is used, has been
described by Delchar, Eberhagen and Tompkins [142]. In a static
condenser there are no moving parts.

The contact potential difference has also frequently been determined by the diode method, using the space-charge limited region of the characteristic [289,290,378,562]. A negative space charge is built up in front of an emitting electrode at low emission current density. If only a small accelerating voltage is applied, then the emission current is determined by the space charge, and it can be shown that the current under these circumstances depends only on the applied voltage and the work function of the anode. The work function of the cathode hardly influences the current. A change of $\Delta(e_0\phi)$ in the anode work function therefore leads to a corresponding displacement of the current-voltage curve (*Figure 5.6a*). It is convenient to use an incandescent tungsten filament as the cathode in adsorption measurements and the anode is an evaporated metal film. Pritchard's [562] reaction vessel (*Figure 5.6b*) is typical of this arrangement. A significant improvement in technique was achieved by Klemperer and Snaith [374] with their recording diode which allows the current-voltage curves to be drawn automatically during adsorption. Knapp [378] has reviewed the diode methods.

The method which one selects to determine the change of work function $\Delta(e_0\phi)$ depends on the system to be investigated.

The applicability of thermionic emission is determined by two factors: if the work function of the adsorbent is relatively high, then the adsorbent must be heated strongly before appreciable emission current is produced. This can, in fact, only be done for a limited range of materials. Again, at such high temperatures most types of adsorbate

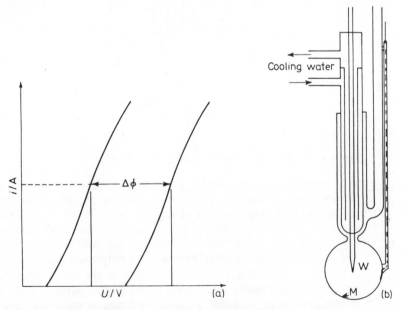

Figure 5.6   Determination of the contact potential difference with the space-charge limited diode method.   (a) current-voltage curves; (b) reaction vessel; M = metal film, W = tungsten filament

are already desorbed. The state of affairs is more favourable, however, when it comes to studying the adsorption of substances which cause a strong depression of the work function. For this reason numerous metal-metal systems have been investigated by use of thermionic emission. Notable among these systems are those in which alkali metals form the adsorbate [478].

The photoelectric method has the advantages of least affecting the system under study and of not needing a reference electrode. The method is limited, nevertheless, to the determination of work functions which lie below about 5.2 eV. This is because of the absorption of UV light of higher energies in the monochromator, in the reaction vessel windows and also, under certain circumstances, in the atmosphere. This occurs even if high-quality quartz glass is used, and it puts the long wave limit at *ca.* 235 nm. At gas pressures above about 10^{-3} Torr impact ionisation is quite liable to occur, and this causes a sudden rise in the emission current which is measured. Photoelectric measurements can therefore only be made at low gas pressures.

When polycrystalline material is used, one measures some sort of average work function because the emitting surface is made up of variously indexed crystal planes. According to equations (5.11) and (5.14), however, the thermionic and photoelectric emission from those crystal planes with a low work function will be weighted in favour of planes with a high work function. The same holds of course for changes in the work function as occasioned by adsorption.

This difficulty does not arise for contact potential difference methods. Nevertheless, in the case of the vibrating condenser method it is hard to find a reference electrode which does not change its work function in the presence of adsorbates.

In the space-charge limited diode method the cathode must be heated to high temperatures. Although the work function is not altered by heating — invariably there is also no adsorption at high temperatures — we do find that many gases are dissociated by the cathode. Dissociation products can then reach the electrode which is being monitored and cause significantly different effects from those produced by the undissociated gases. Savchenko and Boreskov [591] have drawn attention to the existence of this effect in investigations involving the nickel/hydrogen system.

Section 5.6 will include a discussion of the particular advantages to be gained by measuring work functions in a field emission microscope.

Very good agreement is obtained between the various methods, provided that due attention is paid to the possible sources of disturbance which we have mentioned above. Such agreement is demonstrated, for instance, in *Figure 5.7*, which shows results for the nickel/hydrogen system. Uptakes reported by the authors cited [125,323] have been converted to coverages θ for the diagram. Clearly the work function measured at 273 K initially rises in almost direct proportion to the coverage. Beyond 50 per cent monatomic coverage, however, the work function hardly alters any more. We therefore deduce that two states

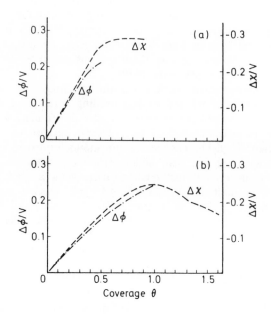

Figure 5.7 *Change of the work function of nickel due to hydrogen adsorption; (a) measured at 273 K; (b) measured at 77 K. After Crossland and Pritchard [125] and Hermann [323]*

exist which show distinct differences from each other. According to the expositions at the beginning of this section, one may take it that hydrogen adsorbed in the initial region is negatively polarised. This cannot, however, be taken as saying that H⁻ ions form.

Measurements at 77 K also reveal two regions below monatomic coverage. These regions are distinguished by their differing rates of rise of the work function with coverage. Above monolayer coverage it is no longer possible to make photoelectric measurements because of impact ionisation. Further coverage, however, can be shown to cause a fall in the work function if use is made of the space-charge limited diode method. This effect is attributed to the adsorption of positively charged molecular hydrogen H_2^+ [473]. In addition, as Savchenko and Boreskov [591] were able to show, there is an atomic species of hydrogen which is adsorbed in this region of coverage, and it also leads to a fall of the work function.

These sorts of observations illustrate how changes in the work function are able to provide information regarding the simultaneous presence of various adsorbed species of one and the same adsorbate. In this respect work function changes are like desorption spectra and infra-red measurements, especially if the work function is measured as a function of the coverage.

The maximum change in work function for the nickel/hydrogen system varies between 0.26 and 0.53 eV [121,128,192,323,379,474], depending on the experimental conditions adopted by the various authors. Considerable interest has recently been shown in the use of single crystals for contact potential difference measurements. Ertl and Küppers [192], for instance, found that 0.40 eV was the maximum increase in the work function during the adsorption of hydrogen on a nickel (110) surface at room temperature. Even more recently, very accurate measurements have been made on Ni(111), (100) and (110) surfaces [121]. These gave the maximum increase in $e_0\phi$ due to hydrogen adsorption as 0.195, 0.170 and 0.530 eV, respectively.

Turning to the adsorption of carbon monoxide on nickel, we find that this system is like nickel/hydrogen in that the gas is chemisorbed provided the coverage does not exceed a monolayer. The maximum increase in the work function has been measured on polycrystalline nickel films as 1.35 eV by Culver, Pritchard and Tompkins [128] and as 1.45 eV by Wedler, Papp and Schroll [698]. These maximum increases agree well with that of 1.4 eV observed by Madden, Küppers and Ertl [435] for the adsorption of carbon monoxide on nickel (110) surfaces. Evidently there is only a relatively small crystal plane effect in the adsorption of carbon monoxide on nickel. Madden *et al.* [435] were also able to assign their work function changes to the occurrence of certain species whose structures differ in the adsorbed state.

The results which we have presented for the systems nickel/hydrogen and nickel/carbon monoxide also apply qualitatively to the adsorption of these two gases on a large number of transition metals.

In contrast to the strong chemisorption just discussed, we shall now give two examples of a weak adsorption. *Figure 5.8* demonstrates the way in which the work function of nickel depends on the uptake of benzene. The experiments were carried out at 90 K because benzene

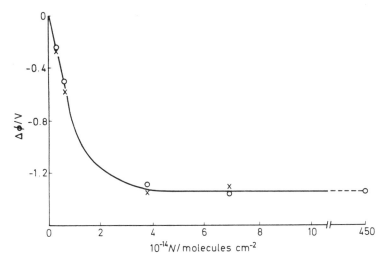

Figure 5.8   Work function of a nickel film as a function of benzene uptake at 90 K [649]

is already decomposed at room temperature on the surface of the clean adsorbent with the formation of hydrogen [643]. At 90 K one observes a strong depression of the work function. This depression is proportional to the uptake at low coverage, but as the monomolecular layer is approached so the change of work function tends to a constant value (−1.37 eV). It follows directly from the cross-sectional area of 45 Å^2 for an adsorbed benzene molecule and the monomolecular uptake of about 2 × 10^{14} benzene molecules per square centimetre extracted from *Figure 5.8* that the benzene molecule must lie flat on the surface of the adsorbent.

The magnitude of the depression of the work function due to physisorption of benzene is determined neither by the structure of the surface nor by the chemical nature of the adsorbent; it is determined only by the value of $e_0\phi_0$, the work function of the clean surface. This is documented in *Figure 5.9*, which collects the work function falls that have been measured for the adsorption of a monomolecular layer of benzene on silver, iron, copper, nickel and palladium. The linear dependence

$$\Delta(e_0\phi) \; = \; c \; + \; a(e_0\phi_{\text{adsorbent}})$$ (5.18)

is also observed in other adsorption systems, and it turns out that it is of no consequence whether the work function of the adsorbent is altered by choosing another material or simply by changing the structure of the adsorbent [648].

The adsorption of carbon monoxide on copper is characterised by enthalpies of adsorption which lie below 15 kcal mol^{-1}. This places

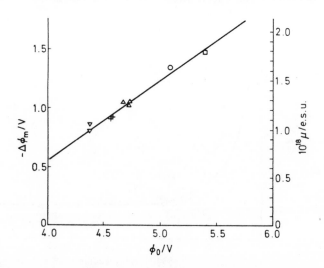

Figure 5.9 The relationship between the work function of the adsorbent and the fall of work function −Δ(e₀φ) due to the adsorption of a monomolecular layer of benzene (+ = Fe, o = Ni, △ = Cu, □ = Pd, ▽ = Ag); after Suhrmann et al. [649]

the adsorption in the transition region between chemisorption and physisorption. A wide variety of methods have been applied to the measurement of work function changes when carbon monoxide is adsorbed by copper films. The methods include the vibrating condenser [62,154], the space-charge limited diode [127] and the photoelectric yield [381, 651], and they all give the same result at a temperature of 77 K: first the work function falls by about 0.35 eV and then $e_0\phi$ rises by about 0.2 eV. This sequence is reproduced in *Figure 5.10(a)*.

It is interesting to note that the maximum fall of the work function depends on the thickness of the copper film (*Figure 5.10b*). This is not so for the subsequent rise of $e_0\phi$. The work function of clean films is also independent of the film thickness. Recently Chesters and Pritchard [116] and Tracy [668] have repeated the measurements of work function changes during carbon monoxide adsorption using a copper (100) surface. These authors find the system behaves qualitatively in the way shown in *Figure 5.10*, although the maximum fall of work function only amounts to 0.2 eV, while the end value is 0.1 eV.

Figures 5.7 and *5.8* demonstrate that in many cases the change of work function, at least at low coverage, is proportional to the coverage.

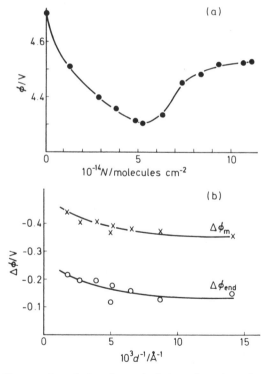

Figure 5.10 Change of work function $e_0\phi$ during adsorption of carbon monoxide on copper: (a) dependence on uptake; (b) dependence of the maximum fall $\Delta(e_0\phi_m)$ and the final value of the fall $\Delta(e_0\phi_{end})$ of the work function on the thickness d of the adsorbent film [381]

As a result one can use work function measurements as an indirect means of establishing the coverage. Ertl and co-workers [192,435] and Tracy [667] have extracted relative coverages in this manner and used them to construct adsorption isotherms and evaluate heats of adsorption.

In much the same way, Pritchard [561] was able to extract the monolayer volume in xenon adsorption by following the variations in surface potential. The monolayer volume, which in turn gives the surface area, corresponds to the distinct kink which is observed in the plot of surface potential against uptake. The variations in work function during adsorption of benzene (*Figure 5.8*) further emphasise the general point that physisorption or chemisorption of many gases can be used to determine the surface area.

Since the variations in work function are often proportional to the gas uptake over a wide range, measurements of the change of work function are suitable for studying the kinetics of adsorption processes or reactions in the adsorbed phase. It is possible to record directly the change of contact potential difference between two metal surfaces during adsorption. This is done by applying an electronic compensation technique [546] to the vibrating condenser or to the static condenser method [144]. The oxidation of aluminium [345,368] and the chemisorption of oxygen on nickel [144] have been investigated in this way, to name but two examples.

Like the other methods, the photoelectric method of determining a work function calls for the measurement of a series of values. These may be temperature dependence of thermionic emission current, current-voltage curves or, in the case of photoelectric measurements, frequency dependence of the photoelectric current. Rapid processes are therefore difficult to follow.

The photoelectric current, however, shows very large changes when the work function of the adsorbent alters, provided that the frequency of the incident light is sufficiently close to the long wavelength cut-off ν_0. This is evident from the horizontal displacement of the 'Fowler curves' in *Figure 5.3(b)*, a rise of work function corresponding to a fall in the photoelectric current and vice versa.

As an example of such current variations during work function changes, we give the decomposition of water on pure nickel films at 273 K. The adsorption of water causes the work function to fall [644], while the products of decomposition raise $e_0\phi$. *Figure 5.11* shows how adsorption first causes a very rapid rise in the photocurrent ($e_0\phi$ falls); a significantly slower reaction (decomposition of water) is then superimposed on this effect and soon causes the reverse movement.

If a reaction occurs between adsorbed molecules of different materials, then the work function is determined not only by the starting species, but also by the products of reaction. Such a reaction occurs, for instance, between adsorbed carbon monoxide and hydrogen – as in the Fischer-Tropsch synthesis – or between oxygen and hydrogen or oxygen and carbon monoxide. Under certain circumstances information

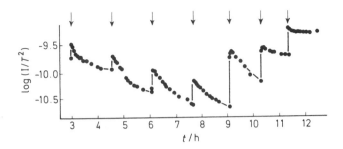

Figure 5.11 Investigation of the decomposition of water on nickel at 273 K. The arrows denote the times at which successive doses of water were admitted to the surface. Wavelength of incident light 248.2 nm; long wavelength cut-off 254 nm. After Suhrmann et al. [644]

concerning the reaction intermediates or the reaction products can thus be obtained from measurements of the work function [610]. This will only be possible where the effects due to the pure starting substances are known.

Although the majority of investigations have been carried out on metallic adsorbents, there is no reason why the method of change of work function should not be just as effective on semiconductors. A semiconducting layer will be formed on the surface of a metal adsorbent by allowing it to react extensively with a suitable adsorbate such as oxygen and the entire process can be followed. In a photoelectric investigation Anderson and Klemperer [15] examined both the oxidation of nickel to nickel oxide and the subsequent reduction of oxide with hydrogen. As is well known, photoelectric and thermionic emission from oxide coatings can be surprisingly high [370]. Bulk compound or elementary semiconductors are also amenable to the change of work function method (see references 320, 581). The ways in which the band structure can influence the work function [670] and the adsorption effects are matters of particular interest. With this in mind Vilesov and Terenin [674], for example, investigated adsorption on semiconducting oxides photoelectrically.

5.2. Electrical conductivity

The significance of the 'electronic factor' in adsorption and catalysis has been much discussed during the 1950s. It was in this connection that one drew attention to the observation that the electron configuration of an adsorbent evidently had a direct influence on the adsorptive properties and catalytic effectiveness of that adsorbent. The influence of the number of d-band holes in transition metals was particularly noticeable. This contention was strengthened by the fact that one observed variations of the electrical conductivity when gases were adsorbed on metals and semiconductors. For such an experiment it was essential that the adsorbent should possess small dimensions. Thus electrical conductivity is a volume effect and it should be noticeably influenced by an adsorption process taking place on the surface.

For this reason many groups of workers have extensively studied the influence of gas adsorption on the electrical resistance of evaporated metal films. Foremost among these groups was that of Suhrmann and his associates. The aim of these investigations was to establish the state of the bound adsorbate by means of conductivity variations. *Figure 5.12* shows a reaction vessel of the type used in more recent work. The metal film is evaporated from a metal coil E on to the

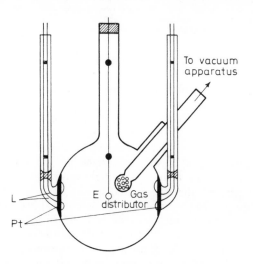

Figure 5.12   Reaction vessel for observing changes of electrical resistance of evaporated metal films caused by adsorption [533]

inside wall of a round-bottomed flask. Resistance is measured between the two ring-shaped contacts Pt, which are made of platinum foil. The electrical lead wires L are taken to the exterior through the rings so that no shadows occur during film evaporation. By using this arrangement the geometric layout is considerably simplified and the specific resistance of the film can be readily calculated. Gas is introduced through a distributing rose so that gas access to the film is uniform.

Interpretation of the observable conductivity changes has been the subject of discussion for many years. This discussion continues even today.

Originally the measured increases or decreases in the electrical resistance of evaporated metal films were ascribed directly to a reduction or an increase in the number of conduction electrons (see, for instance, reference 639). One thought in terms of conduction electrons passing from the metal to the adsorbed molecules or passing from the molecules to the metal. This transfer of electrons was supposed to determine the polar nature of the bond between adsorbent and adsorbate. The resistance variations of 1-3 per cent which were observed for various systems seemed to fit this model because films of *ca.* 100 Å thickness were used. This corresponds to a thickness of about 50 atomic layers.

According to other authors [128], however, the bond formed in chemisorption should be of a predominantly covalent character. Furthermore, it transpired that with continually improving vacuum techniques — that is, with the utilisation of ever-cleaner surfaces — the occurrence of a fall in the resistance became rarer and rarer. It was evidently necessary to discuss the origins of resistance variations anew.

Sachtler and Dorgelo [590], who almost exclusively observed resistance increases, suggested that these increases depended on a demetallisation of the outermost atomic layers of metal films. This part of the film was supposed to stop contributing to the electrical conduction as a result of the formation of a compound with the adsorbate. As before, a resistance increase of about 2 per cent could be accounted for without difficulty in the case of films which are only 100 Å thick. Later investigations, nevertheless, revealed the existence of quite definite resistance decreases or, as in the case of the Cu/CO system, resistance increases of over 30 per cent [651], despite the fact that the carbon monoxide was weakly bound. Effects of this magnitude cannot be explained on the basis of Sachtler's ideas.

More recently there has been a particular preoccupation with the origins of resistance changes. To develop the theory we must first enquire into the mechanism by which films conduct. In principle, one must distinguish between two types of films. 'Ultrathin' films exhibit an island type of structure and essentially the quantum tunnelling of electrons is responsible for their conductivity [215,513,526]. Alternatively, there are thin films which show normal metallic conductivity although their specific resistance does depend on the film thickness (see, for instance, references 59, 625, 694, 719).

Such dependence of the specific resistance on film thickness was explained many years ago by the Fuchs-Sondheimer theory in terms of the so-called free path effect [625]. This theory assumes that the metal film extends to infinity in two dimensions and is bounded in the third by two parallel planes; no grain boundaries exist to disturb the structure. Under these circumstances conduction electrons are taken, at least in part, to be diffusely reflected at the boundary planes. For any bulk metal whose conductivity can be described by a single-band model, the specific resistance ρ_0 is given by [353]

$$\rho_0 = \frac{(2m\ E_F)^{1/2}}{e^{l}{}_N\ e_0^2\ l_0} \tag{5.19}$$

Here m is the mass of the electron, E_F is the Fermi energy, ^{el}N is the number of conduction electrons per cubic centimetre, e_0 is the elementary charge and l_0 is the mean free path of the conduction electrons. This expression is modified by the Fuchs-Sondheimer theory to give a specific resistance ρ for a film of thickness d according to

$$\rho = \rho_0 f\left(\frac{l_0}{d}\right) \tag{5.20}$$

If we also take into account that the resistance $R = F\rho/d$ ($F = $ geometric factor) and replace the Fermi energy by

$$E_F = \frac{h^2}{8m}\left(\frac{3\,^{el}N}{\pi}\right)^{2/3} \tag{5.21}$$

then we obtain

$$R = \frac{A\,f(l_0/d)}{{^{el}N}^{2/3}\,l_0\,d} \tag{5.22}$$

where all constants have been collected together in A.

According to equation (5.22), a change in the electrical resistance could be due to a change in the number ^{el}N of conduction electrons, the mean free path length l_0 (or the mobility) and the film thickness d, or to a simultaneous variation of more than one of these quantities. Despite numerous investigations [265,411,413,744], it has not proved possible to formulate any hypothesis and isolate the effect of adsorption on ^{el}N, l_0 or d. Experiments have included the measurement of resistance changes as a function of film thickness [695] and the variation of temperature coefficients of resistance [508,695]. Wedler and Fouad were, nevertheless, able to exclude any unique influence of ^{el}N and d in the Ni/CO system [695].

Difficulties had already cropped up at an early stage in applying the Fuchs-Sondheimer theory to the variation of specific resistance of thin films with their thickness [694], and doubt was thrown on the applicability of the theory when Chopra and Bobb [119] noticed that the specific resistance of single-crystal copper films showed no dependence on thickness of those films. This result can only be taken to mean that the conduction electrons undergo specular reflection at the surface of the film. On the other hand, a detailed knowledge of the microcrystalline structure of their nickel films was obtained by Suhrmann, Gerdes and Wedler [642] in an electron microscopic investigation and by Wedler and Wissmann [706-708,720] using X-ray techniques. On the basis of these experimental data, Wissmann [719] was able to reproduce the thickness dependence of electrical conductivity more accurately than was possible with the Fuchs-Sondheimer theory. For this purpose he assumed that conduction electrons simultaneously underwent purely specular reflection at the film surface and scattering at the crystallite boundaries. Similar lines of reasoning were developed independently by Mayadas and co-workers (see, for instance, references 444,445). According to Wissmann, the specific resistance $\rho(d)$ at film thickness d comes out to be

$$\rho(d) = \rho_0 \left\{ 1 + [Kl_0/D(d)] \right\} = \frac{\rho_0}{\psi(d)} \tag{5.23}$$

where ρ_0 is the specific resistance of the bulk material, l_0 is the mean free path of the electrons, K is a constant characterising the electron scattering at crystallite boundaries and $D(d)$ is the average crystallite dimension at a film thickness d.

If conduction electrons are specularly reflected at clean film surfaces, then adsorbed molecules can act as scattering centres for the conduction electrons in the same way as do foreign atoms that are alloyed into the metal. The resistance then rises accordingly. Working along these lines, Wedler, Wissmann and co-workers [700,709,721] were, in fact, able to obtain better quantitative agreement than had hitherto been possible for the resistance changes caused by gas adsorption and the dependence of these effects on film thickness. These considerations have received direct support from the recently published work of Panchenko *et al.* [532] in which electronic interaction during adsorption was investigated by use of the skin effect.

By analogy with Matthiessen's rule, the specific resistance ρ of the film at low gas coverages is given by

$$\rho = \rho_F + \Delta\rho \tag{5.24}$$

where ρ_F is the specific resistance of the clean film and $\Delta\rho$ is the additional resistance resulting from gas adsorption. For the latter we have

$$\Delta\rho = k\,\frac{N}{d} \tag{5.25}$$

where k is a 'scattering constant', N is the number of adsorbed molecules per square centimetre of geometric surface and d is the thickness of the film. The rise in resistance may also be related to the atomic percentage x of foreign adsorbed molecules:

$$k' = \frac{\Delta\rho}{x} = {}^{at}N\,k\,10^{-2} \tag{5.26}$$

In this expression, which may be found in the literature [260] for the case of a dilute alloy, ${}^{at}N$ is the number of metal atoms per cubic centimetre.

Figures 5.13 and *5.14* show the changes in specific resistance that are observed for nickel films of about 100 Å thickness when H_2 and CO, respectively, are admitted up to an equilibrium pressure of 10^{-4} Torr at various temperatures.

Figure 5.15 shows the relative changes in electrical resistance that are observed for a copper film of 100 Å thickness when carbon monoxide is adsorbed at 77 K.

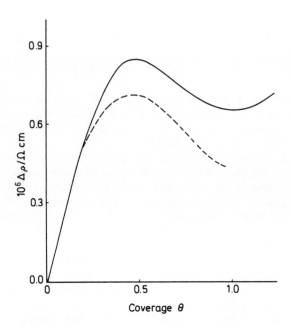

Figure 5.13 Change in specific resistance Δρ for nickel films of about 80 Å thickness when hydrogen is adsorbed up to a pressure of 10^{-4} Torr. Continuous curve at 77 K; dashed curve at 273 K. After reference Wedler and Bröcker [691]

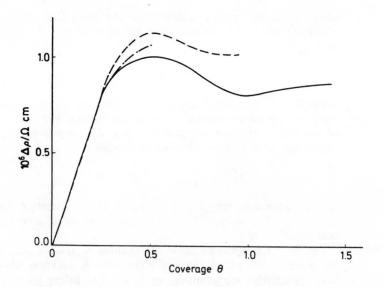

Figure 5.14 Change in specific resistance Δρ for nickel films of about 100 Å thickness when carbon monoxide is adsorbed up to a pressure of 10^{-4} Torr. Continuous curve at 77 K; dashed curve at 273 K; dashed/dotted curve at 353 K. After Wedler et al. [698]

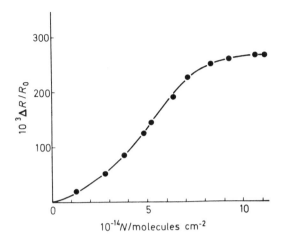

Figure 5.15   Relative change in electrical resistance for a copper film of 100 Å thickness during the adsorption of carbon monoxide at 77 K [381]

According to equation (5.25), as given by Wissmann, the film thickness should be inversely proportional to $(d\Delta\rho/dN)_{N\to0}$, the initial slope of the curve relating $\Delta\rho$, the measured change of specific resistance, with the uptake N (in molecules per square centimetre of geometric surface). Equation (5.25) can therefore be checked by carrying out the same measurements on a series of films of differing thicknesses. *Figures 5.16-5.18* reveal that a straight line of slope -1 does in fact occur when $\log(d\Delta\rho/dN)_{N\to0}$ is plotted against $\log d$. The scattering constant k can be extracted from these linear plots and then, using equation (5.26), one can evaluate the increase k' in the specific resistance per atomic per cent of adsorbed foreign molecules. In the case of the systems presented, k' lies between 1 and 3 $\mu\Omega$ cm mol^{-1} per cent. We may note that this is of the same order of magnitude as the values which are found for binary alloys [402].

Despite these advances, the theoretical interpretation of resistance changes still contains some uncertainties. On the other hand, resistance measurements have turned out to be a valuable aid in the study of adsorption. They enable the point to be established at which monomolecular coverage is completed. They also enable adsorption kinetics and mobility to be studied, and it is possible to follow reactions in the adsorbed phase. Semiconducting elements and compounds can be used in addition to metallic films. Indeed powdered samples, invariably semiconducting oxides (NiO, ZnO, etc.), have proved to be amenable to resistance measurements.

The Ni/H_2 system has been well characterised by a number of authors [101,477,556,559,589,650,691]. At low coverages the resistance

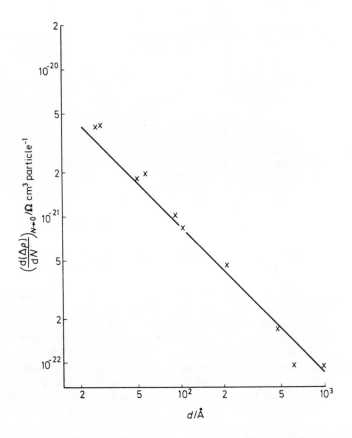

Figure 5.16   Plot of $(d\Delta\rho/dN)_{N\to 0}$ against log d for the system Ni/H_2 at 273 K; after Wedler et al. [700]

rises linearly with the coverage. This is shown in *Figure 5.13*, which also shows how the resistance passes through a maximum at 0.5 atomic coverage. At 273 K the resistance then gradually approaches a limiting value but at 77 K it rises again after the atomic monolayer has been reached. These resistance changes are so accurately reproducible that they afford a direct measure of the coverage θ.

The least we can do is to assign distinguishable species of adsorbed hydrogen to the various sections of the resistance curves which have differing gradient signs. Distinguishable species can also be recognised in other measurements such as the desorption spectra (*Figure 3.16*). We may also note that a close parallel exists between the resistance and the variation of the enthalpy of adsorption which is observed at 273 K (*Figure 3.9*). The heat curve has a minimum which occurs at exactly the same coverage as the maximum in the resistance curve.

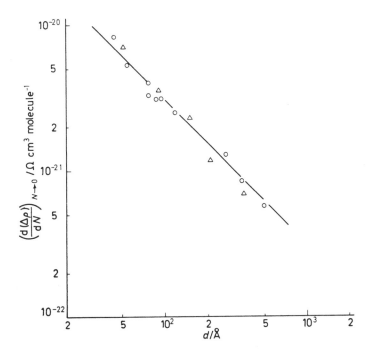

Figure 5.17   Plot of log(d$\Delta\rho$/dN)$_{N\to0}$ against log d for the system Ni/CO at 273 K; after Wedler and Wissmann [709]

Work function changes also bear comparison.   At 273 K the work function $e_0\phi$ of a nickel film first rises during the adsorption of hydrogen (*Figure 5.7*) but then changes little more after the coverage is reached at which there is a maximum in the resistance.   At 77 K, however, $e_0\phi$ continues to rise, if less strongly, up to $\theta = 1$.   At this temperature, therefore, $e_0\phi$ rises while the resistance falls but beyond the monolayer, when the resistance rises again, we find $e_0\phi$ falls.

As *Figure 5.14* shows, there is a marked similarity in the resistance changes shown by the Ni/CO and the Ni/H$_2$ systems.   Thus recent investigation has shown that a maximum in the resistance also exists in the case of the Ni/CO system, indicating that two different species of adsorbed carbon monoxide exist.   The proportion of each species depends on the coverage up to $\theta = 1$ and it is highly probable that the two species exhibit a different structure in the adsorbed phase (see Section 6.1).   Beyond the monolayer coverage ($\theta > 1$) a further species then appears.

Figure 5.14 also shows how temperature influences the amount of gas which can be adsorbed at a certain equilibrium pressure (here 10^{-4} Torr).   The appearance of the various species, however, depends solely on the extent of the coverage.

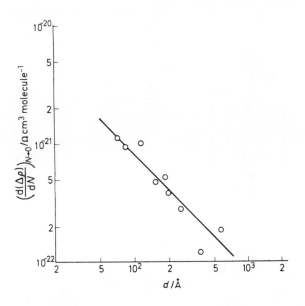

Figure 5.18   Plot of log $(d\Delta\rho/dN)_{N\to 0}$ against log d for the system Cu/CO at 77 K; after Wedler and Wissmann [709]

One can show that the extent of the resistance rise is independent of the strength of the bond in adsorption. This is done by comparing the changes in relative resistance observed during chemisorption of carbon monoxide and hydrogen on nickel films with the effects of carbon monoxide adsorption on copper films (*Figure 5.15*).

Resistance changes have been used to study the mobility of adsorbed molecules [100,654]. *Figure 5.19(a)* shows a reaction vessel which is suitable for this type of investigation. Gas is passed through a thermostat and reaches the upper part of a cylindrical, evaporated film via a distributing rose. The resistance of the film can be measured between a number of different points with platinum ring electrodes. In *Figure 5.19(b)* we can see the effect of adding doses of carbon monoxide (T = 90 K) to a nickel film at 90 K. After the first two doses there is an appreciable rise in the resistance of the upper film section but the lower film section hardly changes. Only when the third dose D_3 is admitted does the monolayer become substantially complete in the upper section and the resistance of the lower section also starts to rise. This result shows that CO molecules adsorbed initially are very firmly bound to their sites. Pumping off the gas phase (P) is without

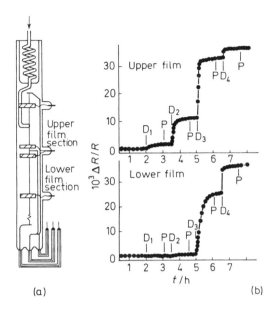

Figure 5.19 Investigation of the mobility of adsorbed molecules (CO on Ni). (a) Reaction vessel; (b) variation of electrical resistance with time for the upper and lower film sections [654]. Gas admitted at D and pumped out at P

effect. Adsorbed molecules only become mobile when the coverage has risen substantially (around the monolayer) and they can then reach the lower section of the vessel by moving over the surface (or, under certain circumstances, through the gas phase). These conclusions are in full agreement with the results of Section 3.5 (*Figures 3.17* and *3.18*).

Reactions in the adsorbed phase have also been fruitfully investigated with the aid of resistance measurements. Examples are the decomposition of water [644] and of methane [640] on nickel; the displacement of hydrogen by carbon monoxide on nickel [699] and of nitrogen by hydrogen on iron [689]; and the interaction of adsorbed molecules (H_2, O_2) [557,558].

Kinetics of adsorption [412,653,684,685] and any kind of conversion in the adsorbed phase can be conveniently studied by observing resistance changes, because these changes are proportional to the coverage, provided the coverage is not too high. The ability to investigate reactions which are relatively fast is a special advantage of the resistance method.

At very low temperatures superconductivity can be turned to the study of adsorption. This has been done by, for example, Rühl [585, 586].

5.3.   Thermoelectric power

It has proved to be exceedingly difficult to make deductions about
the electronic processes which are actually going on during adsorption
by considering only measurements of the change of electrical resistance.
The exploitation of additional parameters which depend on the concentration of electrons has therefore been desirable.   To this end, thermoelectric power and the Hall effect may be studied.   As in the case of
resistance measurements, a favourable ratio of surface area to the
volume of adsorbent must obtain so that changes in thermoelectric
power and the Hall effect may readily be measured during adsorption.

Thermoelectric power measurements have been made during adsorption
of gases on both metal films and pressed powders of metal oxides.   In
view of the experimental difficulties, however, the amount of published
work is small.

For a bulk metal specimen the thermoelectric power S is given [353]
by

$$S = - \frac{\pi^2 k^2 T}{3|e_0|E_F} \left(\frac{\partial \ln \sigma}{\partial \ln E} \right)_{E=E_F} \tag{5.27}$$

where e_0 is the elementary charge, σ is the specific conductivity and
E_F is the Fermi energy.   Recalling that σ depends on the mean free
path length for electrons l as well as the area of the Fermi surface A
according to

$$\sigma = \text{const.}\ l\,A \tag{5.28}$$

− this is a generalisation of equation (5.19) − it follows that

$$S = - \frac{\pi^2 k^2 T}{3|e_0|E_F} \left(\frac{\partial \ln l}{\partial \ln E} + \frac{\partial \ln A}{\partial \ln E} \right)_{E=E_F} \tag{5.29}$$

In the case of a thin film l depends on the film thickness and therefore differs from the mean free path length l_0 for electrons in the
bulk material (see equation 5.20).   Thus the thermoelectric power also
depends on the film thickness.   The combination of equations (5.19)
and (5.20) gives

$$\frac{l}{l_0} = f\left(\frac{d}{l_0} \right) \tag{5.30}$$

so that

$$\frac{\partial \ln l}{\partial \ln E} = \frac{\partial \ln l_0}{\partial \ln E} + \frac{\partial \ln f(d/l_0)}{\partial \ln E} \tag{5.31}$$

and equation (5.29) becomes

$$S = -\frac{\pi^2 k^2 T}{3|e_0|E_F} \left\{ \frac{\partial \ln l_0}{\partial \ln E} \left[1 - \frac{d \ln (l/l_0)}{d \ln (d/l_0)} \right] + \frac{\partial \ln A}{\partial \ln E} \right\}_{E=E_F} \quad (5.32)$$

If we may reckon on free electrons being present, then the radius of the Fermi sphere is proportional to $E^{\frac{1}{2}}$ and the last term of the sum in the curly bracket assumes the value of unity. In this case equation (5.32) reduces to the relationship which Justi, Kohler and Lautz [355] deduced by applying Sondheimer's free path length theory:

$$S = -\frac{\pi^2 k^2 T}{3|e_0|E_F} \left\{ 1 + \frac{d \ln l_0}{d \ln E} \left[1 - \frac{d \ln (l/l_0)}{d \ln (d/l_0)} \right] \right\}_{E=E_F} \quad (5.33)$$

The presence of only free electrons, however, can certainly not be assumed for transition metals. For this reason equation (5.33) can only serve as a first approximation for those transition metals in which the conductivity is determined predominantly by s-electrons [740].

The expression in the square brackets in equation (5.33) cannot be altered by adsorption. Accordingly, the change ΔS_N in thermoelectric power caused by adsorption is given by

$$\Delta S_N = -\frac{\pi^2 k^2 T}{3|e_0|E_F} \left[1 - \frac{d \ln (l/l_0)}{d \ln (d/l_0)} \right] \left[\frac{d \ln l_0}{d \ln E_N} - \frac{d \ln l_0}{d \ln E_0} \right]_{E_F} \quad (5.34)$$

where the subscripts 0 and N attached to the energy refer to the number of molecules taken up before and after adsorption.

According to Mott and Jones [487], the large specific resistance of transition metals is due to the scattering of their s-electrons at d-band holes. For this reason Eley and Petro [182], who did not allow for the effect of dependence on film thickness, assumed that the mean free path length l_0 was inversely proportional to the density of states of d-electrons at the Fermi energy. Should a change in the number of conduction electrons occur during adsorption, then it follows that the Fermi energy must change. At the same time the density of states at the Fermi energy must alter. According to Eley's assumption, this will lead to a change in the mean free path length of the electrons and, according to equation (5.34), it also leads to a change in the thermoelectric power. The sign of the thermoelectric power change would be given by the gradient of the curve giving the density of states at the Fermi energy. Since we do not know the precise nature of the density of states curve, any quantitative treatment of the problem becomes difficult.

It is possible, nevertheless, to take the view that the adsorbed particles act as scattering centres in the same way as do foreign atoms that are mixed into the bulk. We have used this approach in discussing resistance changes and it means that the influence of adsorption on thermoelectric power is best described by starting again from equation (5.27) [700]:

$$S = C\left(\frac{\partial \ln \rho}{\partial \ln E}\right)_{E=E_F} \qquad (5.35)$$

ρ is the specific resistance and all constants have been collected in C. The change ΔS_N of thermoelectric power for N molecules adsorbed then becomes

$$\Delta S_N = C\frac{\Delta\rho_N}{\rho_b + \Delta\rho_N}\left\{\left(\frac{\partial \ln \Delta\rho_N}{\partial \ln E}\right)_{E=E_F} - \left(\frac{\partial \ln \rho_b}{\partial \ln E}\right)_{E=E_F}\right\} \qquad (5.36)$$

The resistance of the bare film ρ_b, which depends on the film thickness, may be replaced by means of equation (5.23) and $\Delta\rho_N$ may be replaced by means of equation (5.25). We can also write $l_0\rho_0P_1$ for k in equation (5.25) and say $\Delta\rho_N \ll \rho_b$ to obtain finally

$$\Delta S_N = Cl_0P_1N\frac{\psi(d)}{d}\left\{\left(\frac{\partial \ln(l_0P_1)}{\partial \ln E}\right)_{E=E_F} - \right.$$

$$\left. \psi(d)\frac{Kl_0}{D(d)}\left[\frac{\partial \ln (Kl_0)}{\partial \ln E}\right]_{E=E_F}\right\} \qquad (5.37)$$

The initial slope of the curve of ΔS against N is then seen to be

$$\left(\frac{d\Delta S_N}{dN}\right)_{N\to0} = \left(\frac{dS}{dN}\right)_{N\to0} = Cl_0P_1\frac{\psi(d)}{d}\left\{\left[\frac{\partial \ln(l_0P_1)}{\partial \ln E}\right]_{E=E_F} - \right.$$

$$\left. \frac{\psi(d)}{D(d)}Kl_0\left[\frac{\partial \ln(Kl_0)}{\partial \ln E}\right]_{E=E_F}\right\} \qquad (5.38)$$

A reaction vessel which is suitable for thermoelectric power measurements is shown in *Figure 5.20*. The spherical vessel resembles the one used for resistance measurement (*Figure 5.12*) but bears an additional assembly which is inserted from above and is used for thermoelectric power and electrical resistance measurements. It consists of a glass substrate S to which two glass tubes have been fused. These tubes contain the thermostating fluids. Four tungsten pins (a-d) have been

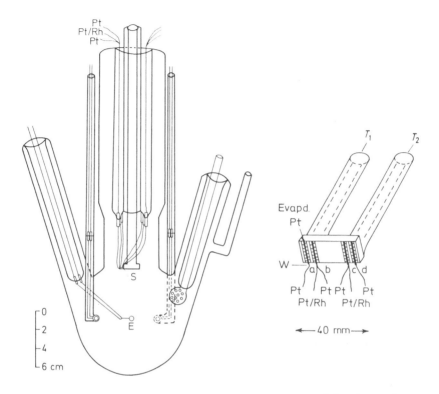

Figure 5.20 Reaction vessel for simultaneous measurement of the changes in thermoelectric power and electrical resistance occasioned by adsorption on metal films [704]

fused into the substrate below these tubes and the substrate has then been ground back until the ground pins are lying in an optically flat surface. To improve contact, narrow strips of platinum (labelled Pt) are evaporated on to the pins and the glass bordering them. The platinum strips bear the platinum and the platinum/rhodium leads which serve to measure the temperature, the thermoelectric power of the specimen against platinum and the resistance of the film. The specimen is a metal film that is evaporated from coil E, and the resistance measurements are made by means of current and voltage leads. A vessel which is suitable for measuring variations of thermoelectric power of powder adsorbents has been described by Squires and Parravano [630].

Figure 5.21 shows the change in thermoelectric power measured for a nickel film at 273 K as a function of the quantity of hydrogen adsorbed. Similar measurements for the adsorption of carbon monoxide on nickel film are shown in *Figure 5.22*.

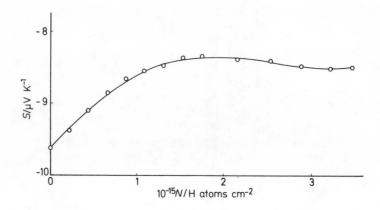

Figure 5.21   Change in the thermoelectric power of a nickel film on adsorbing hydrogen at 273 K; after Wedler et al. [700]. Thickness of film is 98 Å

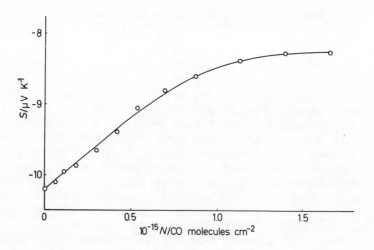

Figure 5.22   Change in the thermoelectric power of a nickel film on adsorbing carbon monoxide at 273 K; after Wedler et al. [700].   Thickness of film is 106 Å

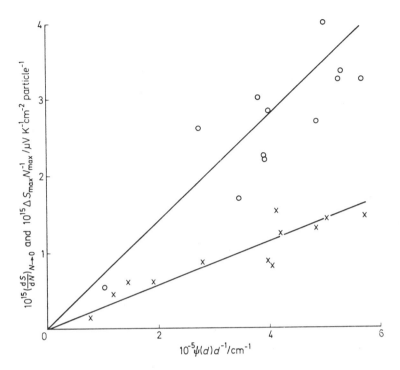

Figure 5.23 Slopes of thermoelectric power curves like those given in Figures *5.21 and 5.22 as a function of $\psi(d)/d$. The plots have been constructed to check equation (5.38). Circles, carbon monoxide; crosses, hydrogen*

To test equation (5.38), one should take data for a number of films of differing thickness and plot the initial slopes of curves such as that given in *Figure 5.22* against $\psi(d)/d$. The result is shown for the adsorption of carbon monoxide as circles in *Figure 5.23*. Since the initial slopes of curves for the adsorption of hydrogen could not be determined with sufficient accuracy, the slopes $\Delta S_{max}/N_{max}$. were taken over a range of half atomic coverage. These slopes, which are only about half of the initial values, have been plotted against $\psi(d)/d$ as the crosses in *Figure 5.23*. We notice that the scatter of points in *Figure 5.23* is too large to enable us to establish a linear relationship with certainty. Particularly in the case of carbon monoxide adsorption, this may be attributed to the extremely small effects one has to contend with.

If the change in thermoelectric power due to adsorption is converted into the effect per mol per cent of adsorbate, then one obtains

$$\Delta S = + 6.5 \ \mu V \ K^{-1} \text{ per mol per cent CO}$$
$$\Delta S = + 5.0 \ \mu V \ K^{-1} \text{ per atom per cent H}$$

These values are of the same order of magnitude as the values found for binary nickel alloys [389].

5.4 Hall effect

The Hall effect depends on the concentration of charge carriers and the thickness of the conductor in the same way as the electrical resistance does. It is nevertheless independent of the mobility of the electrons. In Section 5.2 we raised the question: why do the electronic properties of a metal change during adsorption? We can now see that a particularly suitable way of clarifying this matter should be to combine measurements of electrical resistance and Hall effect.

Suppose that we take an elongated parallelepiped of conductor, pass a current i through it and place it in a transverse magnetic field of magnetic induction B. A potential difference U_H (*Figure 5.24a*) is then observed in a direction perpendicular to both i and B. This potential is given by

$$U_H = R_H \frac{iB}{d}$$ (5.39)

where d is the thickness of the conductor measured in the direction of the magnetic field and R_H is known as the Hall coefficient. So long as there is only one type of charge carrier, R_H depends on the density of carriers. At sufficiently strong fields and for a closed Fermi surface

$$R_H = \frac{-1}{(^{el}N - {}^{ho}N)e}$$ (5.40)

where ^{el}N is the density of electrons and ^{ho}N the density of positive holes. R_H is negative if electronic conduction predominates, but if conduction by holes predominates, then R_H is positive. As in the cases of electrical conductivity and thermoelectric power, the effect of path length becomes noticeable in the Hall voltage of very thin conductors (metal films). Equation (5.40) must therefore be corrected in a suitable manner [447,506,625]. Furthermore, the Hall coefficient for ferromagnetic metals must be divided up between the ordinary and the extraordinary parts.

Hansen and Littmann [301], Murgulescu and Comsa [506], Bastl [32] and Wedler and Wiebauer [705,717], among others, have described suitable arrangements for measuring the variation of Hall voltage due to chemisorption (*Figure 5.24b*). Current i is passed through the evaporated film F via the electrodes A and B. Electrodes C, D and E are used to measure the Hall voltage. The Hall voltage must be read off between points showing no potential difference when the magnetic field is switched off. These points C and C′ are established with the aid of the variable resistances R_1 and R_2. The Hall voltage U_H is then measured by balancing it on the potentiometer P by using galvanometer G, and temperature is measured with a copper-constantan thermocouple.

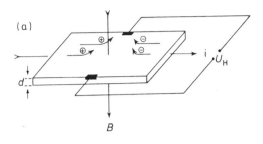

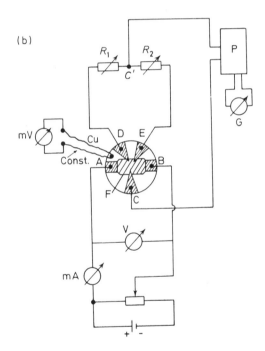

Figure 5.24 Measurement of the Hall voltage. (a) To illustrate equation (5.39);
(b) circuits. After Murgulescu and Comsa [506]

Murgulescu and Comsa [507] studied the variation of Hall voltage during chemisorption of oxygen and carbon monoxide on thin copper films, and Wedler and Wiebauer [705,717] followed the variations in Hall voltage during the chemisorption of carbon monoxide on copper films of different thicknesses.   The effects of adsorbing oxygen on thin nickel films [32] and hydrogen on tungsten films [33] were investigated by Bastl.

When carbon monoxide was adsorbed on nickel and iron films, Hansen and Littmann [301] found that the Hall voltage increased. Since the Hall coefficients of nickel and iron are negative (electron conduction) and positive (hole conduction), respectively, Hansen and Littmann concluded that a reduction of the effective film thickness was responsible for the variation of Hall voltage; this reduction is occasioned by the formation of compounds.   Were one concerned with a variation of the electron concentration, then the Hall voltage for nickel and iron would rise and fall, respectively, during the adsorption of carbon monoxide.   This is because any variation of the electron concentration that occurs in these systems can only be a fall in concentration.

This result runs quite contrary to the mechanisms which have been deduced from measurements of resistance and thermoelectric power. Our discussion of these results has been in very simple terms, especially in view of the fact that the single-band model cannot really be used for iron and nickel.   Before definitive conclusions can be drawn, investigations should be carried out of the way in which variations of the Hall voltage depend on the structure and thickness of films (see, for instance, reference 242).   The first data in this direction are already to hand.   Thus, Wedler and Wiebauer [705,717] investigated the influence of film thickness and temperature on the Hall coefficient of copper films, both in the clean condition and during carbon monoxide adsorption.   The results were interpreted in the light of the more recent work concerning the Fermi surface of copper [603,604] and the Hall effect [346,431,741,742].   It turned out that the effects could only be explained if the adsorbed carbon monoxide molecules acted as additional scattering centres.   Despite the difficulties of interpreting the effects one measures, it is to be expected that informative data will be obtained from investigations of the influence of adsorption on the Hall voltage.   Measurements must be made, however, while the detailed parameters are varied in a systematic way.

Such measurements are not confined to the metal/gas adsorption system.   Chon and Prater [118] have shown that Hall effect measurements can be fruitfully turned to polycrystalline oxides for studying adsorption and reactions in the adsorbed phase.

5.5.   Magnetic properties

The formation of a chemisorbed bond may influence not only the electrical properties of the adsorbent, but also its magnetic properties. This will always occur if the number of unpaired electrons alters as a result of adsorption. Such is the case when a paramagnetic gas is bound to a solid (for instance, NO adsorption [743]) or when previously unpaired electrons of a para- or ferromagnetic adsorbent move into the adsorbed phase. On the other hand, the effect can only occur at the surface, so that if one wishes to study alterations in magnetic properties due to adsorption, it is important to keep the number of surface atoms compared with the number of bulk atoms as large as possible. This means that one has to work with a material that is made up of small particles of adsorbent, as, for instance, in the case of supported catalysts.

Prominent among those who have exploited the possibility of using magnetic measurements for problems in adsorption are Selwood and co-workers [146,149,348,605,611]. In his monograph *Adsorption and Collective Paramagnetism* [606], Selwood gives a detailed introduction to his field of interest and also reviews the results that have been obtained up to about 1961. Subsequent results are reviewed in the same author's *Chemisorption and Magnetization* [606].

If a body is placed in an external magnetic field H (in oersteds), then it becomes magnetised. The magnetic induction B (in gauss) that is effective internally is made up of H and the magnetisation M according to

$$B = H + 4\pi M \qquad (5.41)$$

Magnetisation is proportional to field strength:

$$M = \kappa H \qquad (5.42)$$

where κ is called the magnetic susceptibility per unit volume. The susceptibility per gram χ can be obtained by use of the density ρ:

$$\chi = \frac{\kappa}{\rho} \qquad (5.43)$$

The quantities M and χ will be of particular interest to us.

As is well known, χ enables materials to be divided into those which are diamagnetic ($\chi < 0$), paramagnetic ($\chi > 0$) and ferromagnetic ($\chi \gg 0$). Most matter is diamagnetic, paramagnetism only occurring when there are unpaired electrons. In both cases one is concerned with properties of the atoms themselves. Diamagnetic susceptibility is independent of the field strength and the temperature. But paramagnetism, although it is independent of the field strength, depends on the temperature. Paramagnetic susceptibility per mole of atoms (χ_A) is given by

$$\chi_A = \frac{N_L \mu_A^2 \beta^2}{3\,kT} \qquad (5.44)$$

where N_L is Avogadro's number, μ_A the magnetic moment per atom expressed in Bohr magnetons, β the Bohr magneton, k the Boltzmann constant and T the absolute temperature.

Paramagnetic susceptibility is thus inversely proportional to temperature.

Ferromagnetic materials may be distinguished from paramagnetic ones in that they become very strongly magnetised at moderate temperatures, that the magnetisation approaches a limiting value (saturation magnetisation) as the field strength rises, that the magnetisation is retained after the external field has been switched off and that above a certain temperature (the Curie temperature) ferromagnetism ceases. Above the Curie temperature these materials behave as if they were paramagnetic. Ferromagnetism therefore cannot be a property of the atoms. It arises because macroscopic regions of the crystals (Weiss domains) exhibit parallel orientation of the atomic moments.

Para- and ferromagnetic adsorbents are of particular interest for investigations involving adsorption. We have mentioned that the adsorbent should consist of small particles if adsorption effects are to be observed and it is this requirement that complicates matters in the case of ferromagnetism. Frequently the particles may be no larger than the size of a single Weiss domain (diameter < 300 Å). As a result, ferromagnetic materials lose one of their most important criteria, namely the sharp Curie point. Their behaviour can then be described as that of an intermediate state lying between para- and ferromagnetism; it is designated collective paramagnetism or superparamagnetism [606]. The magnetisation of a substance exhibiting superparamagnetism obeys equation (5.44) except for the difference that μ_A is replaced by $\mu = \bar{\mu}_A n$, the moment of a particle built up of n atoms. This moment, divided by the volume v of the particle, gives the spontaneous magnetisation I_{sp}:

$$I_{sp} = \frac{\mu}{v} \qquad (5.45)$$

Deductions about the state of the binding in the adsorbed phase are made by comparing the magnetic moment μ_A of the adsorbent before and after adsorption. μ_A is calculated from the magnetisation by use of equations (5.42)-(5.44). A number of methods are available for measuring magnetisation. However, if we take into account the necessity of keeping the sample in high vacuum, then practical considerations limit us to a few of these methods.

In the Faraday method a mass m of adsorbent is suspended on a quartz spiral in a strong magnetic field. The field has a gradient in the vertical (z) direction. The deflection of the adsorbent that occurs when the field is switched on is observed with a microscope. Since the force K acting on the sample is

$$K = m\chi H \frac{dH}{dz} \tag{5.46}$$

χ can be evaluated with the aid of a calibration curve (deflection = $f(K)$). This, in turn, leads to the magnetisation.

The permeameter described by Selwood is suitable for observing the effect of adsorption directly. As shown in *Figure 5.25*, the adsorbent is surrounded by a small solenoid connected to a second, empty coaxial coil which is wound in opposition. The whole arrangement is surrounded with a primary solenoid which is supplied by alternating current. The EMF induced in the secondary circuit is directly proportional to the magnetisation M of the adsorbent.

We also mention the method of Weiss and Forrer [712], which is eminently suitable for adsorption investigations. This is again an inductive technique (see *Figure 5.26*), which enables the saturation magnetisation to be measured at high field strengths and sufficiently low temperatures to yield data for the saturation magnetisation at absolute zero, M_0; this quantity gives us accurate values of $\overline{\mu}_A$, the magnetic moment per atom. The procedure consists of moving the adsorbent in the magnetic field from a position between two Helmholtz coils

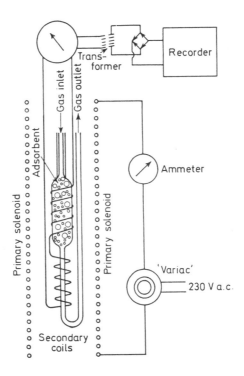

Figure 5.25   Alternating current permeameter; after Selwood [605,606]

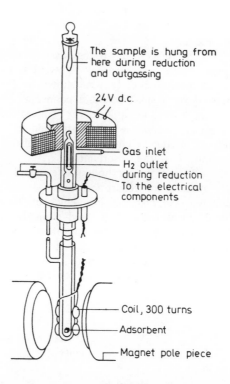

The sample is hung from here during reduction and outgassing

24V d.c.

Gas inlet

H₂ outlet during reduction

To the electrical components

Coil, 300 turns

Adsorbent

Magnet pole piece

Figure 5.26   Apparatus [149] for the measurement of magnetisation by the method of Weiss and Forrer

into another position between two further Helmholtz coils that have been wound in opposition.   The current induced by this movement is integrated by means of a ballistic galvanometer.   The galvanometer deflection is directly proportional to the magnetisation.

The methods we have outlined are not suitable for investigations on evaporated films.   The saturation magnetisation of films is determined by use of, for example, a torsion magnetometer [511].   In this method the film is evaporated onto a substrate and hung in a magnetic field on the end of a torsion suspension.   The saturation magnetisation can be calculated from the extent to which the suspension is twisted (see also reference 383).

The change in magnetisation per adsorbed molecule may be obtained by comparing the saturation magnetisation before and after uptake of a known quantity of gas.   If there are $^{1}N_A$ atoms cm^{-3} of adsorbent with an average magnetic moment of $\bar{\mu}_A\beta$, then the saturation magnetisation M_0 at absolute zero is

$$M_0 = {}^{1}N_A\bar{\mu}_A\beta \tag{5.47}$$

The change in M_0 due to adsorption is

$$\Delta M_0 = \Delta(^1N_A\bar{\mu}_A\beta) \tag{5.48}$$

so that the relative change in magnetisation is

$$\frac{\Delta M_0}{M_0} = \frac{\Delta(^1N_A\bar{\mu}_A)}{^1N_A\bar{\mu}_A} \tag{5.49}$$

As in the measurements of electrical resistance, there is no immediate way of telling whether a change in ^1N_A or in $\bar{\mu}_A$ is occurring.

If ϵ is the apparent change in $\bar{\mu}_A$ caused by the adsorption of one molecule per atom of adsorbent, then

$$\Delta(^1N_A\bar{\mu}_A) = \epsilon\,^1N_S \tag{5.50}$$

where ^1N_S molecules are adsorbed per cubic centimetre of adsorbent. Substituting in equation (5.49) gives

$$\epsilon = \frac{(\Delta M_0/M_0)\,^1N_A\bar{\mu}_A}{^1N_S} \tag{5.51}$$

If the magnetic moment of the adsorbent is due to electron spins only, then $\bar{\mu}_A$ is numerically equal to the number of unpaired electrons. ϵ is now none other than the number of electrons which pair up as a result of the bonding between the adsorbent and an adsorbate molecule. If, however, the magnetic moment of the adsorbent is determined by spin-orbit coupling, then this statement is only correct if the splitting or g-factor is influenced by adsorption. ESR investigations enable this to be checked.

Equations (5.47)-(5.51) are valid for the saturation magnetisation M_0 at absolute zero.

Should saturation magnetisation not obtain during the experiments, as, for instance, in the case of measurements using the a.c. permeameter, then equation (5.44) must be applied. According to equation (5.45), $N\mu^2$ may be replaced by $^1N_i(I_{sp}v_i)^2$, where ^1N_i is the number of adsorbent particles of volume v_i. If now ^1N_S gas molecules are adsorbed on a particle of moment $I_{sp}v_i$, then the moment becomes $I_{sp}v_i - {}^1N_S\epsilon\beta$. We thus have

$$\frac{\Delta M}{M} = \frac{[^1N_i(I_{sp}v_i - {}^1N_S\epsilon\beta)^2\,H/3kT] - [^1N_i(I_{sp}v_i)^2H/3kT]}{^1N_i(I_{sp}v_i)^2H/3kT} \tag{5.52}$$

$$= -\frac{2\,^1N_S\epsilon\beta}{I_{sp}v_i} + \left(\frac{^1N_S\epsilon\beta}{I_{sp}v_i}\right)^2 \tag{5.53}$$

The squared term can usually be neglected [606].

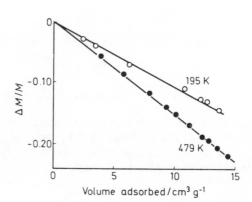

Figure 5.27 *Fractional change* ΔM/M *in the magnetisation of a nickel-silica adsorbent as a function of the quantity of adsorbed hydrogen at 195 K and 479 K [611]*

In *Figure 5.27* the fractional change in the magnetisation of nickel (present as nickel supported on silica gel) is given for the adsorption of hydrogen.

The result verifies equation (5.53), according to which

$$\frac{\Delta M}{M} = - \frac{2 \, ^1N_H \epsilon \beta}{I_{sp} V} \tag{5.54}$$

if the square term is neglected when $\Delta M/M$ is not large: the fractional loss of magnetisation is directly proportional to the number of hydrogen atoms ^1N_H taken up on the total volume V of adsorbent.

According to theory, ϵ is independent of the temperature. The alteration of the slope of the line with temperature is due only to the dependence of spontaneous magnetisation on temperature; it falls with rising temperature.

Although we cannot go into the quantitative treatment of the results here (see reference 606), *Figure 5.27* does enable two facts to be established:

(1) Since the lines are straight, ϵ must be independent of the coverage. ϵ is the number of nickel electrons that are paired for every hydrogen atom adsorbed. There is, therefore, no evidence for a change in the bonding as the coverage rises.

(2) The fall in magnetisation can only be explained by a fall in the number of d-band holes. The adsorbate must therefore be bound with a covalent bond Ni–H or a polar bond Ni⁻–H⁺. The structure Ni⁺–H⁻ is not consistent with the fall in magnetisation.

Bauer, Blechschmidt and von Hellermann [37] studied the influence of adsorbed hydrogen on the magnetisation of thin nickel films. These authors also found a fall in the magnetisation. They concluded that two different species of adsorbed hydrogen exist, because they observed that a part of the effect is irreversible, while the rest is reversible.

In contrast to the Ni/H$_2$ system, the Ni/CO system exhibits no linear trend when $\Delta M/M$ is plotted against $^1N_{CO}$ [146,266,606]. This indicates that ϵ is altering and thus the type of bond is also altering. This result agrees with the conclusions that were drawn from infra-red spectra.

Numerous other systems have been investigated using magnetic measurements. The measurements have also been applied to reactions occurring in the adsorbed phase [606].

Magnetisation of the adsorbent can only be altered by altering the occupancy of the d-band of transition metals, and it is for this reason that magnetic measurements can conveniently be used to distinguish between physisorption and chemisorption.

5.6. Field emission

More or less all the methods we have discussed so far have been indirect. Thus, the details of what is actually happening on the surface of the adsorbent could only be concluded indirectly. In contrast, field emission methods afford a direct insight. These methods are founded on the basic work of E.W. Müller with the field emission microscope [491], field desorption [492] and the field ion microscope [494]. The methods have been widely applied during the last 20 years, with the result that today the literature in this field is so extensive that numerous review articles have necessarily been written [39,172,270,497, 587].

As was described in Section 5.1, an electron must acquire a certain energy before it can leave a metal. This energy, which is the work function, is lowered if a strong electric field is applied, the metal being the cathode. The potential energy $E(x)$ of an electron outside the metal surface is then the sum of two parts. One part arises from the binding energy (work function) and is due to the Coulombic attraction between the electron and its image charge in the metal $-(e_0^2/4x)$. The other part is the energy of the electron due to the electric field $-e_0Fx$. In total

$$E(x) = -\frac{e_0^2}{4x} - e_0Fx \qquad (5.55)$$

The situation is depicted in *Figure 5.28*. Evidently electrons that are beyond a certain distance from the metal possess less energy than electrons within the metal. To extract electrons, it is therefore necessary to move them from left to right across the potential barrier. This can occur in two ways: either the potential barrier is surmounted by

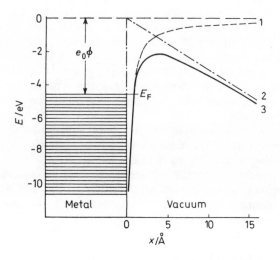

Figure 5.28   Potential energy E(x) of an electron as a function of its distance x from the metal surface.   E$_F$ is the Fermi energy.   After Sachtler [587].
(1) Potential energy curve in field-free space (see Figure 5.1); (2) energy in an electric field; (3) resultant potential energy

the provision of extra energy (as in the photoelectric effect or in thermionic emission) or electrons tunnel through the barrier (quantum mechanical tunnelling effect).

The former possibility is ruled out at low temperatures, but the latter mechanism becomes probable provided the applied field is strong enough to make the potential barrier narrow enough to permit escape.

By making the simplifying assumptions:

(1) the metal behaves as if it were at 0 K,
(2) the electrons within the metal can be regarded as free electrons,
(3) any roughness of the metal surface is small compared with the width of the potential barrier,
(4) the potential energy of electrons outside the metal is given by equation (5.55)

Fowler and Nordheim [236,520] derived a relationship between the current density *j*, the field strength *F* and the work function $e_0\phi$. This relationship, which has become known as the 'Fowler-Nordheim equation', is

$$j = 1.54 \times 10^{-6} \frac{F^2}{e_0\phi t^2(y)} \exp\left[-6.83 \times 10^7 \frac{e_0^{3/2} \phi^{3/2}}{F} f(y)\right] \text{A cm}^{-2}$$

(5.56)

$t(y)$ and $f(y)$ are tabulated functions of $y = (e_0F)^{\frac{1}{2}}/\phi$ [274,671]. The field emission current i that one measures is determined by the current density and the emitting area A according to

$$i = jA \tag{5.57}$$

and the potential difference U between cathode and anode is related to the field strength by a geometric factor β:

$$F = \beta U \text{ V cm}^{-1} \tag{5.58}$$

In general, β is inversely proportional to the radius of curvature ρ of the emitting surface. If one plots $\log (j/F^2)$ against $1/U$, the reciprocal of the applied potential, then a straight line should be obtained according to equation (5.56) and the work function $e_0\phi$ can be extracted from the slope [671].

Although it is still not quite clear to what extent our simplifying assumptions impair the Fowler-Nordheim theory [671], the equation has, nevertheless, acted as a basic stimulant to an extensive area of research.

Field strengths of 10^7-10^8 V cm^{-1} are needed for field emission. Since the β-factor of equation (5.58) is inversely proportional to the radius of the emitting surface, it is possible to attain these field strengths by applying voltages of the order of kV to very finely etched metal tips. The metal tips needed have radii of some 10^{-5} cm and they are always obtained nowadays by chemical or electrochemical etching techniques.

In principle, the field emission microscope (*Figure 5.29*) consists simply of the metal cathode tip mounted in a flask whose interior

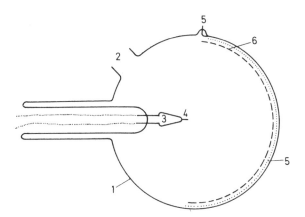

Figure 5.29 Diagram of a field emission microscope; (1) spherical glass vessel; (2) connection to UHV apparatus; (3) heating stirrup and cathode lead; (4) metal tip; (5) anode; (6) fluorescent screen

surface has been rendered conducting and also bears a fluorescent
screen. An electric field is applied between the tip and the flask wall
which acts as anode. If the field is high enough to allow field
emission according to equation (5.56), then electrons leave the surface
of the emitting metal tip perpendicularly, strike the fluorescent screen
and produce a visible image.

The equilibrium shape assumed by a metal tip during the etching
process is a spherical cap. The tip is so small that it invariably consists of a single crystal with the result that its surface is made up of
variously indexed crystal planes in a well-defined way. Unlike macroscopic single crystals, high index planes are well represented on the
surface. *Figure 5.30* shows the way a spherical cap is built up using
a ball model.

One can also see in *Figure 5.30* how the various crystal planes with
different indices are packed with different packing densities. This has
the result (see Section 5.1) that the work function is bound to vary
over the surface, and since field emission is strongly dependent on
work function (equation 5.56), the whole tip will not emit uniformly:
the current density will be higher on crystal planes of low work function than on crystal planes of high work function. Accordingly, the
electrons, which travel along radial trajectories, produce a highly magni-
fied image of the emitting tip as light and dark areas.

The magnification M depends on the tip radius ρ, the distance r
between the tip and the screen and a geometric factor a, which has a
value of about 1.5:

$$M = \frac{r}{a\rho} \tag{5.59}$$

Typically r is about 15 cm and ρ is 10^{-6} cm, so that a 10^6-fold
magnification is achieved. Two points 1 mm apart on the screen therefore correspond to a separation of 10 Å on the emitter. Although it
should be possible to increase the magnification by increasing the ratio
r/ρ until the atomic arrangement of the surface is seen, in practice the
limit of resolution of a field emission microscope is about 20 Å. The
reason for this can be traced to the finite tangential velocity components that emitted electrons possess, the electrons being governed by
Fermi-Dirac statistics. Additional lack of definition arises from electron
diffraction effects.

The metal pattern shown in *Figure 5.31* is typical of the field
emission microscope. This particular pattern is the image of a tungsten
single-crystal tip with its (110) pole in the centre of the screen. One
can see quite clearly how the crystal planes of differing indices show
up with different brightness on the screen. The darkest regions correspond to the projections of the five visible (110) planes, the four (100)
planes and the (112) planes.

If one is to increase the resolving power further, then the particles
employed to image the surface must not be governed by Fermi-Dirac
statistics. Their tangential velocity component should be rendered

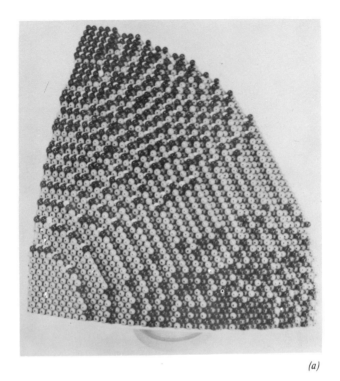

(a)

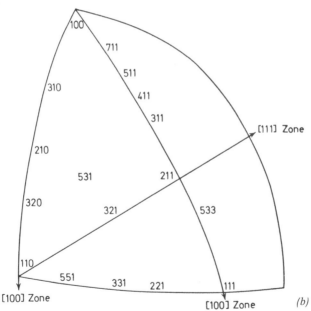

(b)

*Figure 5.30(a) Ball model of the metal emitter tip (body centred cubic) of a field
emission microscope [583]. (b) Miller indices of the crystal planes that can be
distinguished on the ball model*

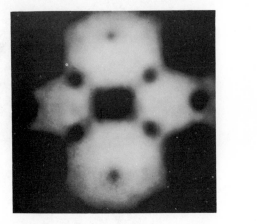

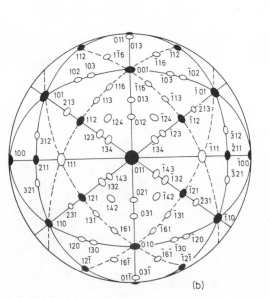

Figure 5.31 (a) Field emission microscope pattern of a tungsten single-crystal tip; (b) corresponding stereographic projection [495]

negligible by cooling to low temperatures and their De Broglie wavelength should be much shorter than the wavelength of electrons. Helium atoms fulfil these criteria. If the metal tip is made the anode, then helium atoms are polarised by the high field and attracted to the tip. Here they are immediately ionised because a helium electron tunnels into the metal under the influence of the large field gradient. The newly formed ion has taken up the temperature of liquid helium or liquid hydrogen with which the tip is cooled and now flies to the cathode, where it makes the phosphor glow. For such field ionisation to occur, the fields must be higher than those used in the field emission of electrons. They should be of the order of several 100 MV cm^{-1}. The helium pressure is kept sufficiently low ($<$ 10^{-3} Torr) to avoid disturbances occasioned by collisions in the gas phase.

At a short distance in front of the metal the equipotential surfaces are smooth and fail to notice unevennesses. This causes the ions to fly radially from the tip. However, the potential gradient in which ionisation occurs lies immediately in front of the atomic structure of the metal surface. The gradient in front of protruding atoms is larger than the gradient between protruding atoms and as a result field ionisation occurs on them more readily than elsewhere. Densely packed, very smooth crystal planes (mostly low-index planes) thus appear as relatively dark areas on the screen. Steps at the edge of a crystal plane will be seen as the brighter regions. Imaging of single atoms becomes possible on very rough crystal planes provided the atoms are at least 5-6 Å apart.

Figure 5.32 shows how detailed the reproduction of structural features on the surface can be: the emergence of a dislocation is marked by the arrow. By comparing the three other equivalent positions in the picture, one can clearly identify the lattice disturbance caused by the dislocation.

Field electron and field ion microscopy are capable therefore of imaging a metallic adsorbent with almost atomic resolution. Nevertheless, without the use of special procedures only a few materials come in question for use as adsorbents. This is because the tip material must normally be very strong and possess a high melting point. The fields necessary for field ion microscopy subject the specimen surface to mechanical stresses which amount to several times the tensile strength of steel, and even at the temperature of liquid hydrogen (20 K) a tungsten tip will evaporate at 550 MV cm^{-1} at a rate of one atomic layer per second. The corresponding figure for molybdenum is 420 MV cm^{-1} On the other hand, this 'field evaporation' process can very well be turned to cleaning and smoothing of tips.

Tips of metals that are neither as strong nor as refractory as tungsten or molybdenum can still be successfully imaged in the field ion microscope by improving the accommodation of helium atoms on the tip. This is done by adding some hydrogen or deuterium (promoter gas) to the imaging gas. (Hydrogen can also be very useful in assisting field evaporation for specimen preparation.) Niobium, iron, steel, cobalt and nickel have been successfully imaged in this way [498,519]. The

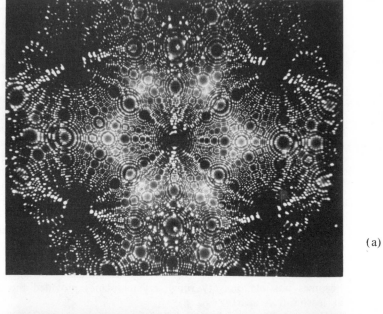

(a)

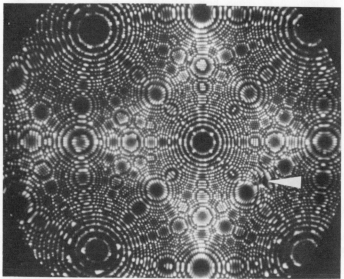

(b)

Figure 5.32   Field ion microscope picture of a tungsten tip (a), and an iridium tip (b).   Figures 5.32(a) and 5.31(a) correspond to similarly oriented crystals. (These photographs have been made available through the courtesy of E.W. Müller)

development of image intensifiers even enables metals like copper, gold and aluminium to be imaged using low fields and imaging gases less noble than helium, viz. neon and argon [85,86].

Apart from the study of the adsorbent itself, numerous possibilities are opened up in the way of adsorption investigations using field emission and field ion microscopy.

In Section 5.1 it was shown how the work function of the adsorbent is affected by the adsorption process. Provided one does not have very extensive areas of single-crystal plane available, the methods described in that section are only capable of yielding the average work function together with its change on adsorption. The situation in field emission microscopy is different. Here various crystal planes are imaged simultaneously on the fluorescent screen, and the relative intensity of the illumination affords a measure of the work functions of each region on the emitter surface. If a gas is adsorbed on the tip of a field emission microscope, this should manifest itself in a change of brightness and so, in this purely visual way, one should be able to observe the adsorption process as a function of crystal plane.

As an example of this effect, *Figure 5.33* illustrates Müller's results [495] for the adsorption of oxygen on a tungsten tip. The starting surface, which is that shown in *Figure 5.31,* was exposed to only 5×10^{-8} Torr of oxygen. The adsorbed layer could therefore only build up slowly. Notice how rising oxygen coverage (*Figure 5.33a-c*) does not cause a similar fall-off in brightness on all planes. The work function rises first in the regions of the [111] zones and in the neighbourhood of the (112) planes. After an appreciable time of adsorption, the total emission current falls five orders of magnitude, but this fall-off can be countered by raising the anode voltage.

If the tip is now heated to high temperatures for 1 min periods with the high tension switched off, then the oxygen layer is progressively desorbed. The field emission pictures obtained during this process (*Figure 5.33d-f*) do not tie up with the pictures obtained during adsorption, because rearrangement processes also occur on the tip during the heating period (compare surface rearrangements in desorption spectra, p. 51, and also reference 31).

This Müller sequence, which is coming to be regarded as a classic, establishes the following points:

(1) Crystal plane specificity exists with respect to adsorption, i.e. not all the crystal planes comprising the surface of the adsorbent adsorb simultaneously or to the same extent.

(2) The adsorbed phase is capable of diffusing laterally over the surface.

(3) The surface itself may undergo reconstruction under the influence of the adsorbed phase; without the adsorbed phase nothing would happen.

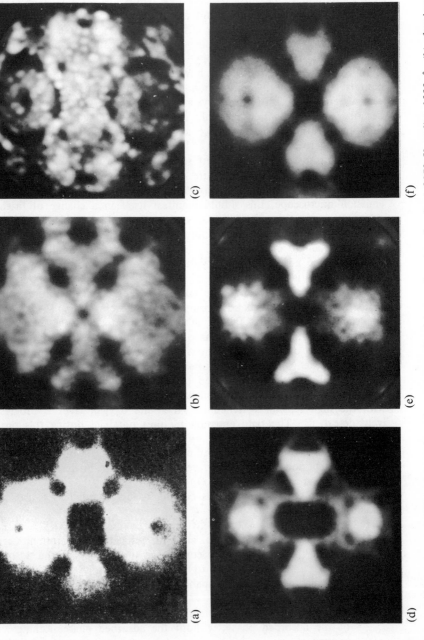

Figure 5.33 Adsorption and desorption of oxygen on tungsten: (a) pure tungsten, 1 μA at 2370 V, radius 1000 A; (b) after impingement of 7 × 10¹⁴ oxygen molecules, 3020 V; (c) after impingement of 5 × 10¹⁵ oxygen molecules, 3760 V; (d) evaporated for 1 min at 1700 K (3200 V); (e) evaporated for 1 min at 1900 K (2850 V); (f) evaporated for 1 min at 2100 K (2470 V)

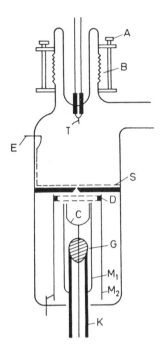

Figure 5.34   Special cell for investigating the emission of individual crystal planes.   A = aligning screw; B = UHV-holding bellows; C = collector; D = double grid; E = metal lead-through (electrically connected to the fluorescent screen S); G = metal-glass pinch seal; K = Kovar tube; M_1 and M_2 = molybdenum cylinders; T = tip (cathode).   After Sachtler [587]

In order to investigate the specificity of adsorption in a field emission microscope, it is best to measure the emission current from each crystal plane separately. This can be done by use of a special device known as the 'probe-hole' tube (*Figure 5.34*). In this device there is a very small hole in the fluorescent screen through which an isolated beam of electrons passes into a Faraday cage situated behind the screen [153,338, 493,516,587,671]. In this way the Fowler-Nordheim equation can be applied to obtain work functions and pre-exponential factors for individual crystal planes. Furthermore, data may be taken for the changes in both these quantities that characterise every adsorption system.

If we compare the averaged changes of work function which are obtained for polycrystalline material using the photoelectric or the contact potential difference method, then it rapidly becomes clear that averaged changes enable very little to be discovered concerning the true situation obtaining on individual crystal planes.

For example, the tungsten/nitrogen system has been investigated at 295 K by the condenser and the diode methods. At maximum coverage $\Delta\phi$ = +0.12 V [564], $\Delta\phi$ = 0.0 V [326,327] or $\Delta\phi$ = +0.09 V [567], depending on the state of the adsorbent. These discrepancies can be explained if one examines the changes of work function on individual tungsten planes. These data (*Table 5.1*) were obtained by Holscher [337] and van Oostrom [672] with the probe-hole field emission microscope. *Table 5.1* contains the work function $e_0\phi_W$ of clean crystal faces and the changes of voltage $\Delta\phi$ which were observed after some 10 min exposure to nitrogen at a pressure of 10^{-6} Torr [337]. *Table 5.1* also gives $\Delta\phi$ after 10^{17} molecules had impinged on every square centimetre of adsorbent, this value being calculated from equation (2.10) [672]. Since the sticking probability differs on different crystal

Table 5.1 Work functions of various crystal planes of tungsten before and after adsorption of nitrogen

(hkl)	$e_0\phi_W/eV$	$\Delta\phi/V$ after 10 min exposure to nitrogen at 10^{-6} Torr and 300 K [337]	$\Delta\phi/V$ after impingement of 10^{17} molecules N_2 cm^{-2} at 295 K [672]
(100)	5.2	−0.9	−0.26
(110)	−	−	0.00
(111)	4.40	+0.30	+0.13
(211)	−	−	+0.40
(310)	4.35	+0.39	−
(311)	4.50	+0.26	+0.27
(321)	−	−	+0.22
(411)	−	−	−0.14
(334)	−	−	+0.25
(441)	−	−	+0.10
(610)	−	−	−0.10
(611)	4.30	+0.29	−
Overall surface	4.50	−0.18	−0.10

faces, the values given in *Table 5.1* refer to different coverages. It is remarkable that nitrogen not only is polarised to varying extents on the individual planes, but even varies in the direction of its polarisation. This is indicated by the sign of $\Delta\phi$. This result emphasises that different species can occur on adjacent areas.

We may note that there are major differences in the atomic structures of the various crystal planes of body centred cubic tungsten. These differences can be held responsible for the large variations in the polarisation of adsorbed nitrogen. It is logical, therefore, to enquire whether face specificity towards nitrogen is spread out to the same extent in the case of a face centred cubic metal, for which the packing density of the low-index planes shows less variation. This question is answered by the work of Nieuwenhuys and Sachtler [516]. Using the field emission microscope, they studied the adsorption of nitrogen on face centred cubic platinum and found that the work function changes did differ on the various crystal faces but that there was less variation on the low-index planes than in the case of tungsten.

Investigations of the diffusion of an adsorbed phase over the surface of an adsorbent are of particular interest. A convenient method of doing this was developed by Gomer and his co-workers [272,273].

The entire field emission tube is drawn off from the pumping line and placed in a Dewar vessel containing liquid helium. The emitter is cleaned by electrical heating, and gas is then liberated from an electrically heated source that is positioned so that gas can only reach one side of the tip (*Figure 5.35*). Since the tip and the tube are at 4 K, the sticking probability of the gas is virtually unity, i.e. every gas molecule arriving at the tip or the wall is immediately adsorbed and

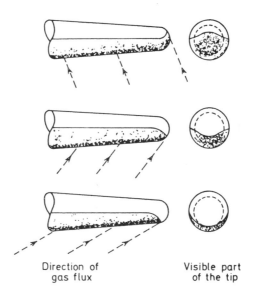

Direction of
gas flux

Visible part
of the tip

Figure 5.35   To illustrate diffusion experiments.   The region of the tip that is covered by gas depends on the position of the gas source.   After Gomer et al. *[273]*

cannot be desorbed. The emitter is now slowly heated, and one can observe on the fluorescent screen at which temperature and in what manner surface diffusion sets in.

It is instructive to compare the diffusion of hydrogen on tungsten, which has a body centred cubic structure, and nickel, which is face centred cubic.

In the tungsten/hydrogen system [273] surface diffusion depends to a marked extent on the topography of the surface. In its detail three different diffusion processes can be clearly distinguished.

(1) If the part of the tip which faces the gas source is heavily overlaid with hydrogen, then diffusion with a sharp front is already observed below 20 K. This may be traced to the existence of

a very mobile physisorbed layer on top of the chemisorbed monolayer. The physisorbed molecules simply precipitate at the edge of the chemisorbed layer and the chemisorbed layer is extended as a result.

(2) If the receiving face of the tip is only covered with about one monolayer, then surface diffusion only sets in above about 180 K. The boundary between covered and uncovered areas now spreads out radially from the most densely packed (110) planes, since surface migration on these planes occurs with the lowest activation energy. The adsorbed gas then slides over the edge of these planes into regions that possess a rougher structure (see *Figure 5.30*) and there it is immobilised.

(3) If the coverage is so low that sites for adsorption are far from completely taken up, then the rate of diffusion is no longer determined by diffusion over the smooth (110) planes. It is now determined by movement via energetically favourable sites on the rougher planes, and the activation energy rises sharply.

The situation is entirely different in the case of the nickel/hydrogen system [726]. Hydrogen was found to spread completely without external heating of the tip at 2 K $< T <$ 4 K if a sufficient amount was deposited. By proper dosing it was possible to obtain partial spreading (without heating) beyond the zone enfiladed by the source; the covered region was then demarcated by a sharp boundary. Such deposits did not contain a fraction mobile at low temperature, since further migration did not occur below 240 K. Above this temperature boundary-free diffusion occurred rapidly, and it is certain that the diffusing species is chemisorbed hydrogen. Unlike the case of tungsten, the lack of a sharp boundary here suggests the absence of topographically determined traps.

The different diffusion behaviour of hydrogen on tungsten compared with nickel is again probably the consequence of the difference in relative packing densities of the planes in body centred cubic and face centred cubic lattices. Bearing in mind, therefore, that the topographic heterogeneity of planes in a face centred lattice is least, one may expect that the adsorption of hydrogen on f.c.c. metals will be much less susceptible to face specificity than it will be on b.c.c. metals. This point of view has been substantiated by the investigations of Rootsaert, van Reijen and Sachtler [583]. The field emission microscope has been used to measure the rise in work function when hydrogen is adsorbed on nickel [714]. The value found, $\Delta\phi$ = 0.36 V, is comparable to that given by the photoelectric or the vibrating condenser methods (Section 5.1).

We have already mentioned several times that an adsorbed gas can be taken up in a number of different states on one and the same adsorbent. In this connection, it would be especially interesting to see if a particular state shows crystal plane specificity. The systems W/CO and W/N$_2$ have been investigated intensively in recent times with such an effect in mind [171,271,339].

A further possibility of applying the probe-hole field emission microscope has been demonstrated by Domke, Jähnig and Drechsler [153]. They measured the stopped-out emission current as a function of tip temperature for a number of equilibrium pressures. Since a particular coverage can be associated with a particular emission current, the family of curves obtained enables one to read off pressure p - temperature T pairs at specific coverages. Isosteric heats of adsorption can therefore be evaluated for several different crystal planes in one experiment. It is clearly important to establish that the measurements are made under conditions of equilibrium and that the adsorption itself does not introduce any changes to the surface, whether due to reconstruction or to ion bombardment. It is also necessary to ensure that the electric field does not influence the experimental results.

An even deeper insight into the processes occurring on the surface of an adsorbent is afforded by investigations in which the field ion microscope is coupled with field emission microscopy. This work has led to the realisation that 'corrosion phenomena' or rearrangements can be brought about on the surface of the adsorbent as a result of the act of adsorption. *Figure 5.36(a)* is again the field ion micrograph of a tungsten tip that has been cleaned by field evaporation. This adsorbent was then exposed to 10^{-5} Torr min of carbon monoxide.

Subsequently the adsorbate was field evaporated. After this the tip picture (*Figure 5.36b*) shows numerous bright points which do not occur in *Figure 5.36(a)* (some have been indicated by arrows). These points must be tungsten atoms which have been crowded out of their equilibrium positions by the adsorption of carbon monoxide. This kind of corrosion phenomenon is not, however, the general rule.

Pictures like *Figure 5.36* can be studied more easily if the two-colour technique [496] is utilised. This technique consists of taking a colour photograph of the first picture with a red filter and of the second with a green filter. The two negatives are printed on top of each other so that atoms which have left their places appear red, transposed atoms appear green and those atoms which remain unchanged in their places appear as white points.

The identification of individually imaged objects in field ion pictures sometimes poses a major problem. Thus, a lively discussion has developed as to whether the newly imaged points after an adsorption process (see *Figure 5.36b*) are to be traced to adsorbed molecules (e.g. CO [171]) or to transposed adsorbent atoms [339,497].

In this connection the atom-probe field ion microscope [499] makes a major advance. This recent instrument combines a probe-hole field ion microscope with a time-of-flight mass spectrometer, as shown in *Figure 5.37*.

As in the probe-hole field emission microscope, the feature of interest in the picture is moved to coincide with a hole in the fluorescent screen. The imaging feature of interest is then torn off by applying a field pulse and shot into the mass spectrometer. Thanks to its high sensitivity, the mass spectrometer is capable of analysing single particles on the basis of their flight times.

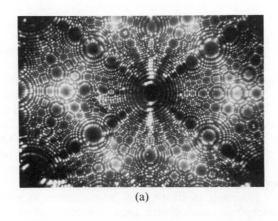

(a)

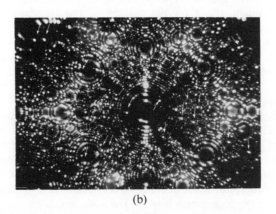

(b)

Figure 5.36 (a) Picture of a tungsten tip cleaned by field evaporation.   (b) The same tip after exposure to 10^{-5} Torr min of CO and field evaporating the adsorbate.   (These photographs have been made available through the courtesy of E.W. Müller)

Although the atom-probe field ion microscope is probably the more sensitive arrangement, a precursor developed by Inghram and Gomer has enjoyed widespread application.   Their field ion mass spectrometer [347] can be used to analyse the species comprising the adsorbed phase and to study the influence of the field upon adsorption [61].

No account of field emission would be complete without mention of the new technique known as field emission spectroscopy of chemisorbed atoms [245].   In this technique the emitted electrons are energy-analysed to give detailed information about the electronic properties of both clean surfaces and those with adsorbed layers.   Some specific adsorption systems on tungsten have been examined.

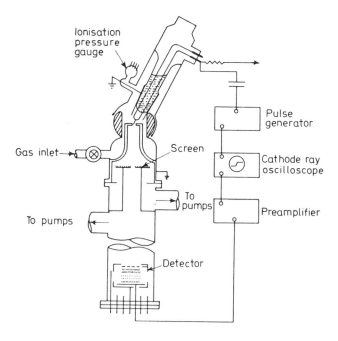

Figure 5.37 Atom-probe field ion microscope [499]

Our presentation of the field emission method has only been able to include a brief survey of the many possibilities of applying these techniques in the field of adsorption. No discussion can be given here of studies of metal/metal systems, of reactions in the adsorbed phase or of kinetic problems.

6

STUDY OF ADSORPTION USING LOW ENERGY ELECTRONS

A number of effects can be observed when clean or gas-covered surfaces are irradiated with low energy electrons. These effects are confined to the surface and may be used to analyse the surface or the adsorbed phase. The depth of penetration or the escape depth of low energy electrons is in fact very small — it has been found to lie between 5 Å and 30 Å. The low energy electron effects which we shall consider are based on elastic and inelastic scattering processes [190,397] with the additional possibility of an interaction between the electrons and the adsorbed particles leading to desorption.

The different scattering processes can be identified in the energy distribution of secondary electrons which are released from the surface by electron bombardment. *Figure 6.1* shows the energy distribution curve for the emitted secondary electrons. $N(E)$ in arbitrary units is given as a function of secondary electron energy E when the surface is bombarded with monochromatic primary electrons of energy E_0. The spectrum may be divided into three regions.

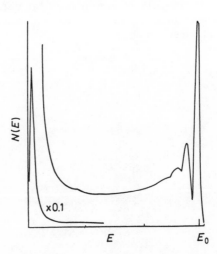

Figure 6.1 Energy distribution N(E) of electrons emitted from a surface for a primary electron energy of E_0 eV

152

(1) There is an intense peak at $E \sim E_0$ corresponding to electrons which have been elastically reflected. These electrons have hardly lost any energy and the process is evidently concerned with the strongly bound core electrons of the atoms which make up the solid lattice or the adsorbed phase. As in the case of X-rays, whose wavelength is of the same order as that of slow electrons, the position, size, shape and intensity of the diffraction reflections enable an investigation of the structure of the solid to be undertaken. This is so-called low energy electron diffraction, or LEED.

(2) Secondary electrons also occur with even greater intensity in the very low energy region. These are genuine secondary electrons which arise from inelastic scattering processes and subsequent cascade processes in the solid.

(3) If the measuring technique is sufficiently sensitive, then the intermediate energy region is found to possess fine structure. This is likewise the result of inelastic scattering processes.

The electrons which give rise to the fine structure either consist of true secondaries which are emitted with a characteristic energy that is independent of the primary electron energy or are electrons which have suffered a characteristic loss of energy. The former group includes the Auger electrons whose occurrence enables information to be extracted about the chemical composition of the surface (Auger electron spectroscopy, or AES). Electrons in the latter group have suffered energy losses due to excitation of phonons, plasmons, interband transitions and surface molecular orbitals. For this reason the method of electron energy loss spectra (EELS) is also a suitable means of studying adsorption processes.

It is well known that X-rays are given off in addition to the emission of secondary electrons when a solid is bombarded with electrons. The X-rays consist of continuous radiation due to the retardation of particles, as well as characteristic lines. If the electron energy is raised continuously, starting from zero, then a step is observed in the total X-ray yield at an energy which is just sufficient to raise a core electron to the Fermi level. The method of appearance potential spectroscopy (APS) [538,540] is concerned with the measurement of this threshold, and it leads to the density of states at the Fermi boundary and in the unoccupied part of the conduction band in metals. These parameters are of importance for adsorption and catalysis, and it is possible to evaluate them quantitatively in this way.

Bombardment of the surface with electrons also leads to the desorption of adsorbed species. This electron impact desorption or electron stimulated desorption (ESD) can be followed with a mass spectrometer, and it is capable of giving valuable information about the condition of the adsorbed phase.

6.1. Low energy electron diffraction

The field emission method enables a deep insight to be obtained into occurrences in the adsorbed phase, and yet, despite the considerable value of the method, it does present certain difficulties and disadvantages. The adsorbing surface is so small that it is impossible to measure the amount adsorbed directly. And doubling up with other methods of investigation is hardly possible if the same adsorbent is used. It is also sometimes difficult to establish that the presence of the high field does not influence the adsorption effects or the reactions which one observes in the adsorbed phase. For these reasons it has become necessary to obtain further information by investigating the structure of the adsorbed phase. The method of low energy electron diffraction which stems from the fundamental work of Davisson and Germer [131] is available to this end.

If one investigates the diffraction of back-scattered or transmitted electrons possessing high energy (50-100 keV), then the diffraction patterns give structural information concerning the solid being investigated. It is possible to confine the structural information to the surface layers of the solid by using grazing incidence and examining the diffraction pattern in reflection — this is called reflection high energy electron diffraction (RHEED). Alternatively, the structure of the top atomic layers is obtained by investigating the diffraction of back-scattered electrons whose incident energy is low (50-250 eV). This technique, in which the incident electrons only penetrate a very small distance, is called low energy electron diffraction, or LEED. The LEED and RHEED methods have been compared by Højlund Nielsen [335].

Not only the top atomic layers of the adsorbent may be investigated with LEED, but also any adsorbed phase. A standard LEED apparatus for investigating surface structures is shown diagrammatically in *Figure 6.2*.

A beam of electrons from the electron gun impinges perpendicularly on the surface of the single-crystal specimen. The diffracted electrons travel towards the fluorescent screen and their impact produces a diffraction pattern. A relatively high proportion of the incident electrons is inelastically scattered. This would lead to a high background of illumination on the screen. The inelastic flux is therefore prevented from reaching the screen by placing retarding grids with a suitable potential on them in front of the screen. The elastically scattered electrons pass through this potential barrier and are then strongly accelerated so that an intense diffraction pattern is obtained.

The set-up shown in *Figure 6.2* only enables the diffraction pattern to be measured. For unambiguous and precise structural information to be obtained, however, one has to measure the intensity as well as the position of the diffracted electron beams. This is generally accomplished by using a Faraday cage to scan the diffraction picture. An early apparatus incorporating such a facility was published by Farnsworth *et al.* [213]. To complete the experimental background, we

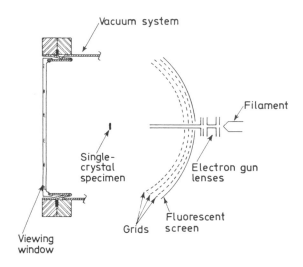

Figure 6.2   Diagram of a standard apparatus for low energy electron diffraction

refer finally to Tucker's [669] apparatus for low energy electron diffraction, in which the diffracted and the inelastically scattered electrons are separated by means of a magnetic field.

The theoretical treatment of the intensity of diffracted electron peaks has been fraught with considerable difficulty from the outset [212,432, 476]. It has, nevertheless, now proved to be possible to calculate exact LEED intensity profiles (see, for instance, reference 571). Because of the complexity involved, one usually restricts oneself to an evaluation of the geometry of the diffraction picture and only if necessary to a qualitative appraisal of the reflection intensities.

The ability to draw conclusions from LEED experiments is enhanced if another study is conducted simultaneously on the specimen. In recent years efforts have therefore been made to couple LEED work with studies of the work function and surface potential [9,116,192,193, 310,354,433,435,667,668], desorption spectra by the flash filament method [9,192,193], mass spectra [192,193,211,523], ellipsometry [454], field emission microscopy [454] and Auger electron spectra [9,310,354, 435,624].

As already mentioned, it is peculiarly difficult to assign a particular structure to an observed diffraction picture by making use of the beam intensities [35,36,201,246,356]. Lander and Morrison [399,400] have proposed a method of tackling this problem. Their method consists of taking a plausible model for the structure of the surface and calculating the intensities of individual diffracted beams as a function of the wavelength of the electron. The calculated intensities are then compared with the experimental ones and in this way the most probable surface structure is finally decided. For their calculations Lander and Morrison assume that the scattering factors of light atoms can be neglected because they are small compared with the scattering factors of heavy atoms. If the surface of a metal oxide or an adsorbed phase is being studied, this assumption is equivalent to saying that the diffraction pattern is due solely to the interaction of electrons with the heavier metal atoms.

Such an evaluation of diffraction patterns led Germer [254] to the conclusion that reconstruction of the surface atoms of the adsorbent must sometimes have occurred as a result of chemisorption. This should be the case, for instance, when hydrogen, carbon and oxygen act on Ni (110) surfaces and the reconstruction should be such as to create an entirely new structure. Place exchange processes have, in fact, been observed in an adsorbent by field ion microscopy (see Section 5.6), although they have not led to the formation of a completely new structure. This would entail a very substantial energy requirement.

Hansen and Hanemann [300] were able to show that the experimental intensities could also be explained if one merely displaced the surface atoms of the adsorbent slightly from their equilibrium positions. On the other hand, Bauer [34] has drawn attention to the possibility of adsorbate atoms having such large scattering factors in their own right that they could be responsible for the diffraction pattern. This applies to atoms such as H, O and C in the systems Ni/H, Ni/O and Ni/C, where the bonding of the adsorbed phase is partly polar in character, and it leads to the contrary of Germer's argument [254]. The whole concept of surface reconstruction has therefore become somewhat questionable [200].

Before describing some surface structures we give a system of nomenclature which is used (see also reference 478). Following Wood [725], the two-dimensional reference structure of the surface is taken simply as one of the lattice planes in the three-dimensional structure which lies parallel to the surface of the solid. In place of the usual three Miller indices there are only two. The size of the unit mesh of the actual two-dimensional surface is given in multiples of the translation vectors which describe the unit mesh of the reference surface. Sometimes it is found that the unit mesh of the surface is twisted through a certain angle with respect to the reference structure. Sometimes it is convenient to choose a unit mesh for the chemisorbed phase which possesses a central atom.

The following particulars are therefore needed to define surface structures:

(1) Designation of the solid.
(2) Indices of the reference plane.
(3) Indication by means of the letter c if the chosen unit mesh of the surface possesses a central atom.
(4) Measurements of the size of the unit mesh of the surface in terms of the substrate reference mesh.

(5) Angle between the translation vectors of the surface mesh and the reference mesh.

(6) Designation of the adsorbate.

This will be illustrated by taking as an example the adsorption of oxygen on the (110) face of a copper single crystal [188] (*Figure 6.3*). *Figure 6.3(a)* shows the diffraction pattern obtained for the clean copper surface. When very small amounts of oxygen are admitted, one notices the appearance of streaks between those diffraction spots which lie further apart (*Figure 6.3b*). The streaks indicate that surface atoms are straying from net points to non-periodic sites. Further oxygen uptake results in the formation of sharp half-order reflections; these appear between the wider reflections in the diffraction pattern of the clean (110) copper face (*Figure 6.3c*).

We accordingly identify a 1 × 2 superstructure (Cu–(110)–1 × 2 – 0). Only when significantly larger amounts of oxygen have been admitted do additional reflections appear. The new features (*Figure 6.3d*) indicate the co-existence of domains of 1 × 2 structure and a second structure, the latter actually being a 3 × (10.25)$^{1/2}$ – R 62° structure which has completely taken over in *Figure 6.3(e)*.

A feature of the present system is that copper shows up at 300 V but the voltage has to be turned down to 100 V before oxygen contributes to the diffraction pattern. The new periodicity observed at 300 V in *Figure 6.3(c)* is therefore due only to copper atoms. Furthermore, no new periodicity appears below 100 V, so that oxygen atoms must possess the same symmetry as copper atoms. *Figure 6.3(f)* demonstrates how one might obtain the 1 × 2 structure taking these observations into account. The black spots give the location of copper atoms in the substrate lattice and the horizontally elongated rectangle gives the associated unit mesh. The small open circles denote the copper atoms in the surface and the large open circles are the oxygen atoms. The surface unit mesh (dashed in) for either copper or oxygen can now be seen to be expanded by a factor of 2 in one direction with respect to the substrate mesh.

It is particularly important that the actual surface structure of a clean adsorbent should be known if adsorption effects are to be interpreted. In the absence of suitable methods of investigating this point, it was formerly assumed that the structure of the surface of the adsorbent (no adsorbate present) was, to a first approximation, identical with the structure of the interior. Nevertheless, this assumption was rather insecure, because the unsaturated nature of the surface atoms obliged one to reckon with at least some structural deformation of the surface. At this stage, low energy electron diffraction appeared to extend a suitable means of clearing up the question.

While older work has told us that the surface structure is definitely distorted, as, for instance, in the case of a nickel single crystal [257], newer work leads more and more to the conclusion that any surface deformation only lies within the limits of experimental accuracy. This

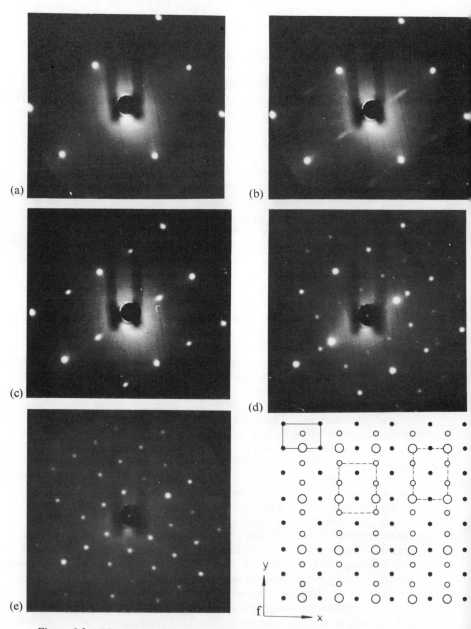

Figure 6.3   Adsorption of oxygen on the (110) face of a copper single crystal [188].   (a) Clean copper surface; (b) oxidation commences; (c) the Cu–(110)–1 × 2–O structure; (d) co-existence of domains of structures (c) and (e); (e) the Cu–(110)–3 × (10.25)$^{1/2}$ – R 62° – O structure; (f) model for the 1 × 2 surface structure

has been shown for nickel single crystals, for example, by Park and Farnsworth [536]. Of particular importance also are the results concerning the structure of epitaxially grown metal films. Haque and Farnsworth [303] investigated nickel films which had been epitaxed on the (111) face of a copper single crystal. They were able to prove that the nickel assumed the same orientation as the copper substrate but that its lattice constant was the same as that for bulk nickel. It is useful to complement low energy electron diffraction with high energy diffraction measurements. This enables the structure of the interior of the specimen to be determined as well as the surface structure.

The measurement of surface areas by physisorption requires a knowledge of the cross-sectional area of an adsorbed atom or molecule. This is tantamount to saying that a knowledge of the structure of the adsorbed phase is needed, and it is clearly of especial interest to know whether any ordered structures characterise physisorption. Investigations of this type were undertaken by Lander and Morrison [401], who studied the physisorption of several adsorbates on graphite, using low energy electron diffraction. They were able to show that the diffraction of low energy electrons is eminently suitable for these investigations and that it yields the required information. The adsorption of xenon on several single-crystal planes of copper and silver was investigated by Chesters, Hussain and Pritchard [115], using LEED and surface potential measurements. They established that adsorbed xenon was hexagonally close packed on each of the surfaces examined (at least to a good approximation) and the site area of an adsorbed xenon atom comes out at 17 Å^2.

To provide further examples of chemisorption, we shall take our usual look at the situation for the adsorption of hydrogen and carbon monoxide on nickel.

We have already mentioned that the adsorption of hydrogen on nickel is capable of leading to definite changes in the diffraction pattern. Germer and MacRae [256] noticed the occurrence of a 2 × 1 structure when hydrogen was adsorbed on a (110) nickel surface. They concluded from this that the nickel surface reconstructs to give rows of nickel atoms and hydrogen atoms lying next to one another. No such reconstruction takes place on the more densely covered (100) and (111) faces [259]. We should bear in mind that considerable doubt exists with regard to the reality of reconstruction processes.

More recently Ertl and co-workers have turned their attentions to this problem. By combining LEED investigations with measurements of thermal desorption spectra and contact potential differences [192], it was possible to establish that a structure which is ordered in one dimension (q_{st} = 19.5 kcal mol^{-1}) initially obtains when hydrogen is adsorbed on a (110) nickel surface at room temperature. This structure slowly converts to the two-dimensional Ni–(110)–1 × 2–H structure which corresponds to a strongly bonded condition. Further studies [120,121] have revealed that definite intensity changes occur in the Ni reflections and in the background as a consequence of hydrogen adsorption on those planes for which no new reflections are observed, viz. the Ni(100) and the Ni(111) planes. The evidence suggests that the adsorbed phase is disordered at room temperature, although at lower temperatures ordered structures might well be formed on these two crystal faces.

The chemisorption of carbon monoxide on nickel single crystals has been investigated by several groups of workers [433,435,535,537,667]. According to Park and Farnsworth [537], a Ni–(100)–c 2 × 2–CO structure is formed on a clean Ni(100) face. This is interpreted to mean that in the adsorbed phase one CO molecule is held by two nickel atoms on the Ni(100) face. Such a stoichiometry clearly suggests that adsorbed CO exists in the 'bridge-bonded' form mentioned in Section 4.1 (p.73). On the other hand, Tracy [667] finds that the surface structure is that of a disordered phase at high temperature and low coverage, a c 2 × 2 structure at sufficiently low temperatures and coverages up to half a monolayer, and a compressible hexagonal phase at coverages between $\theta = 0.61$ and $\theta = 0.69$. He was even able to construct a phase diagram for these phases. Variations have also been reported for the Ni(110) face. Park and Farnsworth [535] observed a Ni–(110)–c 1 × 1–CO structure – that is, a structure in which the unit mesh is preserved. Every adsorbed CO molecule should therefore occupy a single adsorption site and be 'linearly bonded', as in Section 4.1 (p.73). However, two structures were found in recent work by Madden, Küppers and Ertl [435] in which several types of measurement were combined. Up to a coverage of θ 0.7 there is an incoherent linear structure but at higher coverages there is a c 2 × 1 structure. It is remarkable that the maximum uptake which can be accommodated on the latter structure is 1.14×10^{15} molecules cm^{-2}, this being practically the same as the uptake observed by Tracy [667] on the Ni(100) face for a c 2 × 2 structure (1.10×10^{15} CO molecules cm^{-2}). We may add to this the figure of 1.1×10^{15} CO molecules cm^{-2} found by Klier, Zettlemoyer and Leidheiser [377] for the maximum packing density on both nickel (100) and (110) surfaces using a radiotracer method. The inescapable conclusion is that the configuration of adsorbed CO molecules is not determined by the existence of certain sites for adsorption but rather by optimising the mutual disposition of the adsorbed particles. Judging by recent results on other transition metal/ CO systems, this statement seems to have general validity.

In the case of carbon monoxide adsorption on copper (100) faces at low temperature (77 K), a Cu–(100)–c 2 × 2–CO structure was found independently by Tracy [668] and by Chesters and Pritchard [116]. Attack on this system has also been coupled with other methods of investigation to yield a significantly better understanding of the state of affairs in the adsorbed phase. The other methods applied include measurements of surface potentials [116,668] and isosteric enthalpies of adsorption.

There is no change in the low energy electron diffraction pattern of nickel single-crystal surfaces when nitrogen is admitted. Madden and Farnsworth [434] and Germer and MacRae [255] took this to mean that nitrogen is not adsorbed on nickel at room temperature.

In contrast to the gases we have covered above, oxygen reacts very strongly with the single-crystal faces of nickel, and adsorption proceeds uninterruptedly to oxidation [258]. The LEED method is also well suited to the study of adsorption and reorientation of large molecules. The substituted benzenes, for instance, have been fruitfully studied [268].

Low energy electron diffraction is very suitable for studying reactions in the adsorbed phase as well as investigating gas adsorption. It has been applied to decomposition reactions and reactions between different kinds of adsorbate, and Ertl [189,191] has even shown that LEED is suitable for following the kinetics of surface reactions.

6.2.   Auger electron spectroscopy

A number of introductory and review articles concerning Auger electron spectroscopy have appeared in the last few years [36,114,190,547]. Here we shall summarise the essential theoretical and experimental basis.

If an electron is knocked out of an inner atomic shell by a primary electron (or by X-rays or ions), then the vacancy created is filled again within a very short space of time by electron transfer from an outer shell. The energy released in this transfer is either lost in the form of characteristic X-ray emission or – and this is what interests us here – it is given up to another electron without the production of radiation. The electron receiving this energy is then ejected from the atom as an Auger electron possessing corresponding kinetic energy. This energy is not identical with that obtained from X-ray fluorescence measurements, because X-ray fluorescence arises from the formation of simply ionised atoms, whereas in the Auger process a doubly ionised particle is left.

A schematic representation of the process in the case of silicon is shown in *Figure 6.4*. A primary electron knocks an electron out of the $L_{2,3}$ level and the vacancy is filled by an electron from the valency band. The energy released is taken up by another electron in the valency band and this electron leaves the crystal band structure.

Three letters are used to describe an Auger process. The first letter denotes the vacancy produced by the primary electron; the middle letter denotes the source of the electron which fills this vacancy; and the last letter denotes the source of the Auger electron which is ejected. The process represented in *Figure 6.4* is thus an $L_{2,3}$ V_1 V_2 process.

The energy E_A of the emitted Auger electron can be obtained directly from the diagram. It must be

$$E_A = (E_{L_{2,3}} - E_{V_1}) - (E'_{V_2} + e_0 \phi_{eff.})$$
(6.1)

The prime on E'_{V_2} refers to the fact that a doubly ionised particle is formed in the process. $e_0 \phi_{eff.}$ is the effective work function of the analyser material, so that an electron coming from V_2 must have a minimum energy of $E'_{V_2} + e_0 \phi_{eff.}$ in order to be just recorded by the analyser concerned.

It now follows at once that three cases can occur, each of which influences the form of the Auger maximum in its own way. If transitions between sharp energy levels all occur together, then one obtains a sharp maximum. However, if the two participating electrons originate from the valency band, as in the case of *Figure 6.4*, or if they originate from a relatively broad conduction band, then one obtains an Auger maximum which has up to twice the width of the valency or the conduction band. Finally, if the valency or the conduction band exhibits a well-structured density of states, then the Auger maximum is also structured. In this case the structure of the Auger peak enables conclusions to be drawn about the structure of the density of states [488]. In this way chemical shifts can also be recognised and evaluated.

As already stated, the production of Auger electrons is in competition with the emission of X-rays. High sensitivity will therefore be achieved if the probability of producing a vacancy is large yet at the same time there is a small probability of X-ray emission after the vacancy has been filled. The first condition is fulfilled if the primary energy is about two or three times the ionisation energy so long as the energy level of the vacancy remains below 1 600 eV [36]. The second condition is also fulfilled if the energy level of the vacancy stays below 1 600 eV. It follows that one should utilise K-shell ionisation up to Na, L-shell ionisation up to perhaps Ge, and M-shell ionisation for still heavier elements. Under these conditions X-ray emission plays practically no role. The electron guns which are used for Auger electron spectroscopy therefore operate at an energy of about 3 keV; lately this has been extended to 5 keV.

To record an Auger electron spectrum one has to analyse the energy of the secondary electrons. A number of different experimental arrangements have been developed for this purpose.

Excitation is generally obtained by bombarding the specimen with primary electrons either in a perpendicular direction or at almost grazing incidence. A LEED electron gun can be conveniently used for the former arrangement.

At its simplest, the 4-grid LEED optics can be used to analyse the energy of the Auger electrons. The LEED method and Auger electron spectroscopy therefore offer an attractive combination. Over the last few years, however, coaxial cylindrical analysers or spherical analysers have been applied to the analysis of energies to an ever-increasing extent. These analysers enable a better signal-to-noise ratio to be obtained. When the 4-grid LEED optics are used, the middle two of the concentric, hemispherical grids are run at a retarding voltage E so that only those electrons whose energy is in excess of E can surmount

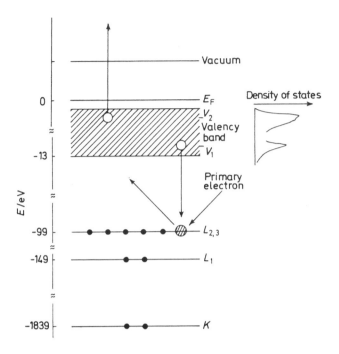

Figure 6.4 Illustration of the Auger process. The energy values shown refer to simple ionisation of the respective levels. E_F *is the Fermi energy*

the energy barrier and reach the phosphor screen, which now acts simply as a collector. If the retarding voltage is modulated by applying an alternating voltage of amplitude ΔE, then a phase-sensitive lock-in amplifier can be used to register just that portion of the electrons lying in the energy interval ΔE, and so one can obtain the energy distribution.

The action of cylindrical or spherical analysers is based on the deflecting effect of an electrostatic field. Electrons are deflected to an extent which depends on their velocity, so that only electrons of a certain energy pass through the output aperture where they may be registered on a secondary electron multiplier. If the deflecting voltage is varied continuously, then the current delivered by the secondary electron multiplier gives the energy distribution. A small modulating voltage may also be superimposed so that a lock-in amplifier can be used to measure $dN(E)/dE$, i.e. the derivative of the energy distribution. There are special advantages attached to monitoring the derivative of the signal. Thus, the position of a maximum is much more clearly defined, particularly if it occurs on the flank of a strong peak such as that of the 'true' secondary electrons. And the 'Auger amplitude', or distance between the maximum and the minimum on the derivative, is also frequently proportional to the area under the Auger peak.

A compilation of Auger electron energies for the entire periodic table is given in an article by Chang [114].

Since Auger electrons can only penetrate an extremely small distance into solids, those Auger electrons which are recorded merely originate from the outermost layers. The escape depth hardly ever exceeds 30 Å and is usually much less. It is for this reason that Auger electron spectroscopy is particularly suitable for surface investigations.

While qualitative chemical analysis using Auger electron spectroscopy presents no difficulties, quantitative analysis does not follow straightforwardly. It is possible nevertheless to carry out a calibration for quantitative analysis in a given experimental arrangement under given conditions. A few per cent of one monomolecular layer can be measured without difficulty, the limit of detection being 10^{13} atoms cm^{-2}.

From the foregoing it is easy to appreciate that Auger electron spectroscopy has been applied intensively to the monitoring of surface cleanliness. *Figure 6.5* shows the Auger spectrum of the surface of a Cu-Ni alloy [190]. The first curve (a) was recorded after extended

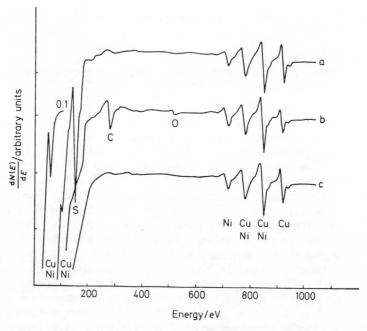

Figure 6.5   Auger electron spectrum for the (110) face of a Cu-Ni alloy containing 55 atomic per cent copper: (a) after flashing in ultrahigh vacuum, showing contamination with sulphur; (b) after removal of the upper atom layers by argon ion bombardment; (c) clean surface after annealing the crystal.   After Ertl [190]

heating in ultrahigh vacuum. It reveals clear evidence of sulphur contamination. Argon ion bombardment then served to remove the uppermost atomic layers together with the sulphur contamination (curve b). The process has, however, resulted in some slight contamination with carbon and oxygen which probably originates from the CO in the residual gases. These elements are driven off during annealing so that the final curve (c) only shows the signals corresponding to the two alloy components.

Since the Auger signal strength for an adsorbed phase is proportional to the surface coverage of that adsorbate, one can use Auger electron spectroscopy to determine the extent of the coverage. This is particularly valuable where adsorption measurements on small surfaces in metal apparatus are concerned, because it is not possible to determine the amount adsorbed volumetrically. For the adsorption of oxygen on copper and nickel, Ertl and Küppers [193] have checked that proportionality exists between the coverage and the signal height by determining that the signal height of the oxygen peak was proportional to the change in work function. Palmberg [530] used the intensity of the Auger electron signal to follow the variation of the sticking probability for Xe adsorbing on Pd, and Bonzel [75] has followed the adsorption of hydrogen sulphide on Cu(110) and its conversion to adsorbed sulphur as well as the kinetics of subsequent oxidation to SO_2.

By varying the angle of incidence of the primary electron beam, one can vary the depth to which the primary electrons penetrate and with it the escape depth of Auger electrons. In this manner it is possible to ascertain concentration gradients perpendicular to the surface. *Figure 6.6* shows the result of such an experiment using an oxygen-covered Ni-Cu alloy. Clearly, the intensity of the oxygen signal alters relative to the nickel signal but the intensity of the copper signal remains unchanged relative to the nickel signal. This means that the concentration ratio of Ni:Cu is the same on the surface as it is in the inside; oxygen, however, is located at the surface [190].

On the other hand, the diffusion of foreign atoms into the bulk can be followed by maintaining a constant angle of incidence for the primary electron beam. It is then simply a matter of observing the time dependence of the intensity of the Auger electron signal, and in the ideal case, as Sparnaay, van Bommel and van Tooren [628] have shown, it can lead to an evaluation of the diffusion coefficient.

The transfer of charge is a topic which is of special importance in the study of adsorption and catalysis. It can occur as a result of polarisation effects or be due to changes of oxidation state. In so far as the density of states in the valency band depends on the chemical environment, we may expect the position and the shape of an Auger peak to reflect charge transfer if the peak is characteristic of transitions involving the valency electrons. One should therefore be able to observe a chemical shift. Bauer [36] could, in fact, identify such a shift in the $L_{2,3}$ VV Auger spectrum of aluminium and silicon as a result of oxidation. This type of analysis should also be capable of establishing

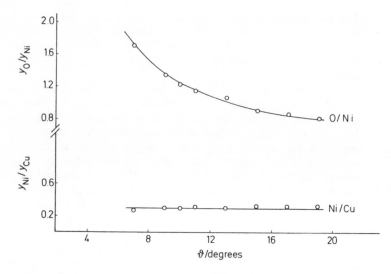

Figure 6.6 Auger signals y from the (100) surface of a Ni-Cu alloy after covering with oxygen. The ratio of Auger signal heights O:Ni and Ni:Cu is given as a function of the angle ϑ contained by the electron beam and the surface. After Ertl [190]

chemical identities. It should be possible, for instance, to say whether a peak is due to carbon or carbon monoxide and thereby provide vital information for many investigations of adsorption and catalysis. Other authors, e.g. Somorjai [624] or Fiermans and Vennik [219], have reported investigations involving the chemical shift of transitions between inner shells of the catalytically interesting vanadium oxides.

For all the positive aspects which the application of Auger electron spectroscopy offers to surface and adsorption investigations, one should not lose sight of the disadvantages. Two shortcomings in particular may be singled out. Hydrogen is incapable of giving an Auger electron spectrum, and yet this gas is of overriding interest in chemisorption and catalysis. Furthermore, changes on the surface and in the adsorbed phase can actually be caused by the action of the primary electron beam. One should therefore couple Auger electron spectroscopy with other methods of investigation as far as is possible.

6.3. Electron energy loss spectroscopy

As in the case of Auger electron spectroscopy, electron energy loss spectroscopy can be carried out with the set-up which is normally employed for LEED investigations. Primary excitation can be effected with a LEED electron gun, and energy analysis of the back-scattered electrons may then be carried out with the 4-grid LEED optics.

By examining the loss spectrum of a clean surface at sufficiently high sensitivity it can be established that there are loss peaks which only rise a few per cent above the background. Küppers' work [397] provides an example of this for the case of a Ni(100) surface. The existence of two loss maxima could be established, one at 8 eV and a second, using higher primary energies, at 18 eV. These loss maxima are independent of the primary energy, but their intensity, particularly that of the second peak, does depend strongly on the primary energy. In agreement with other methods of measurement, the two loss peaks could be assigned, respectively, to surface and volume plasmon excitation.

If the surface is now covered with a gas, then additional loss peaks are found to occur. This is illustrated in *Figure 6.7*, which compares the electron energy loss spectrum of a clean Ni(110) surface with the spectra observed for the same surface after adsorption of CO, H_2 and O_2.

Energy loss peaks are produced at 13.5 and 5.5 eV as a result of CO adsorption and at 15 and 7.5 eV as a result of H_2 adsorption, the latter peak only forming slowly after an extended period of time. The adsorption of O_2 produces peaks at 15 and 8 eV. It would appear from *Figure 6.7* that gas adsorption has resulted in the submergence of the loss peak which was assigned to surface plasmon excitation on the

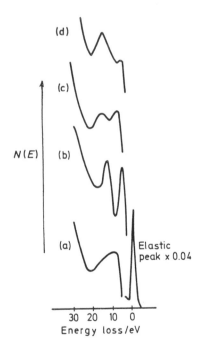

Figure 6.7 Electron energy loss spectra for a clean Ni(110) surface (a) and the same surface after it has been covered with CO (b), H_2 (c) and O_2 (d). The primary beam energy was 62 eV. After Küppers [397]

clean surface. Detailed investigations, however, have revealed that the losses due to adsorption and the surface plasmon occur independently and at the same time.

It is not yet possible to give a satisfactory explanation of the losses which are due to chemisorption. Conceivably the electron density in the surface region is displaced by chemisorption and the plasmon energies are therefore also displaced. However, it appears to be more a matter of individual electron excitation losses, meaning that electrons in the chemisorption orbitals are raised to higher unoccupied energy states in the complex. Several observations [397] combine to indicate that — in the case of CO chemisorption on Ni(110) — the lowest unoccupied level lies 5.5 eV above the Fermi level. If this is so, then the deeper occupied level in the chemisorption bond lies 8 eV below the Fermi edge and there is another occupied level directly below the Fermi edge. The former is in agreement with the photoelectron spectroscopic investigations of Eastman and Cashion [164] and the theoretical calculations of Grimley [281].

We may note that these assignments cannot be regarded as entirely certain at the present time. What does seem to be certain, however, is that electron energy loss spectra will make their contribution in the future towards bringing about a deeper insight into the bonding situation in the chemisorption complex.

6.4. Appearance potential spectroscopy

Appearance potential spectra [87,89,195,344,517,538-540] are recorded in the following manner. Thermionic electrons are produced by a V-shaped tungsten cathode and accelerated on to the specimen by connecting a variable voltage supply (0 to 1000 or 2000 V) between the cathode and the specimen. The electron bombardment produces soft X-ray emission which falls on to a cylinder surrounding the assembly. Photoelectrons are consequently liberated at the cylinder and collected on a positively charged collector. An alternating voltage of small amplitude is superimposed on the voltage which is applied between the cathode and the specimen, so that the photoelectric current can be amplified with a lock-in amplifier. The derivative of the X-ray yield can then be recorded directly as a function of the incident electron energy. In interpreting the data one must allow for the appearance potential energy being larger than the electron acceleration energy by an amount equal to the work function of the cathode. The acceleration energy only represents the difference between the Fermi levels of the cathode and the specimen being used.

Fundamental to the power of appearance potential spectroscopy is the fact that the X-ray emission depends on the density of states of the core electrons and the density of states which exists above the Fermi level [344]. Additional X-ray emissions derive from the excitation of core electrons to unfilled states lying above the Fermi level.

Nilsson and Kanski [517] have used APS to observe the appearance potentials of several simple metals such as Al, Mg and Be. They also investigated the density of states in the unoccupied part of the conduction band. The method was used on Ni and Co surfaces by Burr [108] a Cr surface was investigated by Houston and Park [344], and Dev and Brinkman [147] studied a Cu surface.

The electronic structure of binary alloys is of particular importance to matters concerning adsorption and catalysis. This is especially true of the Ni-Cu alloys which have now been investigated by Ertl and Wandelt [195] using APS. These authors came to the significant conclusion that d-band holes still exist at the Ni sites, even with alloys containing 55 per cent Cu, while such holes are entirely absent at Cu sites.

Appearance potential spectra of surfaces are influenced by the uptake of gases in the same way that Auger electron spectra are affected. New peaks which are ascribed to the bound adsorbate appear in both cases and chemical shifts may be observed as a result of the interaction between the adsorbate and the adsorbent. These effects were studied by Houston and Park [344] for the uptake of oxygen by chromium. A chemical shift could also be observed by Konishi, Murata and Kato [384] for the action of oxygen on iron. The extent of the shift was observed to vary for iron oxides of differing compositions. Ertl and Wandelt [196] carried out a detailed investigation of the initial stages of oxidation of nickel. They found that the APS spectrum consisted of a superposition of the clean nickel spectrum and the NiO spectrum without any trace of a continuous variation in the oxidation state of Ni atoms. These results seem to indicate that APS is not a suitable tool for showing up changes in electronic properties during the adsorption of oxygen and before the formation of small NiO particles sets in. This type of change should therefore be examined by other techniques, such as UPS.

Whereas APS is useful for clarifying questions in solid state and surface physics, only time will show to what extent it may be applied to the problems of adsorption and catalysis.

6.5. Electron stimulated desorption

In the introduction to Chapter 6 we have already referred to the fact that adsorbed particles may be desorbed, among other things, when electrons bombard a surface covered with an adsorbed film. This 'electron stimulated desorption' undoubtedly occurs as a disturbing effect in various measurements one makes, e.g. in LEED or Auger investigations. On the other hand, the effect itself is capable of yielding valuable information for the study of chemisorption.

Electron stimulated desorption belongs to the category of inelastic interactions between electrons and adsorbate molecules. Various processes may be observed as a consequence of electron impact:

(1) Desorption of neutral atoms or molecules in the ground state.
(2) Desorption of excited neutral particles.
(3) Desorption of positive ions.
(4) Conversion of one adsorbed state into another.

The experimental and theoretical fundamentals of electron stimulated desorption (otherwise known as electron impact desorption or electron induced desorption) have been laid down in a number of articles. We refer particularly to the two detailed reviews of Menzel [457] and Madey and Yates [439]. It has been established experimentally that the process is not concerned with thermal desorption. It is an isolated process involving only primary electrons and the adsorbate. Application of the principles of energy and momentum conservation shows that the direct transfer of momentum from electron to adsorbate is insufficient to explain the effects in the case of the low energy electrons which one uses. Such direct energy and momentum transfer could at most lead to the desorption of weakly physisorbed species [460].

A mechanism involving the Franck-Condon principle was proposed independently by Menzel and Gomer [460] and Redhead [568]. According to this mechanism, the electron impact gives rise to a Franck-Condon transition which produces an excited or ionised surface complex. This complex can then decompose, followed by desorption of the adsorbed particles in the ionic or neutral state. For a detailed exposition of these processes we refer to references 439,457.

Two groups of experimental methods are available for the investigation of electron stimulated desorption:

(1) One follows the desorption by measuring a parameter which is proportional to the changes in coverage caused by electron bombardment.
(2) One follows the desorption by monitoring the emitted particles directly.

The first group has the advantage that one can easily obtain a quantitative measure of the adsorbed amount. The disadvantages are that neither the nature nor the energy of the desorbed species can be obtained, although the nature can sometimes be obtained indirectly. The second group, on the other hand, readily yields both a qualitative analysis and the energy of desorbed particles, while the quantitative aspect of the desorbed flux is now associated with greater experimental difficulties.

The investigations of Menzel and Gomer [459] provide an example of the first group. They carried out electron stimulated desorption experiments in a field emission microscope, using the work function variations, as determined from the Fowler-Nordheim equation, to determine coverage changes. Ermrich [186] refined this procedure by applying the probe-hole technique. This enabled him to extract additional information about the processes on individual crystal planes. Of course, the other methods of determining the work function which have been mentioned in Section 5.1 can also be applied to determine coverage changes. The same holds for flash desorption, ellipsometry or Auger electron spectroscopy. The LEED method' has been turned to this end as well [10].

The second group of methods may be further divided. Thus one can confine oneself to analysing just the desorbed ions. The works of Moore [482] and of Lichtman, McQuistan and Kirst [422], among others, fall into this category. They called the method electron-probe surface mass spectrometry. Depending on the conditions, one makes use of one of the various possibilities in mass spectrometry.

The desorbed neutral particles may be ionised if an ionisation chamber is added [455,456] and they can then be recorded in the same way as the ions (see *Figure 6.8*). In this way it is possible, therefore, to obtain both the ions desorbed and the neutral particles desorbed.

We note that the drawback of these particular methods lies in the fact that only an unknown, small fraction of the total flux of particles desorbed can be accommodated by the analyser.

Redhead [568] and Madey *et al.* [441], however, showed that the total ion flux could be collected by suitably designing the arrangement of grid and electrodes (hemispherical analyser). Their arrangement

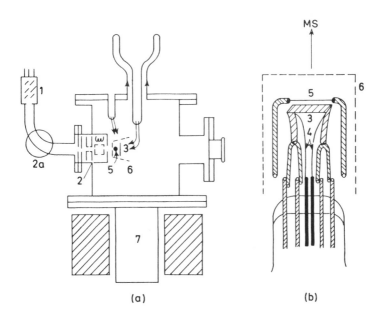

(a) (b)

Figure 6.8 (a) Apparatus for the measurement of desorbed ions and neutral particles; (b) construction of the anode assembly. After Menzel [455]; MS = mass spectrometer; 1 = secondary electron multiplier; 2 = ion source; 2a = mass spectrometer magnet; 3 = anode (tungsten ribbon); 4 = voltage leads; 5 = incandescent filament cathode; 6 = screening grid; 7 = ion pump

enabled the absolute cross-sectional area for electron stimulated desorption to be evaluated. Furthermore, they could also measure the distribution of the kinetic energy of the desorbed ions with the help of retarding potentials, although the arrangement yielded no mass data for the desorbed particles.

An analysis of both the mass and the energy of desorbed ions can be achieved by combining a quadrupole mass spectrometer with a hemispherical analyser [438].

The cross-sectional area or cross-section, q, is a central quantity in any discussion of electron stimulated desorption. Information concerning q is obtained both from measurements on the adsorbent and from analysis of the desorbate.

Let N_i particles per square centimetre be adsorbed in a particular state i and $\dot{N}_e$ be the number of electrons impinging on the adsorbed phase per square centimetre per unit time. Since the interaction on impact is first order with respect to electrons, the rate of desorption dN_i/dt is given by

$$-\frac{dN_i}{dt} = \dot{N}_e \, q_i \, N_i \tag{6.2}$$

The constant q_i has the dimensions of cm^2 and is called the total desorption cross-section for particles in state i because equation (6.2) embraces both the desorbed neutrals as well as the desorbed ions. q_i is, in fact, the parameter which describes the effectiveness of interaction. Integration of equation (6.2) leads to

$$\frac{N_i(t)}{N_i \, (t = 0)} = \exp\left(-q_i \dot{N}_e t\right) \tag{6.3}$$

if N_i ($t = 0$) is taken as the number of adsorbed particles per square centimetre in state i at the commencement of electron bombardment.

Let us suppose that the primary electron current is large and the gas pressure is low, so that the rate of adsorption can be neglected in comparison with the rate of desorption. Under these circumstances equation (6.3) describes the process which is responsible for the change in coverage of the state i. This process may therefore be followed by measuring any physical property X_i which is proportional to coverage (such as the change in work function $e_0\phi$) and we may write

$$\frac{N_i(t)}{N_i \, (t = 0)} = \frac{\Delta X_i(t)}{\Delta X_i \, (t = 0)} \tag{6.4}$$

or

$$\frac{\Delta X_i(t)}{\Delta X_i \, (t = 0)} = \exp(-\dot{N}_e q_i t) \tag{6.5}$$

The total desorption cross-section q_i is then determined by plotting log ΔX_i against t, the primary electron current being known. This method is based on the indirect determination of coverage (first group of methods given above).

The cross-section for desorption can also be found by measuring the ion current i_i^+ (second group of methods given above). Making the same assumptions as before leads to

$$i_i^+ = \dot{N}_e q_i^+ N_i \qquad (6.6)$$

where q_i^+ is the cross-section for desorption of ions. Substitution of equation (6.6) into equation (6.2) gives

$$-\frac{di_i^+}{dt} = \dot{N}_e q_i i_i^+ \qquad (6.7)$$

Integrating this equation,

$$\frac{i_i^+(t)}{i_i^+ (t = 0)} = \exp(\dot{N}_e q_i t) \qquad (6.8)$$

The time dependence of the ion current may now be used to ascertain both the cross-section for desorption of ions and the total desorption cross-section for particles in the state i. If N_i is known and constant (so small a primary electron current $\dot{N}_e$ that N_i remains sensibly constant), then q_i^+ can be obtained from equation (6.6). If N_i is falling (so large a primary electron current $\dot{N}_e$ that rapid desorption occurs), then q_i is obtained by use of equation (6.8).

The same considerations apply to the flux of neutral particles. Using N to denote neutral particles, the various impact cross-sections may be summed:

$$q = \Sigma q^+ + \Sigma q^N$$

Experiment has shown that cross-sections for desorption of ions are generally orders of magnitude less than cross-sections for desorption of neutral particles. The two cross-sections for desorption differ markedly from the effective cross-sections which are found for electron induced processes in free molecules (10^{-16}-10^{-15} cm^2).

The desorption cross-section is observed to depend strongly on the state of adsorption and the energy of the primary electrons. In contrast to electron impact processes in free molecules, for which the curve of impact cross-section against primary electron energy always shows a maximum, cross-sections for desorption do not necessarily behave in the same way [518]. The desorption cross-section falls as the primary energy is lowered, reaching zero at a threshold energy. This energy coincides with the minimum energy which is needed to

effect the process being considered, and it provides an additional para
meter for characterising the adsorption system and discussing the
mechanism of excitation.

The W/CO system has attracted most attention in electron stimulated
desorption work. This system had already been thoroughly studied by
other methods, particularly flash desorption and field emission microscopy. It was therefore particularly appropriate that observations of
electron stimulated desorption should be undertaken.

As already stated, the various states of adsorption are distinguished
by their cross-section for desorption. And it turned out quite generally
[457] that q-values became progressively smaller as the bond strength
between the species and the adsorbent increased. Sometimes one can
also observe that the various species produce distinguishable products
on electron stimulated desorption [455,456]. In the W/CO system,
for instance, CO^+ and O^+ are such desorbed products, whose differing
kinetic energy also enables them to be distinguished [569,736]. In
this way it has been possible to prove that the a-state of CO really
consists of two different states.

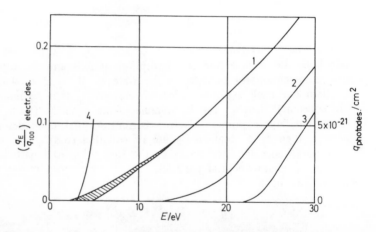

*Figure 6.9   Threshold region for electron stimulated desorption and for photo-
desorption of a-CO on tungsten; after Menzel and co-workers [455,462]. Curve
(1) electron stimulated desorption of CO; curve (2) electron stimulated desorption
of CO$^+$; curve (3) electron stimulated desorption of O$^+$; curve (4) photodesorption
of CO*

Nevertheless, the occurrence of differing desorption products in no
way proves the existence of differing adsorbed species, because a certain species may be capable of producing various desorption products
under electron stimulation. In such a case the products can usually be
distinguished by their threshold energies (see *Figure 6.9*). Menzel [455]
has compiled a list of products together with their properties for the
W/CO system. Goymour and King [276] and Yates [731] compare
the results obtained from desorption spectra and electron stimulated
desorption.

The literature [187,460,461] repeatedly refers to the fact that electron bombardment is capable of inducing the conversion of one state to another. One can, however, work with such low current densities that the coverage is not noticeably altered by electron bombardment. Electron stimulated desorption then serves solely as a probe to determine the coverage. In this mode, it is sometimes possible to elucidate what the coverage of a certain state is. Certainly this mode enables the kinetics of surface processes to be studied. Simon, Lichtman and Kirst [612] used the method (which they called electron-probe surface mass spectrometry) to study the Ni/H_2 system. Unfortunately some doubt has been cast on the cleanliness of their nickel surfaces [439], so we refrain from giving here a detailed discussion of the specific results of this interesting work.

A number of more recent works concerned with the W/H_2 and W/D_2 systems [349-351] have now appeared. They indicate how many different pieces of information may be obtained concerning the adsorptive properties of a system if electron stimulated desorption is consistently and exhaustively applied by the above-mentioned methods or if ESD is combined with other methods of investigation [437].

7

STUDY OF ADSORPTION USING ENERGETIC PHOTONS

In the same way that bombardment of the surface with low energy electrons has a wide range of consequences, irradiation of a clean or gas-adsorbed surface with photons leads to the most diverse variety of effects.

Relatively low energy photons excite vibration and are absorbed (see Section 4.1). Photons in the visible or ultra-violet spectral region excite the adsorbed molecules to higher electronic states and are likewise absorbed (see Section 4.2).

As the energy of the photons is raised, electron emission occurs as an additional effect. In Section 5.1 we have already described an emission of photoelectrons from the upper edge of the conduction band of a metallic adsorbent. High energy photons are also capable of causing the emission of photoelectrons from deeper levels. This effect is exploited in photoelectron spectroscopy.

Finally, the absorption of sufficiently high energy photons can bring about desorption of the adsorbed species and one then speaks of photodesorption.

7.1. Photoelectron spectroscopy

Although photoelectron spectroscopy has been very successfully applied to chemical problems for quite some time, there has been a certain amount of hesitation in using the technique to investigate surfaces and adsorbed phases. This is primarily due to the experimental difficulties. A review of developments up to 1973 is given by Menzel [458] and Bradshaw, Cederbaum and Domcke [88] have recently reviewed the ultra-violet photoelectron spectroscopy of adsorbed gases.

If one bombards a surface with photons, then the absorption process results in the promotion of a bound electron to an unoccupied level. Given enough photon energy $h\nu$, the new state may lie above the vacuum level. In this case the electron leaves the system with a certain kinetic energy E_{kin} whose magnitude enables the original binding energy E_B of the electron to be evaluated. This is because

$$h\nu = E_B + E_{kin}. \tag{7.1}$$

This simple relationship assumes that the photoelectron has not lost any energy prior to emission (compare Chapter 6). The binding energy E_B has also been taken relative to the vacuum level. In the case of solids, however, it is more convenient to measure binding energies relative to the Fermi level E_F. This binding energy is distinguished as E_B^F, where

$$E_B^F = E_B - e_0\phi_s \tag{7.2}$$

$e_0\phi_s$ is the work function of the specimen. Furthermore, due notice must be taken of the contact potential difference between the specimen and the spectrometer. This is because we measure a kinetic energy $E'_{kin.}$ in the spectrometer, where

$$E'_{kin.} = E_{kin.} + e_0(\phi_s - \phi_{sp}) \tag{7.3}$$

$e_0\phi_{sp}$ is the work function of the spectrometer. Combining equations (7.1)-(7.3) yields

$$E_B^F = h\nu - E'_{kin.} - e_0\phi_{sp} \tag{7.4}$$

It is customary to subdivide photoelectron spectroscopy according to the excitation energy employed. The excitation can be effected with very short-wave UV light, in which case one speaks of UPS. Alternatively, soft X-rays can be used and then one speaks of XPS (also called ESCA). Various sources are used to produce the required radiation, the commonest being the He discharge lamp (He I and He II with photon energies of 21.2 eV and 40.8 eV, respectively), and the Al or Mg X-ray tube (Al $Ka_{1,2}$ and Mg $Ka_{1,2}$ with photon energies of 1486.6 eV and 1256 eV, respectively).

The difference between the energies of these sources illustrates how UPS and XPS embrace different energy regimes. In general, UPS gives access to valency levels and yields information about the band structure and the density of occupied states. With XPS the core levels also become accessible, so that, in addition to information about the valency states, information can be secured about the binding energy of electrons in inner levels. In adsorption investigations one is more concerned with the chemical shift caused by environmental influences than with the identification of the particles (ESCA). These shifts enable one to recognise the chemical state of the atoms under study.

In order to apply photoelectron spectroscopy to the investigation of surfaces and adsorption systems, one has to stipulate that the information obtained actually refers only to the region near the surface. This requirement is in fact assured on both experimental and theoretical grounds. The escape depth of photoelectrons with an energy of, say, 20 eV is 10 Å, while that of 40 eV photoelectrons is 5 Å and that of 1500 eV is 20 Å [405,578]. The precise escape depth depends, of course, on the nature of the material; nevertheless, it does not seem to vary by more than a factor of 2 with the material.

Apart from the photon sources, spectrometers for UPS and XPS do not differ much in their experimental arrangements. It has proved to be expedient to build a combined apparatus [607] in which both types of photoelectron spectroscopy may be pursued.   Indeed, it has not been unusual to include the ability to make further measurements such as LEED, Auger electron spectroscopy, surface potential determinations and thermal desorption spectra [123,398].   Essential features of the apparatus are the ability to evacuate to best UHV (in the region of 10^{-11} Torr) and to record the energy distribution of photoelectrons with the highest possible resolution.   For the latter purpose, hemispherical and cylindrical mirror analysers have been particularly successful.   Brundle *et al.* [106] give a detailed description of a suitable apparatus.

7.1.1.   DETERMINATION OF THE DENSITY OF STATES IN THE VALENCY BAND

The aim of these investigations is to obtain from the measured energy distribution curve the density of occupied states and its variation due to adsorption.   In this way one may accumulate data concerning the band structure and the energy of the intrinsic surface valence levels expected theoretically for a clean surface [231-233,288].   One also obtains data concerning the energy of the extrinsic surface valence levels which arise from the presence of an adsorbed species.   There are a number of theoretical difficulties and experimental restrictions which limit the interpretation of spectra.   On the theoretical side, the density of the final states and the matrix elements exerts an uncertain influence, while on the experimental side neither the radiation from the discharge lamp nor the radiation from the X-ray tube is accurately monochromatic (containing up to 10 per cent of radiation at other frequencies) and one also has to contend with a superimposed flux of secondary electrons.   Despite these problems, it is still possible to secure densities of states with sufficient accuracy.   Both UPS and XPS have proved to be favourable starting points for obtaining these sorts of data [607].

The experimental results which have been obtained to date show that, in general, photoelectron spectroscopy fulfils the promise expected of it in the field of surface and adsorption investigations.   Early work was usually directed at elucidating the band structure of metals such as, for example, Cu, Ag and Au [163].   More recently it has been possible to record the surface states which are demanded by theory and mentioned above.   They have been detected, for instance, on W(100) [217,679] and already the least amount of adsorption causes them to disappear.

Eastman, Cashion and Switendick [165] were then able to detect a band in the β-Pd/H system which was due to the energy structure induced by hydrogen.   A short while later they were the first to report electronic energy states for chemisorbed gases.   They tackled the adsorption of CO and oxygen on evaporated nickel films [164], observing two levels at 7.5 eV and 10.7 eV below the Fermi level for CO, while a broadening level formed for oxygen as chemisorption proceeded. This level turned into a wide valency band with stronger oxidation. Measurements made later on a Ni(100) surface [38] showed that these results were correct in general. The levels which arise in CO adsorption are ascribed to orbitals which derive from the σ2p and π2p orbitals of the free CO molecule.

Other authors [30,680] have studied the adsorption of CO on W and found chemisorption levels which may be assigned to the various different species of adsorbed CO.

Measurements have also been made for the adsorption of hydrogen on tungsten [218].

Ertl and co-workers [123,398] investigated the adsorption of various gases on polycrystalline palladium and on Pd(110) surfaces. The results were similar to those of Eastman *et al.* for CO adsorption on nickel (see above). Two levels were found for chemisorbed CO at 7.9 eV and 10.8 eV below the Fermi edge, and there was a considerable fall in the emission immediately below the Fermi edge. *Figure 7.1* shows the difference between the traces obtained for emission from a CO-covered Pd(110) surface and a clean Pd(110) surface.

In addition to the fall in photoelectron emission immediately below the Fermi edge, the adsorption of NO on Pd(110) leads to a peak at 9.4 eV and the adsorption of oxygen to a broad maximum at 5.8 eV. For the adsorption of hydrogen the authors only observed a slight fall in intensity just below the Fermi edge. In addition to these findings, they were able to demonstrate that UPS is suitable for following displacement reactions and decomposition reactions in the adsorbed phase.

Although it is possible to correlate UPS peaks qualitatively with the energy states of free atoms and molecules, an exact, quantitative assignment should not be expected in the near future. For all this, it is already known now from the investigations made to date that levels which appear as a result of chemisorption are, in general, well localised. These investigations have probed the density of states to as much as 15 eV below the Fermi edge.

XPS has proved to be a valuable tool for investigating band structure, but this technique has not led to any significant results concerning the detection of chemisorption levels.

7.1.2. DETERMINATION OF THE ENERGY OF CORE LEVELS

The goal in these investigations is to determine the energy structure of the core levels so that the chemical composition of the surface or the adsorbed phase may be established. It is also desirable to obtain the chemical shift, because this enables conclusions to be drawn regarding the chemical environment and the state of binding in the adsorbate. Such an approach should be particularly fruitful in the investigation of core levels of adsorbed particles where, in the appropriate energy range,

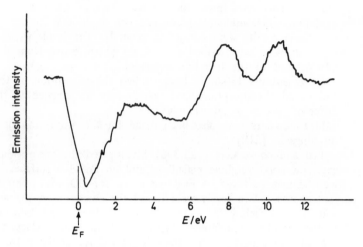

Figure 7.1   Difference in photoelectron emission of a CO-covered and a clean Pd(110) surface; after Conrad et al. [123]

the presence of adsorbent only leads to a background of emission. The possibility even exists that distinguishable chemical shifts will be found for different states of adsorption. For a more detailed discussion of these questions we refer to the literature [104,581].

Less information has been obtained as yet with the help of this method than has been brought to light by determinations of the density of states in the valency band. It has been of more immediate interest to apply the core level method to finding the electronic structure of inorganic compounds. Schön, for instance, has conducted comparison XPS studies on metals and metal oxide powders. He investigated Cu, Cu_2O and CuO [593] and Ag, Ag_2O and AgO [594]. In the case of silver oxide he was able to obtain unambiguous O 1s spectra and to establish from the Ag 3d level that a distinct chemical shift occurred in going from Ag to Ag_2O and further to AgO.

Published adsorption work has initially tended to confine itself to demonstrating that core level spectroscopy is a suitable technique for the investigation of adsorption. Thus, Schön and Lundin [595] also investigated the adsorption of oxygen on nickel and compared the spectrum with that obtained for nickel oxide. They established that the O 1s electrons in adsorbed oxygen have a higher binding energy than they have in nickel oxide.

The surface sensitivity of the method was studied by Fraser *et al.* [239] by looking at caesium adsorption on molybdenum. Their work showed that the photoelectron spectrum definitely depends on the incident angle, especially where the surface region is concerned.

Brundle and Roberts [105] showed by means of Hg adsorption on Au that the sensitivity of the method is sufficient to detect 0.2 per cent of a monolayer.

The first investigations of consequence on adsorption systems were reported by Madey, Yates and Erickson [440] and Menzel [458] for the adsorption of oxygen and carbon monoxide on tungsten. Yates, Madey and Erickson [735] managed to follow the adsorption events on a tungsten ribbon by measuring the O 1s and C 1s core levels. In particular, it was possible to follow the thermal desorption of various species of adsorbed CO by means of these photoelectron peaks. Not only could a chemical shift be unequivocally demonstrated, but also the shift could be identified with respect to the various species.

Atkinson, Brundle and Roberts [24] have reported the first XPS measurements for the chemisorption of carbon monoxide on molybdenum and tungsten films. The same authors [25] recently used XPS to characterise various binding states for the adsorption of CO on Mo. Their results indicate that there is a thermally induced conversion of a 'virgin state' adsorbed CO to the β-state. As already mentioned, XPS and UPS measurements can be combined to advantage.

The work which has appeared so far shows that both XPS and UPS are very sensitive methods for investigating adsorption systems. The quantitative interpretation, however, still awaits the answer to a number of theoretical problems. This is especially true of the chemical shifts that one measures.

7.2. Photodesorption

Many efforts have been made to identify the existence of photodesorption [2,403,479,480] and yet the results have been contradictory. This is partly due to experimental inadequacies and partly because it is so difficult to separate photodesorption and thermal desorption.

Photodesorption in the W/CO system was definitely established by Kronauer and Menzel [395] by using scrupulous experimental techniques and eliminating thermal desorption. Fabel, Cox and Lichtman [209] carried out a heat flow calculation which enabled an upper limit to be set on the heating of the surface resulting from incident radiation. Any possible influence of thermal desorption can be estimated accordingly.

As in the case of electron stimulated desorption, two methods are chiefly available for investigating photodesorption [395]. The amount desorbed may be ascertained by monitoring a parameter, such as the work function, for example, which is proportional to the coverage. The same considerations as those outlined for electron stimulated desorption (see Section 6.5) then also apply. Provided that the photon flux density (in photons s^{-1} cm^{-2}) has been determined previously with a thermopile, one can therefore evaluate a desorption cross-section for photodesorption according to equation (6.5). On the other hand, it is also possible to follow the desorption by measuring the partial or the total pressure.   In the case of a small apparatus, it is well worth using just an ionisation gauge as pump, running the gauge at high emission current.   The way in which the measured pressure variations are worked up has been described by Lange [403], Lange and Riemersma [404] and Adams and Donaldson [2].

Kronauer and Menzel [395] studied the systems W/CO and W/O₂. They were only able to establish photodesorption in the former system, using photon energies up to 5 eV.   Both the probability of photo-desorption and the cross-section for photodesorption were found to depend strongly on the photon energy, the threshold energy being 2.7 eV.   Weaker photons were unable to desorb any CO, and this may be regarded as further proof of the absence of thermal desorption occasioned by the radiation.   As with electron stimulated desorption, photodesorption may be used as a probe in coverage determinations. Thus, Kronauer and Menzel [395] illuminated the specimen with light of a certain frequency and observed the photodesorption signal as a function of the adsorbent temperature.   They found that the species responsible for photodesorption was thermally desorbed below 600 K. This demonstrates that the species concerned is weakly bound a-CO.

A particularly fruitful comparison of experimental data was made by Menzel, Kronauer and Jeland [462] for electron stimulated desorption and photodesorption.   Working with a-CO on W, they observed that both the threshold energies and also both the desorption cross-sections (at similar excitation energy) were the same.   The latter is about 5×10^{-21} cm² at 5 eV and the effect is illustrated by curve 4 in *Figure 6.9*, which refers to photodesorption.   This is tantamount to saying that the desorption of a-CO on tungsten proceeds by the same primary step whether light or electrons are used.

One may confidently expect that the use of higher excitation ener-gies will lead to additional information.   Higher energies should also enable a decision to be reached as to which of the mechanisms currently under discussion is the right one.

8

STUDY OF ADSORPTION USING ION BEAMS

Beams of particles interact with clean surfaces or adsorbed phases in a number of ways. As with low energy electron beams, interaction with the heavier particles is also capable of providing a deep insight into the conditions and events on surfaces. Of atomic, molecular and ionic beams, more analytical significance is currently being attached to ion beams, although the application of thermal beams of atoms or molecules has also produced valuable results [366,531]. Energetic ion beams will provide an analysis of the concentration profile to quite considerable depths, but investigations involving low energy ions yield information which is confined, in the main, to the outermost atom layers. Even with low energy ion beams, however, analysis of the concentration profile may be undertaken to a certain extent by taking advantage of sputtering processes. The *International Conference on Ion Beam Surface Layer Analysis, Yorktown Heights, New York* [453] reviews the state of the art as at 1973, although this conference was more concerned with the application of high energy ion beams. Mayer and Turos [452] give a comparison of the various methods of analysing surface layers.

In the interaction of low energy ions with solid surfaces, the different effects which occur [357] include back-scattering of ions [619,657], secondary ion emission [51,203], ion neutralisation [293], photon emission [45,716] and secondary electron emission [626,627]. As far as the aims of this book are concerned, the first three of these effects are particularly important and we shall be explaining them in more detail in the following sections.

Back-scattered low energy ions (primary energy generally 0.5-2 keV) may be energy analysed to establish the chemical composition of the uppermost one or two atom layers. The analysis is particularly successful for elements of low or intermediate mass.

Secondary ion mass spectrometry is concerned with a mass analysis of the positive and negative secondary ions which are emitted. These ions originate from the uppermost atom layers and, like energy analysis, mass analysis enables the surface layer to be chemically analysed. Both these methods suffer from the disadvantage, however, that their use entails the removal of material from the adsorbed layer and the adsorbent. Irreversible changes are therefore caused.

In ion neutralisation spectroscopy one measures the energy distribution of the electrons which are emitted when ions of extremely low energy

(4-10 eV) are neutralised on an adsorbent surface. With this technique, one can obtain the state densities at the solid surface and, hence, evaluate the orbital energy spectra of electrons in chemisorption bonds.

8.1.   Low energy ion back-scattering

The theory, the experimental procedure and the practical application of low energy ion back-scattering — often called ISS (ion scattering spectroscopy) — are covered in a number of review articles which have appeared in recent years [341,342,619,657]. Perusal of these articles clearly reveals that currently there are still many unresolved questions concerning the theoretical interpretation of the spectra obtained [657]. For this reason we shall confine ourselves to an examination of the simplest and clearest cases possible.

Consider the case of an accurately parallel beam of monoenergetic He^+ ions which impinges on a clean copper surface at $45°$ incidence and let the energy distribution be measured for those He^+ ions which are forward-scattered at an angle $\theta = 90°$ to the incident beam. Under these circumstances one obtains a spectrum which usually reveals a single peak, as shown in *Figure 8.1*. It turns out that the energy of the scattered ions can be calculated by saying that a two-body collision occurs between an incoming rare gas ion and the atom it strikes on the solid surface. The impact knocks the solid atom out of the crystal lattice and the principles of conservation of energy and of momentum may be adopted. If the primary energy of the ions is E_0 and the energy after scattering is E_1, while the mass of the ions is m_1 and the mass of the atoms being struck is m_2, then one obtains

$$\frac{E_1}{E_0} = \frac{1}{(1 + m_2/m_1)^2} \left\{ \cos \theta + [(m_2/m_1)^2 - \sin^2 \theta]^{\frac{1}{2}} \right\}^2 \tag{8.1}$$

In the present case $\theta = 90°$ and this expression simplifies to

$$\frac{E_1}{E_0} = \frac{m_2 - m_1}{m_2 + m_1} \qquad (\text{for } m_2 > m_1) \tag{8.2}$$

The mass of the scattering atoms can therefore be found by means of energy analysis of the scattered ions. Equation (8.2) may be rearranged to give

$$m_2 = m_1 \left[\frac{1 + (E_1/E_0)}{1 - (E_1/E_0)} \right] \tag{8.3}$$

This equation opens up the possibility of applying low energy ion backscattering to the chemical analysis of adsorbent surfaces and adsorbed phases.

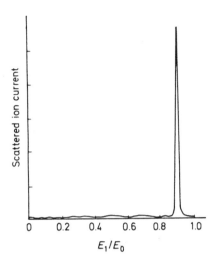

Figure 8.1 *Energy distribution for He$^+$ ions scattered by a copper surface. Incidence angle, 45°; scattering angle, 90°; energy of primary ions, 2 keV. After Smith [619]*

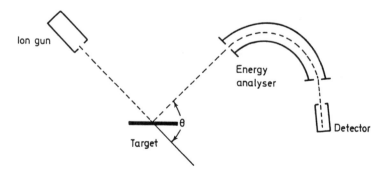

Figure 8.2 *Apparatus for determining the energy distribution of back-scattered ions*

The experimental requirements are self-evident. An ultrahigh vacuum system is necessary; it contains an ion gun capable of delivering an adjustable, parallel beam of strictly monoenergetic ions. A diaphragm system filters off the beam which is scattered from the surface at a specific angle θ to the incident direction. An energy analyser and an ion detector are also needed. *Figure 8.2* indicates the main features of an apparatus used to measure the back-scattering of low energy ions It has proved to be expedient [102,321] to combine the measurements of low energy ion back-scattering with other experimental techniques. The more attractive possibilities for such an additional approach include secondary ion mass spectrometry, Auger electron spectroscopy, LEED, electron stimulated desorption, thermal desorption and ellipsometry. The choice of the type of ion gun, energy analyser and ion detector is determined by the particular problem being tackled. For details concerning the apparatus we refer to the literature [20,102,322,656,715].

According to equation (8.3), the energy distribution of the back-scattered ions should contain as many peaks as there are elements of differing mass in the adsorbent and in the adsorbed phase. The peaks should appear in different places in the spectrum and resolution should improve as one increases the mass of the ion which is used for analysis. These principles are, in fact, confirmed by experiment [619]. Thus, two well-defined peaks are found when a CdS surface is investigated by use of He^+ ions. One peak is due to scattering at Cd atoms and the other is due to scattering at S atoms. Similarly, two peaks (Al and O) are found when an Al_2O_3 surface is investigated, and two peaks (Au and Ni) occur in the spectrum of an Au-Ni alloy. The alloy peaks lie significantly further apart when Ne^+ ions are used instead of He^+ ions. If CO is adsorbed on a nickel surface, then, in addition to the Ni peak, there are two further peaks in the energy spectrum of back-scattered He^+ ions. The additional peaks can be attributed to scattering at C and O atoms [269]. A halogen-covered nickel surface was studied by Brongersma and Mul [102] using Ne^+ ions. The energy spectrum they obtained is shown in *Figure 8.3*. Sensitivity can be quite considerable, the limit of detection being given as 10^{-1}-10^{-3} of a monolayer [657].

Quantitative determinations turn out to be much harder to obtain. They are probably only accessible through calibration runs, and here there is already a problem in defining standard conditions. The intensity of the scattered beam depends on numerous factors. The more important of these include the cross-section, the neutralisation probability, geometric aspects (crystal plane specificity is found), atomic weight and atomic number of the primary ion and the scattered particles, primary energy of the ions and the scattering angle. It should also be stated that equation (8.1) is an oversimplification. It is based on a two-body collision and may only be applied within certain limits. In the case of He^+ ions, equation (8.1) is probably valid for primary energies between 0.5 and 2 keV, provided the scattering angle is sufficiently large. Ne^+ and Ar^+ ions, however, show a more restricted range

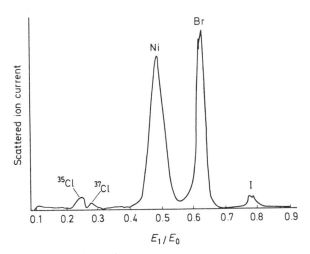

Figure 8.3 Energy spectrum of Ne⁺ ions which have been scattered at 90° to the incident beam from a halogen-covered nickel surface; After Brongersma and Mul [102]

of applicability, as the investigations of Heiland, Schäffler and Taglauer [321] have revealed. One can also use ions of gases which are capable of entering into a stronger interaction with the adsorbent (chemisorption). In such cases the energy spectra show fundamental differences from the spectrum of *Figure 8.1*. For a far-reaching theoretical treatment we refer to the review paper of Suurmeijer and Boers [657].

At the present stage of technical development, ISS involves the removal of 1-4 monolayers before a complete energy analysis can be obtained [342]. One should not overlook the fact that such an amount of material is hardly practicable for adsorption studies. It remains to be seen, therefore, whether the method will assume any appreciable significance in adsorption work. In itself, ISS is an elegant technique for investigating surfaces, and Brongersma and Mul [102] believe it has adsorption applications. They have established that experiments can, if necessary, be carried out in a non-destructive way.

8.2. Secondary ion mass spectrometry

The theory and practice of secondary ion mass spectrometry (SIMS) have been treated in various review articles [51,203,341,631]. Some works deal especially with the technique of this method [202], while others [713] compare the different variations such as static secondary ion mass spectrometry (static SIMS) [50], secondary ion microprobe mass spectrometry (S.I. microprobe M.S. or microprobe SIMS) [423] and secondary ion imaging mass spectrometry (imaging SIMS) [112]. Evans [202] gives a comparison of the different types of instrument.

Some explanation of the method will be given by taking static SIMS [49-51] as an example. This is the variation which is most suitable for adsorption studies.

Suppose that a primary ion with an energy of several keV strikes the surface of a solid. Either the ion can be reflected (see Section 8.1) or it can penetrate into the solid and give up its energy to the lattice points. The energy is then distributed by collisions over a larger region near the surface. If in this process the energy is transferred to surface atoms, then neutrals, charged atoms or charged groups of atoms may be emitted. The flux of charged atoms is invariably much smaller than the flux of neutrals and one also observes an emission of electrons and photons. SIMS is only concerned with the emission of the positive and negative ions.

Figure 8.4 shows a diagram of the salient features which make up a secondary ion mass spectrometer. The spectrometer is part of an ultrahigh vacuum apparatus in which residual pressures in the region of 10^{-11} Torr may be achieved. A beam of monoenergetic ions of one mass (typically Ar^+) is produced in the ion gun and directed onto the target. A sensitive mass spectrometer [52] is placed so that it can analyse secondary ions which leave the surface at an angle of $70°$ with respect to the primary ion beam. Not only magnetic mass spectrometers may be used, but also quadrupole or time-of-flight mass spectrometers.

Normally, the concentration of the adsorbed phase will vary during the time taken to make a measurement because secondary ion emission depletes the surface layer according to an exponential decay:

$$\theta(t) = \theta(0) \exp(-t/\bar{t}) \tag{8.4}$$

Here $\theta(t)$ is the coverage at time t and $\bar{t}$ is the average time of life of a monolayer. In static SIMS, however, the current density of the primary ions is chosen to be so low ($\sim 10^{-9}$ A cm^{-2}) that $\bar{t}$ lies in the region of several hours and the method is therefore particularly suitable for adsorption work. Severe fall-off of the secondary ion current is, in fact, very effectively compensated by bombarding a large area of the adsorbent (~ 0.1 cm^2) with primary ions. It is even possible to detect as little as 1 part in 10^6 of a monolayer of adsorbate with this method. Slowly occurring changes in a monolayer can also be detected, provided that they do not alter the composition and structure of the surface significantly.

The secondary ion spectra for positive and negative ions are characterised by an unusual wealth of lines. This can be put down to the occurrence of all the possible ion fragments in addition to adsorbate and adsorbent ions. In the case of an oxidised chromium surface, for instance, the following secondary ions are emitted as well as O^- and Cr^+: O^+, O_2^+, CrO^+, CrO_2^+, Cr_2^+, Cr_2O^+, $Cr_2O_2^+$, $Cr_2O_3^+$, Cr_3^+, Cr_3O^+, Cr_4^+, O_2^-, CrO^-, CrO_2^-, CrO_3^-, CrO_4^-, $Cr_2O_4^-$, $Cr_2O_5^-$ [54]. Benninghoven [51] also examined the emission from molybdenum

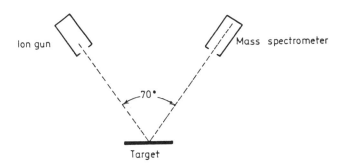

Figure 8.4   Apparatus for measuring secondary ion mass spectra

surfaces covered with a hydrocarbon or an alcohol, and found that there was a strong resemblance between the structures of the secondary ion spectra and the known mass spectra of these substances.

The static method of secondary ion mass spectrometry has been employed to good advantage by Benninghoven and co-workers for the surface analysis of a silver catalyst which was being used for the oxidation of ethylene [51] and for investigating the oxidation of chromium [54], vanadium, niobium and tantalum [489], magnesium, strontium and barium [56], titanium, nickel and copper [490] and silicon [55]. In these studies, as in others, it is expedient to double up with another method such as electron stimulated desorption [53].

Although it has been possible to carry out successful qualitative analyses of adsorbed layers using the static SIMS method, there are formidable difficulties to be overcome before quantitative analyses may be undertaken. Thus, the secondary ion emission of a certain ion is strongly dependent on the presence of other constituents, particularly the presence of oxygen. With the possible exception of oxygen desorption and oxidation, quantitative conclusions can only be obtained under precisely defined conditions and then with the help of calibrations.

8.3.   Ion neutralisation spectroscopy

Only a small proportion of the ions which impinge on a metallic surface is back-scattered in the manner described in Section 8.1. A substantial part of the arriving ions is neutralised on approaching the metallic surface [357]. An intensive study of this ion neutralisation has been the prerogative of Hagstrum [291-294]. It turned out that the neutralisation process is linked to an Auger process which supplies secondary electrons. *Figure 8.5* shows an electron energy diagram for ion neutralisation on the surface of a clean metal. When an ion approaches the metal surface to within a certain distance S,

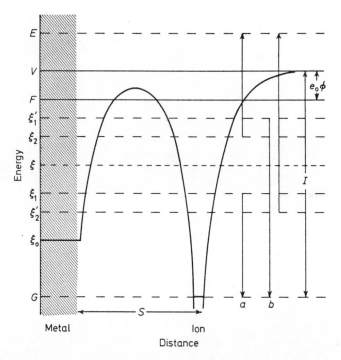

Figure 8.5   Electron energy diagram for the neutralisation of an ion on a clean metal surface. E = *kinetic energy of the secondary electron;* V = *vacuum level;* F = *Fermi level;* ξ = *energies within the conduction band;* G = *ground state of the atom;* I = *ionisation energy of the atom;* $e_0\phi$ = *work function of the metal; a and b denote possible transitions*

then an electron initially in level ξ_1 or ξ_1' makes a radiationless transfer to the ground level of the atom, thereby neutralising the ion. The energy is passed on to an electron in state ξ_2 or ξ_2' and this electron is emitted into the vacuum as a secondary electron with kinetic energy E. One notices immediately that in this process electrons of very variable primary energy give rise to secondary electrons with a specific kinetic energy E. Since the process involves two electrons, the electron emission is evidently concerned with a pair of electrons whose initial energies must always be arranged symmetrically about an energy ξ; the energy ξ lies exactly midway between E and G. In this way, one specific kinetic energy E is to be correlated with an infinite number of energy pairs. The local density of states in the surface region must therefore be reflected indirectly in the energy distribution of the secondary electrons. It is the aim of ion neutralisation spectroscopy to evaluate the state densities from the measured energy distribution of secondary electrons. To accomplish this is no mean assignment in computation [291-294].

In adsorption, 'surface molecules' may be formed and this will manifest itself (see Sections 6.2, 6.3, 7.1, 7.2) in the appearance of new maxima in the state densities at the surface. This, in turn, leads to new maxima in the energy distribution of secondary electrons.

The experimental set-up has been described in detail by Hagstrum and co-workers [293,294,296]. Its purpose is to ascertain the orbital energy spectra of electrons in chemisorption bonds by recording ion neutralisation spectra. Ultrahigh vacuum apparatus is used and the basic requirements are an ion gun and a high-resolution energy analyser with high sensitivity. The ion gun produces a beam of monoenergetic ions whose energy is between 4 and 10 eV. The apparatus enables LEED reflections and changes in the work function of the adsorbent to be recorded simultaneously.

The viability of the method has been demonstrated for chemisorption of oxygen, sulphur and selenium on a Ni(100) crystal face by Hagstrum and Becker [295,296]. They confirmed that changes in state densities of the type postulated above were really occurring and that they could be used to draw a number of definite and noteworthy conclusions: the appearance of several peaks shows that the four degenerate p-electrons in the chalcogens enter surface orbitals which can be distinguished from one another in that they differ as to degree of bonding and ionicity. The width of the orbital energy peaks indicates that there is a high hopping frequency for electrons and holes between the surface bonds and the electron bands of the solid. The structure of the adsorbed phase is likewise revealed in the ion neutralisation spectrum.

This technique has not been applied much to date. The reason for this probably lies to a large extent in the considerable effort demanded for an evaluation of the spectra.

9

SYSTEMATIC SURVEY OF ADSORPTION SYSTEMS

Chapters 3-8 have been concerned with a description of how the adsorption of various gases on solid surfaces manifests itself in the alteration of numerous properties of the adsorbents and the adsorbates. The alteration of such a property may often be explained on the basis of several different hypotheses. In this connection we have only to recall the discussion of adsorption isotherms (Section 3.1), of desorption spectra (Section 3.4), of optical spectra (Sections 4.1 and 4.2), of changes in electrical conductivity (Section 5.2), of LEED measurements (Section 6.1) or of electron stimulated desorption (Section 6.5). In fact, it is often only possible to obtain information about the true state of the bonding by combining several experimental methods.

In looking at the characteristics of a large number of adsorption systems, one eventually recognises a certain order. One can collect together either adsorbates with similar characteristics or adsorbents with similar characteristics.

9.1. Comparison of the approaches; the systems Ni/H_2 and Ni/CO

The state in which a particular adsorption system is revealed may be taken from the body of material in Chapters 3-8. To illustrate this, we summarise the data for the two systems which are of special interest to catalytic problems, namely Ni/H_2 and Ni/CO. The most significant results which have been reported for these two systems in Chapters 3-8 are collected together in *Tables 9.1* and *9.2*, together with the conclusions which have been or may be drawn.

Table 9.1 The system nickel/hydrogen

Method of investigation	Result	Conclusion
Adsorption isotherm	Isotherms generally obtained for dissociative adsorption at 77 K and at 273 K; for molecular adsorption only at 77 K and high coverage	Atomically adsorbed; molecular adsorption only occurs when the coverage exceeds a monolayer
Isosteric heat of adsorption	For coverages appreciably below monomolecular, 23 kcal mol^{-1} on (111) planes and 19.5 ... 21.5 kcal mol^{-1} on (110) planes; for coverage in excess of monomolecular, of the order of a few kcal mol^{-1}	Atomic chemisorption in the submonomolecular region with weak face specificity; physisorption of H$_2$ molecules in the region above monomolecular
Calorimetric heat of adsorption	Markedly differing values between 18 and 40 kcal mol^{-1} H$_2$, depending on the preparation of the adsorbent and the vacuum; low values for pure, well-annealed films	A number of different adsorption states in the region of atomic adsorption; the magnitude of values indicates covalent bonding
Entropy of adsorption	At 278 K, from configurational entropy → from translational entropy →	Atomic adsorption immobile at low coverage, mobile at higher coverage
Desorption spectra	Maxima at 90, 310 and 380 K → second order desorption kinetics → little difference between the various crystal faces →	One physisorption and two chemisorption states atomic chemisorption weak face specificity
Isotope exchange measurements	No exchange at 77 and 90 K, partial exchange at 150 K, free exchange above 195 K with the gas phase; exchange always sets up the HD equilibrium	No mobility below 90 K, mobile adsorption above 195 K, dissociative adsorption, a number of species with varying bond strengths in the chemisorption region
Sticking probabilities	Coverage dependence reveals two regions	At least two different states of adsorption
Electron spin resonance	Intensity of ESR signal from Ni falls when hydrogen is adsorbed	Interaction between hydrogen and unpaired electrons of nickel (d-band holes)
Work function	For films: at 77 K the work function rises (in two sections) up to the monatomic layer, then falls off at higher coverage; at 273 K there is a sharp rise up to half atomic coverage followed by only a small rise; on single crystals: $\Delta(e_0\phi_{max})$ on Ni(111), (100) and (110) is 0.195, 0.170 and 0.530 eV, respectively	At least two chemisorbed species, polarised as H$^{\delta-}$; physisorbed state is H$_2{}^{\delta+}$; polarisation is clearly specific to the face
Electrical conductivity	A maximum occurs in the resistance, followed by a resistance fall above monatomic coverage at 77 K	At least two chemisorbed and one physisorbed states
Thermoelectric power	Different effects below and above half atomic coverage	At least two chemisorbed states

Method of investigation	Result	Conclusion
Magnetic measurements	Magnetisation falls; proportionality between relative fall in magnetisation and amount of hydrogen	Fall in the number of d-band holes, either covalent bonding or polar bonding Ni⁻H⁺, no change in the bonding type as coverage rises
Field emission microscopy	Sharp boundary between covered and uncovered surface at low coverages below 240 K; at higher coverages hydrogen spreads over the entire cap	Immobile adsorption at low temperature, mobile adsorption at higher temperature; no marked crystal face specificity, also not in surface diffusion
Low energy electron diffraction	After adsorption a new structure appears on Ni(110); only intensity variations on Ni(111) and Ni(100)	Ordered structure on Ni(110), probably with rearrangement; disordered structure on Ni(111) and Ni(100)

Table 9.2 The system nickel/carbon monoxide

Method of investigation	Result	Conclusion
Isosteric heat of adsorption	30 kcal mol⁻¹ at low coverage and independent of the crystal face, plateau at *ca.* 25 kcal mol⁻¹ at about half the monolayer	No marked crystal face specificity, two states of chemisorption
Calorimetric heat of adsorption	Initial heat of adsorption is between 35 and 42 kcal mol⁻¹ CO depending on the preparation of the adsorbent; on pure well-annealed films at low coverage 30 kcal mol⁻¹, on the plateau at about half the monolayer 25 kcal mol⁻¹	Two states of chemisorption; bond strength comparable with that in nickel tetracarbonyl
Desorption spectra	Maxima at 150, 310-360, 460-490 K	Two states of chemisorption, one weakly bound state
Isotope exchange measurements	The first species which is adsorbed at low temperature only exchanges with the gas phase at higher temperatures; no intermolecular isotope exchange	Evident heterogeneity in the site energies of the adsorbent, no mobility below 100 K, complete mobility above 195 K, no dissociative adsorption below 300 K
Sticking probabilities	Coverage dependence reveals three regions	At least three different states of adsorption
IR spectroscopy	Several bands; relative intensity is coverage dependent	Several different adsorbed species, bound linearly and bridge-bonded; type of bonding depends on the coverage
Work function	The maximum work function rise of 1.4 eV is independent of the crystal face	Polarised as $CO^{\delta-}$; no crystal face specificity

Method of investigation	Result	Conclusion
Electrical conductivity	A maximum occurs in the resistance, followed by a resistance rise above monomolecular coverage at low temperature;	At least two chemisorbed and one weakly bound state;
	geometric effect at 77 K but not at 273 K	immobile adsorption at 77 K but mobile adsorption at 273 K
Thermoelectric power	Different effects below and above monolayer coverage	At least two chemisorbed states
Hall effect	Hall voltage rises	Formation of covalent bond
Magnetic measurements	Magnetisation falls and is not proportional to the amount of CO adsorbed	Decrease in the number of d-band holes, covalent bonding, change of bond type with rising coverage
Low energy electron diffraction	Phase change which is independent of the crystal face occurs with rising coverage	No marked crystal face specificity, existence of two interconvertible states
Photoelectron spectroscopy	Formation of two discrete levels	Formation of well-defined bonds

In studying *Tables 9.1* and *9.2* it will be noticed that, in general, there is agreement between the results obtained by different methods of investigation for a particular system. Occasionally, however, one finds contradictory deductions, although only those works which are regarded as reliable have been tabulated. It may accordingly be concluded that diverging effects can even crop up for one and the same system. This could result from differening techniques of preparation which lead in turn to adsorbents of differing structure or simply of differing surface cleanliness.

Nevertheless, one may currently say with certainty that in the nickel/hydrogen system there are various species of chemisorbed and physisorbed hydrogen. At least two chemisorbed states are known, these being polarised negative. In addition, there is a physisorbed form which is molecular and is polarised positive. At high coverages yet another type of atomic hydrogen is adsorbed. This type seems to lower the work function. The negatively polarised, atomic hydrogen is predominantly attached with a covalent bond. At low temperature (< 90 K) adsorption is localised but at higher temperature (>145 K) adsorption becomes mobile.

In the nickel/carbon monoxide system one similarly identifies various species, two of which are chemisorbed. They may be distinguished in the structure of the adsorbed phase and convert into each other when the coverage is altered. At high coverage and low temperatures there is also a weakly bound form. Chemisorbed carbon monoxide is negatively polarised and the bonding is predominantly covalent. No dissociation of the molecule occurs below 300 K. Between 100 K and 150 K the localised adsorption becomes mobile.

Our remarks have been confined to two systems, but all the other systems which have been investigated can also be discussed in the same way. This has occurred to some extent in the literature [12,318]. It is not the aim of the present treatment, however, to give a detailed description of every individual system.

9.2. Summary from the adsorbate point of view

The Introduction to this book has already drawn attention to the way in which the type of bond found in adsorption spans a wide range. At one extreme there is pure van der Waals bonding, depending on dispersion forces, and at the other extreme there is normal chemical bonding. Two partners contribute to a bond, so the expected type of bond obviously cannot be considered in the absence of either the adsorbate or the adsorbent. Nevertheless, it is possible to achieve a separate classification for both adsorbates and adsorbents which turns out to have quite general validity.

Oxygen is an adsorbate which could certainly be classed as outspokenly 'aggressive'. The heat of adsorption for many metal/oxygen systems is almost the same as the heat of formation of the oxide; this means that the bond in chemisorbed oxygen is very similar to the bond in an oxide. Chemisorption complexes with oxygen therefore represent one of our limits, viz. the transition to chemical bonding. Numerous experiments have been directed at disclosing a difference between chemisorbed and chemically bonded oxygen. In the majority of cases this distinction has simply not been possible. The difference should be shown up best by comparing the structure of the chemisorption complex with the structure of the oxide. Yet the structural transition to oxide is frequently gradual. This may already be inferred from the quantity of 'adsorbed' oxygen. When the adsorbent is a transition metal, even very low oxygen pressures are found to effect 'oxidation' to the extent of several atom layers; see, for instance, reference 685. In all known cases of oxygen adsorption, oxygen is negatively polarised.

Halogens have been little studied as adsorbates but also tend to be 'aggressive' and electronegative.

Like oxygen, hydrogen is predominantly adsorbed in atomic form. Another similarity in the adsorption is the way the surface effect often overlaps with a volume effect. The latter is the occlusion of hydrogen and it occurs when atoms from the adsorbed phase are able to diffuse into the interior of the adsorbent. This is especially the case with systems such as Pd/H_2, Ti/H_2, Y/H_2 and Cr/H_2. Such 'getter action' of metals is popularly exploited in the production of vacua with getter pumps. For the moment, however, we shall confine our interest to genuine adsorption on the surface. In general, hydrogen is chemisorbed dissociatively, at least on the transition metals. In this condition it is negatively polarised and can occur as different species. At the higher coverages and low temperatures there is a molecular, positively polarised species. The bond between hydrogen and a metal is significantly weaker than the oxygen bond. As a result, it is frequently possible to desorb hydrogen at temperatures which are not too high. The number of adsorbents which adsorb hydrogen is far smaller than the number which chemisorb oxygen.

Judging by the character of its bulk compounds, one might well expect nitrogen to be relatively strongly chemisorbed too. This surmise is only partially supported by experiment. Nitrogen is actually chemisorbed quite strongly on those adsorbents which take up nitrogen by dissociating the molecule. But dissociation has such a high energy requirement that on numerous adsorbents nitrogen is only physisorbed as molecules.

Turning to carbon monoxide, we find that these molecules are much more active in chemisorption than nitrogen molecules. This is due to the favourable electronic configuration of CO, which is such as to allow chemisorption to proceed in the molecular condition. Next to oxygen, CO is the most strongly chemisorbed of the simple gases. It can rarely be desorbed without raising the adsorbent to relatively high temperatures, and because of its universal occurrence it is often responsible for the difficulty one experiences in achieving extreme vacua and perfectly clean adsorbent surfaces. Characteristic of the adsorption of carbon monoxide is the fact that CO can be bonded as different species. These species are distinguished by differing structures in the adsorbed phase. In the majority of cases CO is attached via the C atom. Adsorption via the oxygen atom has only been proposed in a few cases, an example being afforded by the bonding on copper.

Carbon dioxide also bonds very strongly to numerous adsorbents.

The counterpart to highly reactive oxygen is given by the rare gases. Their adsorptive ability is just as outspokenly weak as one might be led to expect from their marked chemical inactivity, and as an example of physisorption they furnish the standard case.

Many substances become fundamentally altered as a result of adsorption. The water molecule is only adsorbed as such on many adsorbents at low temperature. At higher temperatures, often lying below room temperature, H_2O decomposes to give H and OH radicals which then proceed to interact with the adsorbent [644,645]. The same goes for the ammonia molecule [253].

For saturated hydrocarbons such as methane [640,641] one observes weak physisorption at low temperatures, hardly any measurable uptake at intermediate temperatures, and chemisorption with decomposition of the molecule at higher temperatures.

Similar decomposition is found to occur when unsaturated hydrocarbons or aromatics such as benzene [643] are adsorbed on metals. In these cases, only one of the decomposition products is often left on the surface at higher coverages. The other product (usually hydrogen) is displaced from the surface, and it can be picked up in the gas phase mass spectrometrically.

9.3. Summary from the adsorbent point of view

In classifying adsorbents, it is convenient in the first instance to divide them into: metals; semiconducting elements; oxides and sulphides; and ionic crystals.

Among the metals, the transition metals show the largest tendency to attach polar and non-polar adsorbates to their surfaces with a relatively strong bond. The behaviour of Ti, Cr, Mn, Fe, Co, Ni, Y, Zr, Mo, Rh, Pd, Ta, W and, to a certain extent, Pt towards the adsorption of hydrogen and carbon monoxide is thus very similar.

Considering the resemblance between the transition metals and Cu, Ag and Au, it is surprising that the Group 1B metals possess entirely different adsorptive properties. These three metals come directly after the transition metals in the periodic table and they possess the same crystal packing as their preceding elements. The lattice constants are also very similar. If hydrogen can still be induced to chemisorb in very small amounts on Cu, this is no longer the case with Ag and Au. And carbon monoxide, which raises the work function on transition metals, causes a lowering of work function on Cu, Ag and Au. CO is therefore polarised on these metals in the opposite direction to that in which it is polarised on transition metals. From these examples one recognises that it cannot only be the geometric factor which is responsible for what happens in adsorption; rather the band structure of the adsorbent must play a decisive role.

The metals W, Ta, Mo, Ti and Zr chemisorb nitrogen very strongly. Fe and Ni, however, only take up nitrogen at low temperatures and that uptake is in a molecular, physisorbed form. The ability to bond nitrogen in atomic form could be determined here by whether or not the adsorbent is capable of forming a triple bond with the adsorbate.

Metals without d-band vacancies, such as the elements following Cu, Ag and Au, have been but little investigated. It is known, nevertheless, that they only show a slight tendency to chemisorb gases and when they do, it is to form surface compounds with aggressive adsorbates.

Semiconducting elements such as Ge or Si have been studied intensively because of their great technical importance. They exhibit adsorption tendencies which lie between those of the d- and the sp-metals.

In the case of oxide and sulphide adsorbents, a chemical reaction often follows the actual adsorption step. One gets, for example

$$CO_2 \longrightarrow CO_3^{2-}$$

or

$$H \longrightarrow OH^-$$

These 'chemical' reactions on the surface depend very much on the pretreatment of the adsorbents and they are very much influenced by the surroundings. Aluminium oxide surfaces, for instance, show either neutral or basic properties depending on the acid with which they are treated. Clearly this is crucial in determining the adsorptive characteristics.

Table 9.3 Summary of adsorption systems

Adsorbent	Adsorbate				
	O_2	CO	H_2	N_2	CO_2
Li	+	−	−	−	
Be	+	−	−	−	
B	+	+	+	+	
C	+	−	−	−	
Na	+	−	−	−	
Mg	+	−	−	−	
Al	+	+	−	−	
Si	+	−	+	−	+
K	+	−	−	−	
Ca	+	+	+	+	+
Ti	+	+	+	+	+
V	+	+	+		
Cr	+	+	+	+	+
Mn	+	+	+	+	+
Fe	+	+	+	−	+
Co	+	+	+	−	+
Ni	+	+	+	−	+
Cu	+	−	−	−	
Zn	+	−	−	−	−
Ga	+	−	−	−	
Ge	+	−	+	−	+
Rb	+	−	−	−	
Sr	+	+	+	+	+
Y	+	+	+		
Zr	+	+	+	+	+
Nb	+	+	+	+	+
Mo	+	+	+	+	+
Ru			+		
Rh	+	+	+	−	−
Pd	+	+	+	−	−
Ag	+	−	−	−	
Cd	+	−	−	−	
In	+	−	−	−	
Sn	+	−	−	−	
Cs	+	−	−	−	
Ba	+	+	+	+	+
La	+	+	+	+	+
Hf			+		
Ta	+	+	+	+	+
W	+	+	+	+	+
Re	+	+	+	+	+
Os	+				
Ir	+	+	+	−	−
Pt	+	+	+	−	−
Au	−	−	−	−	
Hg	+	−	−	−	
Tl	+	−	−	−	
Pb	+	−	−	−	
Th			+		

It is well known that solid oxides and sulphides frequently deviate from the ideal stoichiometric composition. The partial pressure of oxygen or sulphur in the gas phase has an effect on these adsorbents. It is therefore hardly surprising that these solids show different adsorptive properties depending on the preparation and outgassing procedures adopted. Many systems have been investigated, particularly systems in which the adsorbent is NiO or ZnO. Nevertheless agreement has still not been reached regarding the mechanism of adsorption; see, for instance, reference 307.

In addition to metal and oxide adsorbents, there is a type of adsorbent which is formed by dispersing metal as a thin layer on a semi-conducting oxide support or vice versa. Schwab and co-workers [601, 602] have studied the properties of these binary catalyst systems. They reached the conclusion that the properties of a semiconductor can 'get out' through the metal or that metallic properties can 'get out' through the semiconductor. Systematic adsorption studies of these interesting systems have yet to be made.

9.4.   Specificity in chemisorption

If we waive any consideration of the finer details and simply enquire whether there is chemisorption or not, then it is possible to construct the tabular summary shown. In *Table 9.3*, which is based on the compilation of Hayward [311], + denotes chemisorption and – denotes no chemisorption. The systems listed are restricted to those which have been intensively studied and which are of technical or theoretical interest.

REFERENCES

1. ABRAGAM, A., *The Principles of Nuclear Magnetism* (Clarendon Press, Oxford, 1961)
2. ADAMS, R.O. and DONALDSON, E.E., *J. Chem. Phys.*, **42**, 770 (1965)
3. AHRENS-BOTZONG, R., HESS, P. and SCHÄFER, K., *Ber. Bunsenges. Physik. Chem.*, **77**, 1157 (1973)
4. ALEXANDER, C.S. and PRITCHARD, J., *J. Chem. Soc. Faraday I*, **68**, 202 (1972)
5. AMENOMIYA, Y. and CVETANOVIC, R.J., *J. Phys. Chem.*, **67**, 144 (1963)
6. AMENOMIYA, Y. and CVETANOVIC, R.J., *J. Phys. Chem.*, **67**, 2046 (1963)
7. AMENOMIYA, Y. and CVETANOVIC, R.J., *J. Phys. Chem.*, **67**, 2705 (1963)
8. AMENOMIYA, Y. and CVETANOVIC, R.J., *J. Phys. Chem.*, **68**, 52 (1964)
9. ANDERSON, J. and ESTRUP, P.J., *J. Chem. Phys.*, **46**, 563 (1967)
10. ANDERSON, J. and ESTRUP, P.J., *Surface Sci.*, **9**, 463 (1968)
11. ANDERSON, J.C. (Editor), *The Use of Thin Films in Physical Investigations* (Academic Press, London, 1966)
12. ANDERSON, J.R. (Editor), *Chemisorption and Reactions on Metallic Films*, Vols. 1 and 2 (Academic Press, London, 1971)
13. ANDERSON, J.R. and BAKER, B.G., *J. Phys. Chem.*, **66**, 482 (1962)
14. ANDERSON, J.S., FAULKNER, E.A. and KLEMPERER, D.F., *Australian J. Physics*, **12**, 469 (1959)
15. ANDERSON, J.S. and KLEMPERER, D.F., *Proc. Roy. Soc. (London)*, **A 258**, 350 (1960)
16. ANDREEV, A., *C.R. Acad. Bulg. Sci.*, **20**, 1309 (1967)
17. ANDREEV, A.A. and SELWOOD, P.W., *J. Catalysis*, **8**, 98 (1967)
18. ANDREEV, A.A. and SELWOOD, P.W., *J. Catalysis*, **8**, 375 (1967)
19. ANDREEV, A.A. and SELWOOD, P.W., *J. Catalysis*, **11**, 261 (1968)
19a. ANDREW, E.R., in *Progress in NMR Spectroscopy* (ed. J.W. Emsley, J. Feeney and L.H. Sutcliffe), Vol.8, p.1 (Pergamon Press, Oxford, 1972)
20. ANDREW, R., RILEY, M., ARMOUR, D.G. and CARTER, G., *Vacuum*, **22**, 587 (1972)
21. ANTONINI, J.F. and HOCHSTRASSER, G., *Surface Sci.*, **32**, 665 (1972)
22. ASTON, J.G., in *The Solid-Gas Interface* (ed. E.A. Flood), Vol. 2, p.895 (Marcel Dekker, New York, 1967)
23. ATKINSON, R. and LISSBERGER, P.H., *Thin Solid Films*, **17**, 207 (1973)

24. ATKINSON, S.J., BRUNDLE, C.R. and ROBERTS, M.W., *J. Electron Spectrosc.*, **2**, 105 (1973)

25. ATKINSON, S.J., BRUNDLE, C.R. and ROBERTS, M.W., Discussion of the Faraday Division of the Chemical Society, No.58, p.62, *Photo-Effects in Adsorbed Species*, Cambridge (1974)

26. BADHARA, N.M., BUCKMAN, A.B. and HALL, A.C. (Editors), Proceedings of the Symposium on Recent Developments in Ellipsometry, *Surface Sci.*, **16**, (1969)

27. BADIA, M., *Thin Solid Films*, **13**, 329 (1972)

28. BAGG, J. and TOMPKINS, F.C., *Trans. Faraday Soc.*, **51**, 1071 (1955)

29. BAKER, F.S., BRADSHAW, A.M., PRITCHARD, J. and SYKES, K.W., *Surface Sci.*, **12**, 426 (1968)

30. BAKER, J.M. and EASTMAN, D.E., *J. Vacuum Sci. Technol.*, **10**, 223 (1973)

31. BASSETT, D.W., *Trans. Faraday Soc.*, **64**, 489 (1968)

32. BASTL, Z., *Collect. Czech. Chem. Commun.*, **33**, 4133 (1968)

33. BASTL, Z., *Thin Solid Films*, **10**, 311, (1972)

34. BAUER, E., *Surface Sci.*, **5**, 152 (1966)

35. BAUER, E., *Surface Sci.*, **7**, 351 (1967)

36. BAUER, E., *Z. Metallkunde*, **63**, 437 (1972)

37. BAUER, H.J., BLECHSCHMIDT, D. and VON HELLERMANN, M., *Surface Sci.*, **30**, 701 (1972)

38. BECKER, G.E. and HAGSTRUM, H.D., *J. Vacuum Sci. Technol.*, **10**, 31 (1973)

39. BECKER, J.A., *Advan. Catal.*, **7**, 136 (1955)

40. BECKERT, D., *Physics Lett.*, **25a**, 502 (1967)

41. BECKMANN, K.H., *Angew. Chem.*, **80**, 213 (1968)

42. BEEBE, R.A., *Trans. Faraday Soc.*, **28**, 761 (1932)

43. BEECK, O., *Advan. Catal.*, **2**, 182 (1950)

44. BEECK, O., COLE, W.A. and WHEELER, A., *Disc. Faraday Soc.*, **8**, 314 (1950)

45. BEEZHOLD, W., *Thin Solid Films*, **19**, 387 (1973)

46. BENNDORF, C. and THIEME, F., *Z. Physik. Chem. (Frankfurt/M.)*, **87**, 40 (1973)

47. BENNETT, M.J. and TOMPKINS, F.C., *Trans. Faraday Soc.*, **53**, 185 (1957)

48. BENNET, W.H., *Phys. Rev.*, **74**, 1222 (1948)

49. BENNINGHOVEN, A., *Phys. Status Solidi*, **34**, K169 (1969)

50. BENNINGHOVEN, A., *Z. Physik*, **230**, 403 (1970)

51. BENNINGHOVEN, A., *Surface Sci.*, **35**, 427 (1973)

52. BENNINGHOVEN, A. and LOEBACH, E., *Rev. Sci. Instrum.*, **42**, 49 (1971)

53. BENNINGHOVEN, A., LOEBACH, E., PLOG, C. and TRIETZ, N., *Surface Sci.*, **39**, 397 (1973)

54. BENNINGHOVEN, A. and MÜLLER, A., *Surface Sci.*, **39**, 416 (1973)

55. BENNINGHOVEN, A. and STORP, S., *Appl. Phys. Lett.*, **22**, 170 (1973)

56. BENNINGHOVEN, A. and WIEDERMANN, L., *Surface Sci.*, **41**, 483 (1974)

57. BERRY, R.W., HALL, P.M. and HARRIS, M.T., *Thin Film Technology* (Van Nostrand, Princeton, N.J., 1968)

58. BERSOHN, M. and BAIRD, J.C., *An Introduction to Electron Paramagnetic Resonance* (Benjamin, New York, 1966)

59. BLIZNAKOV, G.M., LAZAROV, D.L. and MANEV, S.G., *C.R. Acad. Bulg. Sci.*, **25**, 1213 (1972)

60. BLJUMENFELD, L.A., WOJEWODSKI, W.W. and SEMJONOW, A.G., *Die Anwendung der paramagnetischen Elektronenresonanz in der Chemie* (Akademische Verlagsgesellschaft Geest und Portig, Leipzig, 1966)

61. BLOCK, J., *Z. Physik. Chem. (Frankfurt/M.)*, **39**, 169 (1963)

62. BLOYAERT, F., D'OR, L. and MIGNOLET, J., *6e Réunion de la Société de Chimie Physique 1956*, p.274

63. BLYHOLDER, G., *J. Chem. Phys.*, **36**, 2036 (1962)

64. BLYHOLDER, G., *J. Phys. Chem.*, **68**, 2772 (1964)

65. BLYHOLDER, G., in *Proc. 3rd Intern. Congr. Catalysis* (ed. W.M.H. Sachtler, G.C.A. Schuit and P. Zwietering), p.657 (North-Holland, Amsterdam, 1965)

66. BLYHOLDER, G. and ALLEN, M.C., *J. Phys. Chem.*, **69**, 3998 (1965)

67. BLYHOLDER, G. and ALLEN, M.C., *J. Amer. Chem. Soc.*, **91**, 3158 (1969)

68. BLYHOLDER, G. and COULSON, C.A., *Trans. Faraday Soc.*, **63**, 1782 (1967)

69. BLYHOLDER, G. and NEFF, L.D., *J. Phys. Chem.*, **66**, 1464 (1962)

70. BLYHOLDER, G. and RICHARDSON, E.A., *J. Phys. Chem.*, **66**, 2597 (1962)

71. BLYHOLDER, G. and RICHARDSON, E.A., *J. Phys. Chem.*, **68**, 3882 (1964)

72. BOND, G.C., *Catalysis by Metals* (Academic Press, London, 1962)

73. BOND, G.C., *Disc. Faraday Soc.*, **41**, 200 (1966)

74. BOND, G.C., *Platinum Metals Rev.*, **10**, 87 (1966)

75. BONZEL, H.P., *Surface Sci.*, **27**, 387 (1971)

76. BOOTSMA, G.A. and MEYER, F., *Surface Sci.*, **13**, 110 (1969)

77. BOOTSMA, G.A. and MEYER, F., *Surface Sci.*, **14**, 52 (1969)

78. BOOTSMA, G.A. and MEYER, F., *Surface Sci.*, **18**, 123 (1969)

79. BORELLO, E., ZECCHINA, A. and MORTERRA, C., *J. Phys. Chem.*, **71**, 2938 (1967)

80. BORELLO, E., ZECCHINA, A., MORTERRA, C. and GHIOTTI, G., *J. Phys. Chem.*, **71**, 2945 (1967)

81. BORESKOV, G.K. and VASSILEVICH, A.A., *Dokl. Akad. Nauk SSSR*, **127**, 1033 (1959)

82. BORESKOV, G.K. and VASSILEVICH, A.A., in *Actes du Deuxième Congrès International de Catalyse, Paris, 1960*, Vol.1, p.1094 (Editions Technip, Paris, 1961)

83. BORN, M., *Optik, Ein Lehrbuch der Elektromagnetischen Lichttheorie* (Springer-Verlag, Berlin, 1945)

84. BORN, M. and WOLF, E., *Principles of Optics*, 5th edn (Pergamon Press, Oxford, 1975)

85. BOYES, E.D. and SOUTHON, M.J., *Vacuum*, **22**, 447 (1972)
86. BOYES, E.D., TURNER, P.J. and SOUTHON, M.J., in *Proc. 25th Anniversay Meeting of the Electron Microscopy and Analysis Group of the Institute of Physics, Cambridge, 1971* (ed. W.C. Nixon), p.256 (Institute of Physics, London, 1971)
87. BRADSHAW, A.M., in *Specialist Periodical Reports, Surface and Defect Properties of Solids* (ed. M.W. Roberts and J.M. Thomas), Vol.3, p.153 (The Chemical Society, London, 1974)
88. BRADSHAW, A.M., CEDERBAUM, L. and DOMCKE, W., in *Structure and Bonding* (ed. J.D. Dunitz *et al.*), Vol.24, p.133 (Springer-Verlag, Berlin, 1975)
89. BRADSHAW, A.M. and MENZEL, D., *Phys. Status Solidi (b)*, **56**, 135 (1973)
90. BRADSHAW, A.M. and PRITCHARD, J., *Surface Sci.*, **17**, 372 (1969)
91. BRADSHAW, A.M. and PRITCHARD, J., *Proc. Roy. Soc. (London)*, **A 316**, 169 (1970)
92. BRADSHAW, A.M., PRITCHARD, J. and SIMS, M.L., *Chem. Commun.*, 1519 (1968)
93. BRADSHAW, A.M. and VIERLE, O., *Ber. Bunsenges. Physik. Chem.*, **74**, 630 (1970)
94. BRENNAN, D., *Disc. Faraday Soc.*, **41**, 106 (1966)
95. BRENNAN, D. and GRAHAM, M.J., *Phil. Trans. Roy. Soc. (London)*, *Ser. A*, **258**, 325 (1965)
96. BRENNAN, D., GRAHAM, M.J. and HAYES, F.H., *Nature*, **199**, 1152 (1963)
97. BRENNAN, D. and HAYES, F.H., *Trans. Faraday Soc.*, **60**, 589 (1964)
98. BRENNAN, D. and HAYES, F.H., *Phil. Trans. Roy. Soc. (London)*, *Ser. A*, **258**, 347 (1965)
99. BRENNAN, D., HAYWARD, D.O. and TRAPNELL, B.M.W., *Proc. Roy. Soc. (London)*, **A 256**, 81 (1960)
100. BRENNAN, D. and JACKSON, J.M., *Proc. Chem. Soc. (London)*, 375 (1963)
101. BRÖCKER, F.J. and WEDLER, G., *Disc. Faraday Soc.*, **41**, 87 (1966)
102. BRONGERSMA, H.H. and MUL, P.M., *Surface Sci.*, **35**, 393 (1973)
103. BRUNAUER, S., EMMETT, P.H. and TELLER, E., *J. Amer. Chem. Soc.*, **60**, 309 (1938)
104. BRUNDLE, C.R., in *Specialist Periodical Report, Surface and Defect Properties of Solids* (ed. M.W. Roberts and J.M. Thomas), Vol.1, p.171 (The Chemical Society, London, 1972)
105. BRUNDLE, C.R. and ROBERTS, M.W., *Chem. Phys. Lett.*, **18**, 380 (1973)
106. BRUNDLE, C.R., ROBERTS, M.W., LATHAM, D. and YATES, K., *J. Electron Spectrosc.*, **3**, 241, (1974)
107. BURGE, D.K. and O'HANDLEY, R.C., *Surface Sci.*, **37**, 548 (1973)
108. BURR, A.F., *Advan. X-ray Anal.*, **13**, 426 (1973)
109. BUTCHER, E.C., DYER, A.J. and GILBERT, N.E., *J. Phys. D, Appl. Phys.*, **1**, 1674 (1968)

110. CALVET, E. and PRAT, H., *Recent Progress in Microcalorimetry* (Pergamon Press, Oxford, 1963)
111. CANNON, W.A., *Nature,* **197,** 1000 (1963)
112. CASTAING, R. and SLODZIAN, G., *J. Microscopie,* **1,** 395 (1962)
113. CERNÝ, S., *Disc. Faraday Soc.,* **41,** 102 (1966)
114. CHUANG, C. Chang, *Surface Sci.,* **25,** 53 (1971)
115. CHESTERS, M.A., HUSSAIN, M. and PRITCHARD, J., *Surface Sci.,* **35,** 161 (1973)
116. CHESTERS, M.A. and PRITCHARD, J., *Surface Sci.,* **28,** 460 (1971)
117. CHESTERS, M.A., PRITCHARD, J. and SIMS, M.L., *Chem. Commun.,* 1454 (1970)
118. CHON, H. and PRATER, C.D., *Disc. Faraday Soc.,* **41,** 380 (1966)
119. CHOPRA, K.L. and BOBB, L.C., in *Single Crystal Films* (ed. M. Francombe and H. Sato), p.373 (Pergamon Press, Oxford, 1964)
120. CHRISTMANN, K., ERTL, G. and SCHOBER, O., *Surface Sci.,* **40,** 61 (1973)
121. CHRISTMANN, K., SCHOBER, O., ERTL, G. and NEUMANN, M., *J. Chem. Phys.,* **60,** 4528 (1974)
122. CLARKE, J.K.A., FARREN, G. and RUBALCAVA, H.E., *J. Phys. Chem.,* **71,** 2376 (1967)
123. CONRAD, H., ERTL, G., KÜPPERS, J. and LATTA, E.E., Discussion of the Faraday Division of the Chemical Society, No.58, p.116 *Photo-Effects in Adsorbed Species,* Cambridge (1974)
124. CONWAY, B.E., in *The Solid-Gas Interface* (ed. E.A. Flood), Vol.2, p.714 (Marcel Dekker, New York, 1967)
125. CROSSLAND, W.A. and PRITCHARD, J., *Surface Sci.,* **2,** 217 (1964)
126. CROWELL, C.R., KAO, T.W., ANDERSON, C.L. and RIDEOUT, V.L., *Surface Sci.,* **32,** 591 (1972)
127. CULVER, R., PRITCHARD, J. and TOMPKINS, F.C., in *Proc. 2nd Intern. Congr. Surface Activity* (ed. J.H. Schulman), Vol.2, p.243 (Butterworths, London, 1957)
128. CULVER, R., PRITCHARD, J. and TOMPKINS, F.C., *Z. Elektrochem., Ber. Bunsenges. Physik. Chem.,* **63,** 741 (1959)
129. CULVER, R.V. and TOMPKINS, F.C., *Advan. Catal.,* **11,** 67 (1959)
130. CVETANOVIC, R.J. and AMENOMIYA, Y., *Advan. Catal.,* **17,** 103 (1967)
131. DAVISSON, C.J. and GERMER, L.H., *Phys. Rev.,* **30,** 705 (1927)
132. DE BOER, J.H., *Electron Emission and Adsorption Phenomena* (Cambridge University Press, Cambridge, 1935)
133. DE BOER, J.H., *The Dynamical Character of Adsorption,* 2nd edn (Clarendon Press, Oxford, 1968)
134. DE BOER, J.H. and KRUYER, S., *Proc. Kon. Nederl. Akad. Wetensch.,* **B55,** 451 (1952)
135. DE BOER, J.H. and KRUYER, S., *Proc. Kon. Nederl. Akad. Wetensch.,* **B56,** 67 (1953)

136. DE BOER, J.H. and KRUYER, S., *Proc. Kon. Nederl. Akad. Wetensch.*
      B56, 236 (1953)
137. DE BOER, J.H. and KRUYER, S., *Proc. Kon. Nederl. Akad. Wetensch.*
      B56, 415 (1953)
138. DE BOER, J.H. and KRUYER, S., *Proc. Kon. Nederl. Akad. Wetensch.*
      B57, 92 (1954)
139. DE BOER, J.H. and KRUYER, S., *Proc. Kon. Nederl. Akad. Wetensch.*
      B58, 61 (1955)
140. DEININGER, D., GESCHKE, D. and HOFFMANN, W-D., *Z. Physik. Chem*
      (Leipzig), **255**, 273 (1974)
141. DEININGER, D. and MICHEL, D., *Wiss. Z. Karl-Marx-Univ. Leipzig,
      Math.-Naturwiss. R.*, **22**, 551 (1973)
142. DELCHAR, T., EBERHAGEN, A. and TOMPKINS, F.C., *J. Sci. Instrum.*,
      40, 105 (1963)
143. DELCHAR, T.A. and EHRLICH, G., *J. Chem. Phys.*, **42**, 2686 (1965)
144. DELCHAR, T.A. and TOMPKINS, F.C., *Proc. Roy. Soc. (London)*,
      A 300, 141 (1967)
145. DELL, R.M., KLEMPERER, D.F. and STONE, F.S., *J. Phys. Chem.*,
      60, 1586 (1956)
146. DEN BESTEN, I.E., FOX, P.G. and SELWOOD, P.W., *J. Phys. Chem.*,
      66, 450 (1962)
147. DEV, B. and BRINKMAN, H., *Ned. Tijdschr. Vacuumtechniek*, **8**,
      176 (1970)
148. DIELS, K. and JAECKEL, R., *Leybold Vakuum-Taschenbuch* (Springer-
      Verlag, Berlin, 1958)
149. DIETZ, R.E. and SELWOOD, P.W., *J. Chem. Phys.*, **35**, 270 (1961)
150. DIGNAM, M.J. and MOSKOVITS, M., *J. Chem. Soc., Faraday II*, **69**,
      56 (1973)
151. DIGNAM, M.J. and MOSKOVITS, M., *J. Chem. Soc., Faraday II*, **69**,
      65 (1973)
152. DIGNAM, M.J., MOSKOVITS, M. and STOBIE, R.W., *Trans. Faraday
      Soc.*, **67**, 3306 (1971)
153. DOMKE, M., JÄHNIG, G. and DRECHSLER, M., *Surface Sci.*, **42**,
      389 (1974)
154. DORGELO, G.J.H. and SACHTLER, M.W.H., *Naturwissenschaften*, **46**,
      576 (1959)
155. DORN, R., LUTH, H. and IBACH, H., *Surface Sci.*, **42**, 583 (1974)
156. DOWDEN, D.A., in *Coloquio Sobre Quimica Fisica de Procesos en
      Superficies Solidas*, p.177 (Liberia Cientifica Medinacel, Madrid,
      1965)
157. DUNKEN, H.H., *Z. Physik. Chem. (Leipzig)*, **246**, 329 (1971)
158. DUNKEN, H.H., FRITSCHE, H.G., KADURA, P., KÜNNE, L.D., MÜLLER,
      H. and OPITZ, C., *Z. Chem.*, **12**, 433 (1972)
159. DUNKEN, H. and HOBERT, H., *Z. Chem.*, **3**, 398 (1963)
160. DUNKEN, H.H. and OPITZ, C., *Z. Physik. Chem. (Frankfurt/M.)*, **60**,
      25 (1968)

161. DUNKEN, H.H. and OPITZ, C., *Z. Physik. Chem. (Leipzig)*, **239**, 161 (1968)

162. DUSHMAN, S. and LAFFERTY, J.M., *Scientific Foundations of Vacuum Technique*, 2nd edn (Wiley, New York, 1962)

163. EASTMAN, D.E. and CASHION, J.K., *Phys. Rev. Lett.*, **24**, 310 (1970)

164. EASTMAN, D.E. and CASHION, J.K., *Phys. Rev. Lett.*, **27**, 1520 (1971)

165. EASTMAN, D.E., CASHION, J.K. and SWITENDICK, A.C., *Phys. Rev. Lett.*, **27**, 35 (1971)

166. EBERHAGEN, A., *Fortschr. Physik*, **8**, 245 (1960)

167. EHRLICH, G., *J. Chem. Phys.*, **23**, 1543 (1955)

168. EHRLICH, G., *J. Appl. Phys.*, **32**, 4 (1961)

169. EHRLICH, G., *J. Chem. Phys.*, **34**, 29 (1961)

170. EHRLICH, G., *J. Chem. Phys.*, **34**, 39 (1961)

171. EHRLICH, G., *Disc. Faraday Soc.*, **41**, 7 (1966)

172. EHRLICH, G., *Ann. Rev. Phys. Chem.*, **17**, 295 (1966)

173. EISCHENS, R.P., *Z. Elektrochem., Ber. Busenges. Physik. Chem.*, **60**, 782 (1956)

174. EISCHENS, R.P., FRANCIS, S.A. and PLISKIN, W.A., *J. Phys. Chem.*, **60**, 194 (1956)

175. EISCHENS, R.P. and JACKNOW, J., in *Proc. 3rd Intern. Congr. Catalysis* (ed. W.M.H. Sachtler, G.C.A. Schuit and P. Zwietering), p.627 (North-Holland, Amsterdam, 1965)

176. EISCHENS, R.P. and PLISKIN, W.A., *Advan. Catal.*, **9**, 662 (1957)

177. EISCHENS, R.P. and PLISKIN, W.A., *Advan. Catal.*, **10**, 2 (1958)

178. EISCHENS, R.P., PLISKIN, W.A. and FRANCIS, S.A., *J. Chem. Phys.*, **22**, 1786 (1954)

179. ELEY, D.D., *Disc. Faraday Soc.*, **8**, 34 (1950)

180. ELEY, D.D., *Z. Elektrochem., Ber. Bunsenges. Physik. Chem.*, **60**, 797 (1956)

181. ELEY, D.D., MORAN, D.M. and ROCHESTER, C.H., *Trans. Faraday Soc.*, **64**, 2168 (1968)

182. ELEY, D.D. and PETRO, J., *Nature*, **209**, 501 (1966)

183. EMMETT, P.H. and CINES, M.R., *J. Phys. Chem.*, **51**, 1248 (1947)

184. EMMETT, P.H. and DE WITT, T.W., *J. Amer. Chem. Soc.*, **65**, 1253 (1943)

185. ERKELENS, J. and LIEFKENS, Th.J., *J. Catalysis*, **8**, 36 (1967)

186. ERMRICH, W., *Nuovo Cimento Suppl.*, **5**, 582 (1967)

187. ERMRICH, W. and VAN OOSTROM, A., *Solid State Commun.*, **5**, 471 (1967)

188. ERTL, G., *Surface Sci.*, **6**, 208 (1967)

189. ERTL, G., *Surface Sci.*, **7**, 309 (1967)

190. ERTL, G., *Ber. Bunsenges. Physik. Chem.*, **75**, 967 (1971)

191. ERTL, G. and GIOVANELLI, T., *Ber. Bunsenges. Physik. Chem.*, **72**, 74 (1968)

192. ERTL, G. and KÜPPERS, J., *Ber. Bunsenges. Physik. Chem.*, **75**, 1017 (1971)

193. ERTL, G. and KÜPPERS, J., *Surface Sci.*, **24**, 104 (1971)

208 References

194. ERTL, G. and NEUMANN, M., *Z. Naturforsch.*, **27a**, 1607 (1972)
195. ERTL, G. and WANDELT, K., *Phys. Rev. Lett.*, **29**, 218 (1972)
196. ERTL, G. and WANDELT, K., *Z. Naturforsch.*, **29a**, 768 (1974)
197. ESCHBACH, H.L., *Praktikum der Hochvakuumtechnik* (Akademische Verlagsgesellschaft Geest und Portig, Leipzig, 1962)
198. ESPE, W., *Materials of High Vacuum Technology*, Vol.1, *Metals and Metalloids* (Pergamon Press, Oxford, 1966)
199. ESPE, W., *Materials of High Vacuum Technology*, Vol.2, *Silicates and Oxides* (Pergamon Press, Oxford, 1968)
200. ESTRUP, P.J. and ANDERSON, J., *Surface Sci.*, **8**, 101 (1967)
201. ESTRUP, P.J. and McRAE, E.G., *Surface Sci.*, **25**, 1 (1971)
202. EVANS, C.A. Jr., *Anal. Chem.*, **44**, 67A (1972)
203. EVANS, C.A. Jr., *Thin Solid Films*, **19**, 11 (1973)
204. EVERETT, D.H., *Trans. Faraday Soc.*, **46**, 453 (1950)
205. EVERETT, D.H., *Trans. Faraday Soc.*, **46**, 942 (1950)
206. EVERETT, D.H., *Trans. Faraday Soc.*, **46**, 957 (1950)
207. EVERETT, D.H., *Proc. Chem.Soc. (London)*, 38 (1957)
208. EVERETT, D.H. and YOUNG, D.M., *Trans. Faraday Soc.*, **48**, 1164 (1952)
209. FABEL, G.W., COX, S.M. and LICHTMAN, D., *Surface Sci.*, **40**, 571 (1973)
210. FAHRENFORT, J. and HAZEBROEK, H.F., *Z. Physik. Chem. (Frankfurt/M.)*, **20**, 105 (1959)
211. FARNSWORTH, H.E., *J. Phys. Chem.*, **74**, 2912 (1970)
212. FARNSWORTH, H.E., in *Grundprobleme der Physik Dünner Schichten* (ed. R.Niedermayer and H. Mayer), p.6 (Vandenhoeck and Ruprecht, Göttingen, 1966)
213. FARNSWORTH, H.E., SCHLIER, R.E., GEORGE, T.H. and BURGER, R.M. *J. Appl. Phys.*, **29**, 1150 (1958)
214. FAUCHER, I.A., McMAMIS, G.M. and TRURNIT, H.J., *J. Opt. Soc. Amer.*, **48**, 51 (1958)
215. FEHLNER, F.P., in *1965 Trans. 3rd Intern. Vacuum Congr.* (ed. H. Adam), Vol.2, Part 3, p.691 (Pergamon Press, Oxford, 1967)
216. FENZKE, D., *Physics Lett.*, **13**, 215 (1964)
217. FEUERBACHER, B. and FITTON, B., *Phys. Rev. Lett.*, **29**, 786 (197?
218. FEUERBACHER, B. and FITTON, B., *Phys. Rev. B.*, **8**, 4890 (1973)
219. FIERMANS, L. and VENNIK, J., *Surface Sci.*, **35**, 42 (1973)
220. FLECHSIG, W., *Z. Physik*, **162**, 570 (1961)
221. FLECHSIG, W., *Z. Physik*, **170**, 176 (1962)
222. FLECHSIG, W., *Z. Physik*, **176**, 380 (1963)
223. FLECHSIG, W., *Z. Physik*, **191**, 423 (1966)
224. FLECHSIG, W., *Z. Physik*, **200**, 304, (1967)
225. FLOOD, E.A. (Editor), *The Solid-Gas Interface*, Vol.1 (Marcel Dekker, New York, 1967)
226. FLOOD, E.A. (Editor), *The Solid-Gas Interface*, Vol.2 (Marcel Dekker, New York, 1967)
227. FLUCK, E., *Die Kernmagnetische Resonanz und ihre Anwendung in der Anorganischen Chemie* (Springer-Verlag, Berlin, 1963)

228. FOLMAN, M. and YATES, D.J.C., *Proc. Roy. Soc. (London)*, **A 246**, 32 (1958)

229. FOLMAN, M. and YATES, D.J.C., *Trans. Faraday Soc.*, **54**, 1684 (1958)

230. FOLMAN, M. and YATES, D.J.C., *J. Phys. Chem.*, **63**, 183 (1959)

231. FORSTMANN, F. and HEINE, V., *Phys. Rev. Lett.*, **24**, 1419 (1970)

232. FORSTMANN, F. and PENDRY, J.B., *Z. Physik*, **235**, 69 (1970)

233. FORSTMANN, F. and PENDRY, J.B., *Z. Physik*, **235**, 75 (1970)

234. FOWLER, R.H., *Phys. Rev.*, **38**, 45 (1931)

235. FOWLER, R.H., *Proc. Cambridge Phil. Soc.*, **31**, 260 (1935)

236. FOWLER, R.H. and NORDHEIM, L., *Proc. Roy. Soc. (London)*, **A 119**, 173 (1928)

237. FRANCIS, S.A. and ELLISON, A.H., *J. Opt. Soc. Amer.*, **49**, 131 (1959)

238. FRANCOMBE, M.H. and SATO, H. (Editors), *Single Crystal Films* (Pergamon Press, Oxford, 1964)

239. FRASER, W.A., FLORIO, J.V., DELGASS, W.N. and ROBERTSON, W.D., *Surface Sci.*, **36**, 661 (1973)

240. FREUNDLICH, H., *Colloid and Capillary Chemistry* (Methuen, London, 1926)

241. FRICKE, K., Dissertation, Technische Universität Hannover (1966)

242. FRITSCHE, L. and SEUFERT, H., *Z. Naturforsch.*, **18a**, 1013 (1963)

243. FROST, A.A. and PEARSON, R.G., *Kinetics and Mechanism, a Study of Homogeneous Chemical Reactions*, 2nd edn (Wiley, New York, 1961)

244. GADZUK, J.W., HARTMAN, J.K. and RHODIN, T.N., *Phys. Rev.*, **B4**, 241 (1971)

245. GADZUK, J.W. and PLUMMER, E.W., in *Solid State Surface Science* (ed. M. Green), Vol.3, p.165 (Marcel Dekker, New York, 1973)

246. GAFNER, G., *Surface Sci.*, **2**, 534 (1964)

247. GARLAND, C.W., *J. Phys. Chem.*, **63**, 1423 (1959)

248. GARLAND, C.W., LORD, R.C. and TROIANO, P.F., *J. Phys. Chem.*, **69**, 1195 (1965)

249. GARNER, W.E. and VEAL, F.J., *J. Chem. Soc. (London)*, 1436 (1935)

250. GASSER, R.P.H., ROBERTS, K. and STEVENS, A.J., *Trans. Faraday Soc.*, **65**, 3105 (1969)

251. GASSER, R.P.H., ROBERTS, K. and STEVENS, A.J., *Surface Sci.*, **20**, 123 (1970)

252. GENTSCH, H., *Z. Physik. Chem. (Frankfurt/M.)*, **35**, 69 (1962); Dissertation, Technische Universität Hannover (1961)

253. GERLACH, J., Dissertation, Technische Universität Hannover (1962)

254. GERMER, L.H., *Surface Sci.*, **5**, 147 (1966)

255. GERMER, L.H. and MacRAE, A.U., *J. Chem. Phys.*, **36**, 1555 (1962)

256. GERMER, L.H. and MacRAE, A.U., *J. Chem. Phys.*, **37**, 1382 (1962)

257. GERMER, L.H., MacRAE, A.U. and HARTMANN, C.D., *J. Appl. Phys.*, **32**, 2432, (1961)

258. GERMER, L.H., MAY, J.W. and SZOSTAK, R.J., *Surface Sci.*, **7**, 430 (1967)

259. GERMER, L.H., SCHEIBNER, E.J. and HARTMANN, C.D., *Phil. Mag.*, **5**, 222 (1960)

260. GERRITSEN, A.N., in *Handbuch der Physik* (ed. S. Flügge), Vol.19, p.137 (Springer-Verlag, Berlin, 1956)

261. GERSON, F., *Hochauflösende ESR-Spektroskopie* (Verlag Chemie, Weinheim/Bergstra., 1967)

262. GESCHKE, D., Z. *Naturforsch.*, **23a**, 689 (1968)

263. GESCHKE, D., Z. *Physik. Chem. (Leipzig)*, **249**, 125 (1972)

264. GESCHKE, D. and PFEIFER, H., Z. *Physik. Chem. (Leipzig)*, **232**, 127 (1966)

265. GEUS, J.W., KOKS, H.L.T. and ZWIETERING, P., *J. Catalysis*, **2**, 274 (1963)

266. GEUS, J.W., NOBEL, A.P.P. and ZWIETERING, P., *J. Catalysis*, **1**, 8 (1962)

267. GLADKICH, N.T., NIEDERMAYER, R. and SPIEGEL, K., *Phys. Status Solidi*, **15**, 181 (1966)

268. GLAND, J.L. and SOMORJAI, G.A., *Surface Sci.*, **41**, 387 (1974)

269. GOFF, R.F. and SMITH, D.P., *J. Vacuum Sci. Technol.*, **7**, 72 (1970)

270. GOMER, R., *Advan. Catal.*, **7**, 93 (1955)

271. GOMER, R., *Disc. Faraday Soc.*, **41**, 14 (1966)

272. GOMER, R. and HULM, J.K., *J. Amer. Chem. Soc.*, **75**, 4114 (1953)

273. GOMER, R., WORTMAN, R. and LUNDY, R., *J. Chem. Phys.*, **26**, 1147 (1957)

274. GOOD, R.H. and MÜLLER, E.W., in *Handbuch der Physik* (ed. S. Flügge), Vol.21, p.176 (Springer-Verlag, Berlin, 1956)

275. GOODENOUGH, J.B., *Magnetism and the Chemical Bond* (Interscience, New York, 1963)

276. GOYMOUR, C.G. and KING, D.A., *J. Chem. Soc., Faraday I*, **69**, 736 (1973)

277. GREENLER, R.G., *J. Chem. Phys.*, **44**, 310 (1966)

278. GREGG, S.J. and SING, K.S.W., *Adsorption, Surface Area and Porosity* (Academic Press, London, 1967)

279. GRIMLEY, T.B., *Advan. Catal.*, **12**, 1 (1960)

280. GRIMLEY, T.B., *Proc. Phys. Soc.*, **90**, 751 (1967)

281. GRIMLEY, T.B., in *Molecular Processes on Solid Surfaces* (ed. E. Drauglis, R.D. Gretz and R.I. Jaffe), p.299 (McGraw-Hill, New York, 1969)

282. GRIMLEY, T.B., *Ber. Bunsenges. Physik. Chem.*, **75**, 1003 (1971)

283. GRIMLEY, T.B., *J. Vacuum Sci. Technol.*, **8**, 31 (1971)

284. GRIMLEY, T.B., in *Adsorption-Desorption Phenomena* (ed. F. Ricca), p.215 (Academic Press, London, 1972)

285. GRUBER, H.L., *J. Phys. Chem.*, **66**, 48 (1962)

286. GRUBER, H.L. and HAUSEN, A., *Kolloid Z.Z. Polym.*, **214**, 66 (1966)

287. GUNDRY, P.M., in *Actes du Deuxième Congrès International de Catalyse, Paris, 1960*, Vol.1, p.1083 (Edition Technip, Paris, 1961)

288. GURMANN, S.J. and PENDRY, J.B., *Phys. Rev. Lett.*, **31**, 687 (1973)

289. GYSAE, B. and WAGENER, S., Z. *Techn. Physik*, **19**, 264 (1938)

290. GYSAE, B. and WAGENER, S., *Z. Physik,* **115**, 296 (1940)
291. HAGSTRUM, H.D., *Phys. Rev.,* **96**, 336 (1954)
292. HAGSTRUM, H.D., *Phys. Rev.,* **122**, 83 (1961)
293. HAGSTRUM, H.D., *Phys. Rev.,* **150**, 495 (1966)
294. HAGSTRUM, H.D. and BECKER, G.E., *Phys. Rev.,* **159**, 572 (1967)
295. HAGSTRUM, H.D. and BECKER, G.E., *Phys. Rev. Lett.,* **22**, 1054 (1969)
296. HAGSTRUM, H.D. and BECKER, G.E., *J. Chem. Phys.,* **54**, 1015 (1971)
297. HAIR, M.L., *Infrared Spectroscopy in Surface Chemistry* (Marcel Dekker, New York, 1967)
298. HANSEN, N., *Vakuum-Technik,* **11**, 70 (1962)
299. HANSEN, N., *Nuovo Cimento Suppl.,* **5**, 389 (1967)
300. HANSEN, N.R. and HANEMAN, D., *Surface Sci.,* **2**, 566 (1964)
301. HANSEN, N. and LITTMANN, W., *Ber. Bunsenges. Physik. Chem.,* **67**, 970 (1963)
302. HANSEN, N. and LITTMANN, W., in *1965 Trans. 3rd Intern. Vacuum Congr.* (ed. H. Adam), Vol.2, Part 2, p.465 (Pergamon Press, Oxford, 1966)
303. HAQUE, C.A. and FARNSWORTH, H.E., *Surface Sci.,* **4**, 195 (1966)
304. HARDEVELD, R. VAN, in *Proc. 3rd Intern. Congr. Catalysis* (ed. W.M.H. Sachtler, G.C.A. Schuit and P. Zwietering), p.638 (North-Holland, Amsterdam, 1965)
305. HARRICK, N.J., *J. Phys. Chem.,* **64**, 1110 (1960)
306. HARROD, J.F., ROBERTS, R.W. and RISSMANN, E.F., *J. Phys. Chem.,* **71**, 343 (1967)
307. HAUFFE, K. and WOLKENSTEIN, Th. (Editors), *Electronic Phenomena in Chemisorption and Catalysis on Semiconductors,* Symp. No.2 of the 4th Intern. Congr. Catalysis, Moscow, 1968 (de Gruyter, Berlin, 1969)
308. HAUL, R. and BODDENBERG, B., in *The Porous Structure of Catalysts and the Role of Transport Processes in Heterogeneous Catalysis,* Symp. No.3 of the 4th Intern. Congr. Catalysis, Novosibirsk, 1968 (ed. G.K. Boreskov), p.309 (Akadémiai Kiadó, Budapest, 1972)
309. HAUSEN, A. and GRUBER, H.L., *J. Catalysis,* **20**, 97 (1971)
310. HAYEK, K., FARNSWORTH, H.E. and PARK, R.L., *Surface Sci.,* **10**, 429 (1968)
311. HAYWARD, D.O., in *Chemisorption and Reactions on Metallic Films* (ed. J.R. Anderson), Vol.1, p.259 (Academic Press, London, 1971)
312. HAYWARD, D.O., KING, D.A., TAYLOR, N. and TOMPKINS, F.C., *Nuovo Cimento Suppl.,* **5**, 374 (1967)
313. HAYWARD, D.O., KING, D.A. and TOMPKINS, F.C., *Chem. Commun.,* **9**, 178 (1965)
314. HAYWARD, D.O., KING, D.A. and TOMPKINS, F.C., *Proc. Roy. Soc. (London),* **A 197**, 321 (1967)
315. HAYWARD, D.O. and TAYLOR, N., *J. Sci. Instrum.,* **44**, 327 (1967)

316. HAYWARD, D.O. and TAYLOR, N., *Trans. Faraday Soc.*, **64**, 1904 (1968)

317. HAYWARD, D.O., TAYLOR, N. and TOMPKINS, F.C., *Disc. Faraday Soc.*, **41**, 75 (1966)

318. HAYWARD, D.O. and TRAPNELL, B.M.W., *Chemisorption*, 2nd edn (Butterworths, London, 1964)

319. HEAVENS, O.S., *Rep. Prog. Physics*, **23**, 1 (1960)

320. HEILAND, G., *Fortschr. Physik*, **9**, 393 (1961)

321. HEILAND, W., SCHÄFFLER, H.G. and TAGLAUER, E., *Surface Sci.*, **35**, 381 (1973)

322. HEILAND, W. and TAGLAUER, E., *J. Vacuum Sci. Technol.*, **9**, 620 (1972)

323. HERMANN, A., Dissertation, Technische Universität Hannover (1960)

324. HESS, P. and SCHULLER, D., *Z. Physik. Chem. (Frankfurt/M.)*, **62**, 320 (1968)

325. HEYNE, H. and TOMPKINS, F.C., *Trans. Faraday Soc.*, **63**, 1274 (1967)

326. HILL, M.P. and PETHICA, B.A., *J. Chem. Phys.*, **36**, 3095 (1962)

327. HILL, M.P. and PETHICA, B.A., *J. Chem. Phys.*, **38**, 567 (1963)

328. HILL, T.L., *J. Chem. Phys.*, **17**, 507, (1949)

329. HILL, T.L., *J. Chem. Phys.*, **17**, 520 (1949)

330. HILL, T.L., *J. Chem. Phys.*, **18**, 246 (1950)

331. HILL, T.L., *Trans. Faraday Soc.*, **47**, 376 (1951)

332. HILL, T.L., *Advan. Catal.*, **4**, 211 (1952)

333. HILL, T.L., *An Introduction to Statistical Thermodynamics* (Addison-Wesley, Reading, 1960)

334. HIROTA, K., KUWATA, K. and NAKAI, Y., *Bull. Chem. Soc. Japan*, **31**, 861 (1958)

335. HØJLUND NIELSEN, P.E., *Surface Sci.*, **35**, 194 (1973)

336. HOLLAND, L., *Vacuum Deposition of Thin Films* (Chapman and Hall, London, 1956)

337. HOLSCHER, A.A., *J. Chem. Phys.*, **41**, 579 (1964)

338. HOLSCHER, A.A., Dissertation, Rijksuniversiteit Leiden (1967)

339. HOLSCHER, A.A. and SACHTLER, W.M.H., *Disc. Faraday Soc.*, **41**, 29 (1966)

340. HONIG, J.M., in *The Solid-Gas Interface* (ed. E.A. Flood), Vol.1, p.371 (Marcel Dekker, New York, 1967)

341. HONIG, R.E., in *Advances in Mass Spectrometry* (ed. A.R. West), Vol.6, p.337 (Applied Science, Barking, 1974)

342. HONIG, R.E. and HARRINGTON, W.L., *Thin Solid Films*, **19**, 43 (1973)

343. HORGAN, A.M. and KING, D.A., in *Adsorption-Desorption Phenomena* (ed. F. Ricca), p.329 (Academic Press, London, 1972)

344. HOUSTON, J.E. and PARK, R.L., *J. Chem. Phys.*, **55**, 4601 (1971)

345. HUBER, E.E. and KIRK, C.T., *Surface Sci.*, **5**, 447 (1966)

346. HURD, C.M., *The Hall Effect in Metals and Alloys*, p.113 (Plenum Press, London, 1972)

347. INGHRAM, M. and GOMER, R., *Z. Naturforsch.*, **10a**, 863 (1955)
348. JACOBSON, P.E. and SELWOOD, P.W., *J. Amer. Chem. Soc.*, **76**, 2641 (1954)
349. JELEND, W. and MENZEL, D., *Chem. Phys. Lett.*, **21**, 178 (1973)
350. JELEND, W. and MENZEL, D., *Surface Sci.*, **40**, 295 (1973)
351. JELEND, W. and MENZEL, D., *Surface Sci.*, **42**, 485 (1974)
352. JOHNSON, D.L. and TAO, L.C., *Surface Sci.*, **16**, 390 (1969)
353. JONES, H., in *Handbuch der Physik* (ed. S. Flügge), Vol.19, p.227 (Springer-Verlag, Berlin, 1956)
354. JOYCE, B.A. and NEAVE, J.H., *Surface Sci.*, **34**, 401 (1973)
355. JUSTI, E., KOHLER, M. and LAUTZ, G., *Z. Naturforsch.*, **6a**, 544 (1951)
356. KAMBE, K., *Z. Naturforsch.*, **22a**, 322 (1967)
357. KAMINSKY, M., *Atomic and Ionic Impact Phenomena on Metal Surfaces* (Springer-Verlag, Berlin, 1965)
358. KAVTARADZE, N.N., *Dokl. Akad. Nauk SSSR*, **138**, 616 (1961)
359. KAVTARADZE, N.N. and SOKOLOVA, N.P., *Dokl. Akad. Nauk SSSR*, **146**, 1367 (1962)
360. KAVTARADZE, N.N. and SOKOLOVA, N.P., *Zh. Fiz. Khim.*, **36**, 2804 (1962)
361. KAVTARADZE, N.N. and SOKOLOVA, N.P., *Zh. Fiz. Khim.*, **38**, 1004 (1964)
362. KEIER, N.P. and ROGINSKII, S.Z., *Izv. Akad. Nauk SSSR, Otdel Khim. Nauk*, 27 (1950)
363. KEMBALL, C., *Advan. Catal.*, **2**, 233 (1950)
364. KING, D.A., *Surface Sci.*, **9**, 375, (1968)
365. KING, D.A., MADEY, T.E. and YATES, J.T. Jr., *J. Chem. Phys.*, **55**, 3236 (1971)
366. KING, D.A. and WELLS, M.G., *Surface Sci.*, **29**, 454 (1972)
367. KINGTON, G.L. and ASTON, J.G., *J. Phys. Chem.*, **73**, 1929 (1951)
368. KIRK, C.T. and HUBER, E.E., *Surface Sci.*, **9**, 217 (1968)
369. KISELEV, A.V., *Quart. Rev.*, **15**, 99 (1961)
370. KLEMPERER, D.F., *J. Appl. Phys.*, **33**, 1532 (1962)
371. KLEMPERER, D.F., in *Surface Area Determination*, Proc. Intern. Symp., Bristol, 1969 (ed. D.H. Everett and R.H. Ottewill), p.55 (Butterworths, London, 1970)
372. KLEMPERER, D.F., in *Chemisorption and Reactions on Metallic Films* (ed. J.R. Anderson), Vol.1, p.39 (Academic Press, London, 1971)
373. KLEMPERER, D.F. and SNAITH, J.C., *Ber. Bunsenges. Physik. Chem.*, **75**, 1078 (1971)
374. KLEMPERER, D.F. and SNAITH, J.C., *J. Phys. E, Sci. Instrum.*, **4**, 860 (1971)
375. KLEMPERER, D.F. and STONE, F.S., *Proc. Roy. Soc. (London)*, **A 243**, 375 (1957)
376. KLIER, K., *Catalysis Rev.*, **1**, 207 (1967)
377. KLIER, K., ZETTLEMOYER, A.C. and LEIDHEISER, H., *J. Chem. Phys.*, **52**, 589 (1970)

378. KNAPP, A.G., *Surface Sci.,* **34,** 289 (1973)
379. KNOR, Z. and PONEC, V., *Collect. Czech. Chem. Commun.,* **31,** 1172 (1966)
380. KNÖZINGER, H. and RESS, E., *Z. Physik. Chem. (Frankfurt/M.),* **59,** 49 (1968)
381. KOCK, H.G., Dissertation, Technische Universität Hannover (1967)
382. KODAMA, T., *J. Phys. D, Appl. Phys.,* **5,** 1160 (1972)
383. KOHLRAUSCH, F., *Praktische Physik,* Vol.2, p.379 (B.G. Teubner, Stuttgart, 1968)
384. KONISHI, R., MURATA, G. and KATO, S., *Surface Sci.,* **44,** 287 (1974)
385. KORTÜM, G., *Reflexionsspektroskopie* (Springer-Verlag, Berlin, 1969)
386. KORTÜM, G. and GRATHWOHL, M., *Ber. Bunsenges. Physik. Chem.,* **72,** 500 (1968)
387. KORTÜM, G. and KOFFER, H., *Ber. Bunsenges. Physik. Chem.,* **67,** 67 (1963)
388. KORTÜM, G. and VÖGELE, H., *Ber. Bunsenges. Physik. Chem.,* **72,** 401 (1968)
389. KÖSTER, W. and GMÖHLING, W., *Z. Metallkunde,* **52,** 713 (1961)
390. KOTTKE, M.L., GREENLER, R.G. and TOMPKINS, H.G., *Surface Sci.,* **32,** 231 (1972)
391. KOUTECKY, J., *Advan. Phys. Chem.,* **9,** 85 (1965)
392. KRAL, H., *Z. Physik. Chem. (Frankfurt/M.),* **61,** 225 (1960)
393. KRAL, H., *Z. Physik. Chem. (Frankfurt/M.),* **75,** 171 (1971)
394. KRAL, H., *Z. Physik. Chem. (Frankfurt/M.),* **76,** 287 (1971)
395. KRONAUER, P. and MENZEL, D., in *Adsorption-Desorption Phenomena* (ed. F. Ricca), p.313 (Academic Press, London, 1972)
396. KRUMME, J.P. and HABERKAMP, J., *Thin Solid Films,* **13,** 335 (1972)
397. KÜPPERS, J., *Surface Sci.,* **36,** 53 (1973)
398. KÜPPERS, J., CONRAD, H., ERTL, G. and LATTA, E.E., *Japan. J. Appl. Phys.,* Suppl.2, Part 2, 225 (1974)
399. LANDER, J.J. and MORRISON, J., *J. Chem. Phys.,* **37,** 729 (1962)
400. LANDER, J.J. and MORRISON, J., *J. Appl. Phys.,* **34,** 1403 and 1411 (1963)
401. LANDER, J.J. and MORRISON, J., *Surface Sci.,* **6,** 1 (1967)
402. LANDOLT-BÖRNSTEIN, *Zahlenwerte und Funktionen,* 6th edn, Vol.4, Part 2b, p.326 (Springer-Verlag, Berlin, 1964)
403. LANGE, W.J., *J. Vacuum Sci. Technol.,* **2,** 74 (1965)
404. LANGE, W.J. and RIEMERSMA, H., in *1961 Transactions of the American Vacuum Society* (ed. L.E. Preuss), Vol.1, p.167 (Pergamon Press, Oxford, 1962)
405. LANGER, D.W., in *Festkörperprobleme XIII, Advances in Solid State Physics* (ed. H.J. Queisser), p.193 (Pergamon Press, Oxford, and F. Vieweg, Braunschweig, 1973)
406. LANGMUIR, I., *J. Amer. Chem. Soc.,* **40,** 1361 (1918)
407. LAPUJOULADE, J. and NEIL, K.S., *C.R. Acad. Sci. Paris,* **273,** 725 (1971)
408. LAPUJOULADE, J. and NEIL, K.S., *J. Chem. Phys.,* **57,** 3535 (1972)

409. LAPUJOULADE, J. and NEIL, K.S., *J. Chim. Phys. Physicochim. Biol.*, **70**, 798 (1973)
410. LAPUJOULADE, J. and NEIL, K.S., *Surface Sci.*, **35**, 288 (1973)
411. LAZAROV, D., *Ann. Univ. Sofia, Fac. Physico-Math.*, **59**, 109 (1955)
412. LAZAROV, D. and BLIZNAKOV, G., *Z. Physik. Chem. (Leipzig)*, **233**, 255 (1966)
413. LAZAROV, D. and BLIZNAKOV, G., *C.R. Acad. Bulg. Sci.*, **20**, 341 (1967)
414. LEFTIN, H.P., *J. Phys. Chem.*, **64**, 1714 (1960)
415. LEFTIN, H.P., *Rev. Sci. Instrum.*, **32**, 1418 (1961)
416. LEFTIN, H.P. and HOBSON, M.C., *Advan. Catal.*, **14**, 115 (1963)
417. LEVINE, J.D. and GYFTOPOULOS, E.P., *Surface Sci.*, **1**, 171 (1964)
418. LIANG, S.C., *J. Appl. Phys.*, **22**, 148 (1951)
419. LIANG, S.C., *J. Phys. Chem.*, **56**, 660 (1952)
420. LIANG, S.C., *J. Phys. Chem.*, **57**, 910 (1953)
421. LIANG, S.C., *Canad. J. Chem.*, **33**, 279 (1955)
422. LICHTMAN, D., McQUISTAN, R.B. and KIRST, T.R., *Surface Sci.*, **5**, 120 (1966)
423. LIEBL, H.J. and HERZOG, R.F.K., *J. Appl. Phys.*, **34**, 2893 (1963)
424. LITTLE, L.H., *Infrared Spectra of Adsorbed Species* (Academic Press, London, 1966)
425. LITTLE, L.H., in *Chemisorption and Reactions on Metallic Films* (ed. J.R. Anderson), Vol.1, p.489 (Academic Press, London, 1971)
426. LÖSCHE, A., *Kerninduktion* (Deutscher Verlag der Wissenschaften, Berlin, 1957)
427. LUCCHESI, P.J., CARTER, J.L. and SINFELT, J.H., *J. Amer. Chem. Soc.*, **86**, 1494 (1964)
428. LUCCHESI, P.J., CARTER, J.L. and YATES, D.J.C., *J. Phys. Chem.*, **66**, 1451 (1962)
429. McCARROLL, B., *J. Chem. Phys.*, **46**, 863 (1967)
430. McCRACKIN, F.L., PASSAGLIA, E., STROMBERG, R.R. and STEINBERG, H.L., *J. Res. Natl. Bur. Stand.*, **67A**, 363 (1963).
431. MacDONALD, D.K.C., in *Handbuch der Physik* (ed. S. Flügge), Vol.14, p.147 (Springer-Verlag, Berlin, 1956)
432. McRAE, E.G., *J. Chem. Phys.*, **45**, 3258 (1966)
433. MADDEN, H.H. and ERTL, G., *Surface Sci.*, **35**, 211 (1973)
434. MADDEN, H.H. and FARNSWORTH, H.E., *J. Chem. Phys.*, **34**, 1186 (1961)
435. MADDEN, H.H., KÜPPERS, J. and ERTL, G., *J. Chem. Phys.*, **58**, 3401 (1973)
436. MADEY, T.E., *Surface Sci.*, **33**, 355 (1972)
437. MADEY, T.E., *Surface Sci.*, **36**, 281 (1973)
438. MADEY, T.E. and YATES, J.T. Jr., *J. Vacuum Sci. Technol.*, **8**, 39 (1971)
439. MADEY, T.E. and YATES, J.T. Jr., *J. Vacuum Sci. Technol.*, **8**, 525 (1971)

440. MADEY, T.E., YATES, J.T. Jr. and ERICKSON, N.E., *Chem. Phys. Lett.,* **19**, 487 (1973)

441. MADEY, T.E., YATES, J.T. Jr., KING, D.A. and UHLANER, C.J., *J. Chem. Phys.,* **52**, 5215 (1970)

442. MANES, L. and MOLINARI, E., *Z. Physik. Chem. (Frankfurt/M.),* **39**, 104 (1963)

442a. MANSFIELD, P., in *Progress in NMR Spectroscopy* (ed. J.W. Emsley, J. Feeney and L.H. Sutcliffe), Vol.8, p.41 (Pergamon Press, Oxford, 1972)

443. MANSOUR EL NABY, H., *Z. Physik,* **174**, 269 (1973)

444. MAYADAS, A.F., FEDER, R. and ROSENBERG, R., *J. Vacuum Sci. Technol.,* **6**, 690 (1969)

445. MAYADAS, A.F., SHATZKES, M. and JANAK, J.F., *Appl. Phys. Lett.,* **14**, 345 (1969)

446. MAYER, H., *Physik Dünner Schichten,* Vol.1 (Wissenschaftliche Verlagsgesellschaft, Stuttgart, 1950)

447. MAYER, H., *Physik Dünner Schichten,* Vol.2 (Wissenschaftliche Verlagsgesellschaft, Stuttgart, 1951)

448. MAYER, H. and ST. V. AUFSCHNAITER, *Z. Physik,* **249**, 400 (1972)

449. MAYER, H. and BLANARU, L.D., *Z. Physik,* **249**, 424 (1972)

450. MAYER, H. and HIETEL, B., *Z. Physik,* **254**, 232 (1972)

451. MAYER, H., NIEDERMAYER, R., SCHROEN, W., STÜNKEL, D. and GÖHRE, H., in *Vacuum Microbalance Techniques* (ed. K.H. Behrndt), Vol.3, p.75 (Plenum Press, London, 1963)

452. MAYER, J.W. and TUROS, A., *Thin Solid Films,* **19**, 1 (1973)

453. MAYER, J.W. and ZIEGLER, J.F. (Editors), International Conference on Ion Beam Surface Layer Analysis, Yorktown Heights, New York, 1973, *Thin Solid Films,* **19** (1973)

454. MELMED, A.J., LAYER, H.P. and KRUGER, J., *Surface Sci.,* **9**, 476 (1968)

455. MENZEL, D., *Ber. Bunsenges. Physik. Chem.,* **72**, 591 (1968)

456. MENZEL, D., *Z. Naturforsch.,* **23a**, 330 (1968)

457. MENZEL, D., *Angew. Chem.,* **82**, 263 (1970); *Angew. Chem. Intern. Edn,* **9**, 255 (1970)

458. MENZEL, D., in *Proceedings of the International Conference on Solid Surfaces,* Madrid, 1973, pub. *Electron. Fis. Apli.,* **17**, 113 (1974)

459. MENZEL, D. and GOMER, R., *J. Chem. Phys.,* **40**, 1164 (1964)

460. MENZEL, D. and GOMER, R., *J. Chem. Phys.,* **41**, 3311 (1964)

461. MENZEL, D. and GOMER, R., *J. Chem. Phys.,* **41**, 3329 (1964)

462. MENZEL, D., KRONAUER, P. and JELAND, W., *Ber. Bunsenges. Physik. Chem.,* **75**, 1074 (1971)

463. MENZEL, E. and GEBHART, J., *Z. Physik,* **168**, 392 (1962)

464. MEYER, F. and BOOTSMA, G.A., *Surface Sci.,* **16**, 221 (1969)

465. MEYER, F., DE KLUIZENAAR, E.E. and BOOTSMA, G.A., *Surface Sci.,* **27**, 88 (1971)

466. MEYER, F. and MORABITO, J.M., *J. Phys. Chem.,* **75**, 2922 (1971)

467. MEYER, F. and SPARNAAY, M.J., *Symp. Faraday Soc.*, No.4, 17 (1970)
468. MICHEL, D., *Z. Naturforsch.*, **22a**, 1751 (1967)
469. MICHEL, D., *Z. Naturforsch.*, **23a**, 339 (1968)
470. MICHEL, D., *Z. Physik. Chem. (Leipzig)*, **252**, 263 (1973)
471. MICHEL, D., *Surface Sci.*, **42**, 453 (1974)
472. MICHEL, D., MEILER, W. and HOPPACH, D., *Z. Physik. Chem. (Leipzig)*, **255**, 509 (1974)
473. MIGNOLET, J.C.P., *Disc. Faraday Soc.*, **8**, 105 (1950)
474. MIGNOLET, J.C.P., *Disc. Faraday Soc.*, **8**, 326 (1950)
475. MILLER, A.R., *The Adsorption of Gases on Solids*, p.57 (Cambridge University Press, Cambridge, 1949)
476. MIYAKE, S. and HAYAKAWA, K., *J. Phys. Soc. Japan*, **21**, 363 (1966)
477. MIZUSHIMA, Y., *J. Phys. Soc. Japan*, **15**, 1614 (1960)
478. MOESTA, H., *Chemisorption und Ionisation in Metall-Metall-Systemen* (Springer-Verlag, Berlin, 1968)
479. MOESTA, H. and BREUER, H.D., *Naturwissenschaften*, **55**, 650 (1968)
480. MOESTA, H., BREUER, H.D. and TRAPPEN, N., *Ber. Bunsenges. Physik. Chem.*, **73**, 879 (1969)
481. MÖNCH, G.C., *Neues und Bewährtes aus der Hochvakuumtechnik* (VEB Wilhelm Knapp Verlag, Halle, 1959)
482. MOORE, G.E., *J. Appl. Phys,*, **32**, 1241 (1961)
483. MOORE, G.E. and ALLISON, H.W., *J. Chem. Phys.*, **23**, 1609 (1955)
484. MOORE, G.E. and UNTERWALD, F.C., *J. Chem. Phys.*, **40**, 2626 (1964)
485. MORRISON, J.A., DRAIN, L.E. and DRUGDALE, J.S., *Canad. J. Chem.*, **30**, 890 (1952)
486. MORRISON, J.A. and LOS, J.M., *Disc. Faraday Soc.*, **8**, 321 (1950)
487. MOTT, N.F. and JONES, H., *The Theory of the Properties of Metals and Alloys* (Oxford University Press, Oxford, 1936)
488. MULAIRE, W.M. and PERIA, W.T., *Surface Sci.*, **26**, 125 (1971)
489. MÜLLER, A. and BENNINGHOVEN, A., *Surface Sci.*, **39**, 427 (1973)
490. MÜLLER, A. and BENNINGHOVEN, A., *Surface Sci.*, **41**, 493 (1974)
491. MÜLLER, E.W., *Z. Physik*, **106**, 541 (1937)
492. MÜLLER, E.W., *Naturwissenschaften*, **29**, 533 (1941)
493. MÜLLER, E.W., *Z. Physik*, **120**, 26 (1943)
494. MÜLLER, E.W., *Z. Physik*, **131**, 136 (1951)
495. MÜLLER, E.W., *Z. Elektrochem., Ber. Bunsenges. Physik. Chem.*, **59**, 372 (1955)
496. MÜLLER, E.W., *J. Appl. Phys.*, **28**, 1 (1957)
497. MÜLLER, E.W., *Ann. Rev. Phys. Chem.*, **18**, 35 (1967)
498. MÜLLER, E.W., NAKAMURA, S., NISHIKAWA, D. and McLANE, S.B., *J. Appl. Phys.*, **36**, 2496 (1965)
499. MÜLLER, E.W., PANITZ, J.A. and McLANE, S.B., *Rev. Sci. Instrum.*, **39**, 83 (1968)
500. MÜLLER, H., *Z. Physik. Chem. (Leipzig)*, **248**, 152 (1971)

218   *References*

501. MÜLLER, H., *Z. Physik. Chem. (Leipzig)*, **249**, 1 (1972)
502. MÜLLER, K., *Z. Physik*, **195**, 105 (1966)
503. MÜLLER, K. and VIEFHAUS, H., *Z. Naturforsch.*, **21a**, 1726 (1966)
504. MULLER, R.H., *Surface Sci.*, **16**, 14 (1969)
505. MULLER, R.H., in *Advances in Electrochemistry and Electrochemical Engineering* (ed. R.H. Muller), Vol.9, p.167 (Wiley, New York, 1973)
506. MURGULESCU, I.G. and COMSA, G., *Rev. Roum. Chimie*, **11**, 1253 (1966)
507. MURGULESCU, I.G. and COMSA, G., in *Proc. 2nd Colloquium on Thin Films*, p.466 (Akadémiai Kiadó, Budapest, 1967)
508. MURGULESCU, I.G. and IONESCU, N.I., *Rev. Roum. Chimie*, **11**, · 1267 (1966)
509. NAKATA, T. and MATSUSHITA, S., *J. Catalysis*, **4**, 631 (1965)
510. NASH, C.P. and DE SIENO, R.P., *J. Phys. Chem.*, **69**, 2139 (1965)
511. NEUGEBAUER, C.A., *Z. Angew. Physik*, **14**, 182 (1962)
512. NEUGEBAUER, C.A., NEWKIRK, J.B. and VERMILYEA, D.A. (Editors), *Structure and Properties of Thin Films* (Wiley, New York, 1959)
513. NEUGEBAUER, C.A. and WEBB, M.B,, *J. Appl. Phys.*, **33**, 74 (1962)
514. NEWNS, D.M., *Phys. Rev. Lett.*, **25**, 1575 (1970)
515. NIEDERMAYER, R. and MAYER, H. (Editors), *Grundprobleme der Physik Dünner Schichten* (Vandenhoeck and Ruprecht, Göttingen, 1966)
516. NIEUWENHUYS, B.E. and SACHTLER, W.M.H., *Surface Sci.*, **34**, 317 (1973)
517. NILSSON, P.O. and KANSKI, J., *Surface Sci.*, **37**, 700 (1973)
518. NISHIJIMA, M. and PROBST, F.M., *Phys. Rev.*, **B2**, 2368 (1970)
519. NISHIKAWA, O. and MÜLLER, E.W., *J. Appl. Phys.*, **38**, 3159 (1967)
520. NORDHEIM, L., *Proc. Roy. Soc. (London)*, **A 121**, 626 (1928)
521. NOVOTNY, D.B., *J. Vacuum Sci. Technol.*, **9**, 1447 (1972)
522. OLDHAM, W.G., *Surface Sci.*, **16**, 97 (1969)
523. ONCHI, M. and FARNSWORTH, H.E., *Surface Sci.*, **11**, 203 (1968)
524. O'NEILL, C.E. and YATES, D.J.C., *J. Phys. Chem.*, **65**, 901 (1961)
525. ORR, W.J.C., *Trans. Faraday Soc.*, **35**, 1247 (1939)
526. ORT, W., *Z. Physik*, **163**, 230 (1961)
527. OTTER, M., *Z. Physik*, **161**, 163 (1961)
528. PACE, E.L., in *The Solid-Gas Interface* (ed. E.A. Flood), Vol.1, p.105 (Marcel Dekker, New York, 1966)
529. PAIK, W.K. and BOCKRIS, J.O 'M., *Surface Sci.*, **28**, 61 (1971)
530. PALMBERG, P.W., *Surface Sci.*, **25**, 598 (1971)
531. PALMER, R.L., SMITH, Joe N. Jr., SALTSBURG, H. and O'KEEFE, D.R., *J. Chem. Phys.*, **53**, 1666 (1970)
532. PANCHENKO, O.A., LUTSISKIN, P.P., PTUSHINSKII, Y.G. and SHISHKOV, V.V., *Surface Sci.*, **34**, 187 (1973)
533. PAPP, H., Diplomarbeit, Universität Erlangen-Nürnberg (1969)
534. PARIISKII, G.B. and KAZANSKII, V.B., *Kinetika i Kataliz (Moscow)*, **5**, 96 (1964)

535. PARK, R.L. and FARNSWORTH, H.E., *J. Chem. Phys.*, **40**, 2354 (1964)
536. PARK, R.L. and FARNSWORTH, H.E., *Surface Sci.*, **2**, 527 (1964)
537. PARK, R.L. and FARNSWORTH, H.E., *J. Chem. Phys.*, **43**, 2351 (1965)
538. PARK, R.L. and HOUSTON, J.E., *Surface Sci.*, **26**, 664 (1971)
539. PARK, R.L. and HOUSTON, J.E., *J. Vacuum Sci. Technol.*, **11**, 1 (1974)
540. PARK, R.L., HOUSTON, J.E. and SCHREINER, D.G., *Rev. Sci. Instrum.*, **41**, 1810 (1970)
541. PARKYNS, N.D. and PATRICK, J.B., *J. Sci. Instrum.*, **43**, 695 (1966)
542. PASSAGLIA, E., STROMBERG, R.R. and KRÜGER, J. (Editors), *Ellipsometry in the Measurement of Surfaces and Thin Films,* Natl. Bur. Standards, Misc. Publ. 256 (U.S. Govt. Printing Office, Washington, 1964)
543. PAUL, W. and STEINWEDEL, H., *Z. Naturforsch.*, **8a**, 448 (1953)
544. PAULING, L., *Proc. Roy. Soc. (London)*, **A 126**, 343 (1949)
545. PAULING, L., *The Nature of the Chemical Bond*, 3rd edn (Cornell University Press, Ithaca, N.Y., 1960)
546. PAULY, L., PETMECKY, H.W. and SCHMIDT, C., *Z. Angew. Physik,* **19**, 207 (1965)
547. PENTENEVO, A., *Catalysis Rev.*, **5**, 199 (1972)
548. PERI, J.B., *Disc. Faraday Soc.*, **41**, 121 (1966)
549. PÉTERMANN, L.A., in *Progress in Surface Science* (ed. S.G. Davison), Vol.3, p.1 (Pergamon Press, Oxford, 1973)
550. PFEIFER, H., in *NMR Basic Principles and Progress* (ed. P. Diehl, E. Fluck and R. Kosfeld), Vo.7, p.53 (Springer-Verlag, Berlin, 1972)
551. PICKERING, H.L. and ECKSTROM, H.C., *J. Phys. Chem.*, **63**, 512 (1959)
551a. PINES, A., GIBBY, M.G. and WAUGH, J.S., *J. Chem. Phys.*, **56**, 1776 (1972)
552. PLISKIN, W.A. and EISCHENS, R.P., *J. Phys. Chem.*, **59**, 1156 (1955)
553. PLISKIN, W.A. and EISCHENS, R.P., *J. Chem. Phys.*, **24**, 482 (1956)
554. PLISKIN, W.A. and EISCHENS, R.P., *Z. Physik. Chem. (Frankfurt/M.)*, **24**, 11 (1960)
555. POHL, R.W., *Einführung in die Optik* (Springer-Verlag, Berlin, 1948)
556. PONEC, V. and KNOR, Z., *Collect. Czech. Chem. Commun.*, **25**, 2913 (1960)
557. PONEC, V., KNOR, Z. and CERNÝ, S., *Collect. Czech. Chem. Commun.*, **29**, 3031 (1964)
558. PONEC, V., KNOR, Z. and CERNÝ, S., *Collect. Czech. Chem. Commun.*, **30**, 208 (1965)
559. PONEC, V., KNOR, Z. and CERNÝ, S., *J. Catalysis*, **4**, 485 (1965)
560. POWELL, C.E., OXLEY, J.H. and BLOCHER, J.M. Jr. (Editors), *Vapor Deposition* (Wiley, New York, 1966)
561. PRITCHARD, J., *Nature*, **184**, 38 (1962)

562. PRITCHARD, J., *Trans. Faraday Soc.*, **59**, 437 (1963)
563. PRITCHARD, J. and SIMS, M.L., *Trans. Faraday Soc.*, **66**, 427 (1970)
564. QUINN, C.M. and ROBERTS, M.W., *J. Chem. Phys.*, **40**, 237 (1964)
565. REDHEAD, P.A., *Trans. Faraday Soc.*, **57**, 641 (1961)
566. REDHEAD, P.A., *Vacuum*, **12**, 203 (1962)
567. REDHEAD, P.A., *J. Chem. Phys.*, **38**, 566 (1963)
568. REDHEAD, P.A., *Canad. J. Phys.*, **42**, 886 (1964)
569. REDHEAD, P.A., *Nuovo Cimento Suppl.*, **5**, 586 (1967)
570. REDHEAD, P.A., HOBSON, J.P. and KORNELSEN, E.V., *The Physical Basis of Ultrahigh Vacuum* (Chapman and Hall, London, 1968)
571. RHODIN, T.N., in *Reactivity of Solids*, Proc. 7th Intern. Symp. on the Reactivity of Solids (ed. J.S. Anderson, M.W. Roberts and F.S. Stone), Bristol, 1972, p.651 (Chapman and Hall, London, 1972)
572. RICCA, F. and BELLARDO, A., *Z. Physik. Chem. (Frankfurt/M.)*, **52**, 318 (1967)
573. RICCA, F., MEDENA, R. and BELLARDO, A., *Gazz. Chim. Ital.*, **97**, 623 (1967)
574. RICCA, F., MEDENA, R. and SAINI, G., *Trans. Faraday Soc.*, **61**, 1492 (1965)
575. RIDEAL, E. and SWEETT, F., *Proc. Roy. Soc. (London)*, **A 257**, 291 (1960)
576. RIENÄCKER, G., in *Proc. 4th Intern. Congr. Catalysis, Moscow, 1968*, Vol.1, p.537 (Akadémiai Kiadó, Budapest, 1971)
577. RIENÄCKER, G., VÖLTER, J. and ENGELS, S., *Z. Chem.*, **10**, 321 (1970)
578. RIVIÈRE, J.C., *Contemp. Phys.*, **14**, 513 (1973)
579. ROBENS, E. and SANDSTEDE, G., *Z. Instrumentenkunde*, **75**, 167 (1967)
580. ROBERTS, J.D., *Nuclear Magnetic Resonance* (McGraw-Hill, New York, 1959)
581. ROBERTS, M.W., in *Specialist Periodical Report, Surface and Defect Properties of Solids* (ed. M.W. Roberts and J.M. Thomas), Vol.1, p.144 (The Chemical Society, London, 1972)
582. RON, A., FOLMAN, M. and SCHNEPP, D., *J. Chem. Phys.*, **36**, 2449 (1962)
583. ROOTSAERT, W.J.M., VAN REIJEN, L.L. and SACHTLER, W.M.H., *J. Catalysis*, **1**, 416 (1962)
584. ROSS, S. and OLIVER, J.P., *On Physical Adsorption* (Interscience, New York, 1964)
585. RÜHL, W., *Z. Physik*, **159**, 428 (1960)
586. RÜHL, W., *Z. Physik*, **176**, 409 (1963)
587. SACHTLER, W.M.H., *Angew. Chem.*, **80**, 673 (1968)
588. SACHTLER, W.M.H., *Le Vide*, **164**, 67 (1973)
589. SACHTLER, W.M.H. and DORGELO, G.J.H., *Bull. Soc. Chim. Belgique*, **67**, 465 (1958)
590. SACHTLER, W.M.H. and DORGELO, G.J.H., *Z. Physik. Chem. (Frankfurt/M.)*, **25**, 69 (1960)

591. SAVCHENKO, V.I. and BORESKOV, G.K., *Kinetika i Kataliz (Moscow)*, **9**, 142 (1968)
592. SCHMIDT, L.D., *Catalysis Rev.*, **9**, 115 (1974)
593. SCHÖN, G., *Surface Sci.*, **35**, 96 (1973)
594. SCHÖN, G., *Acta Chem. Scand.*, **27**, 2623 (1973)
595. SCHÖN, G. and LUNDIN, S.T., *J. Electron Spectrosc.*, **1**, 105 (1972/73)
596. SCHRIEFFER, J.R. and GOMER, R., *Surface Sci.*, **25**, 315 (1971)
597. SCHUELER, D.G., *Surface Sci.*, **16**, 104 (1969)
598. SCHUIT, G.C.A. and DE BOER, N.H., *Rev. Trav. Chim. Pays-Bas*, **72**, 909 (1953)
599. SCHUIT, G.C.A., DE BOER, N.H., DORGELO, G.J.H. and VAN REIJEN, L.L., in *Chemisorption* (ed. W.E. Garner), p.39 (Butterworths, London, 1957)
600. SCHUIT, G.C.A. and VAN REIJEN, L.L., *Advan. Catal.*, **10**, 242 (1958)
601. SCHWAB, G.M. and DERLETH, H., *Z. Physik. Chem. (Frankfurt/M.)* **53**, 1 (1967)
602. SCHWAB, G.M. and SIEGERT, R., *Z. Physik. Chem. (Frankfurt/M.)* **50**, 191 (1966)
603. SEGALL, B., *Phys. Rev. Lett.*, **7**, 154 (1961)
604. SEGALL, B., *Phys. Rev.*, **125**, 109 (1962)
605. SELWOOD, P.W., *J. Amer. Chem. Soc.*, **78**, 3893 (1956)
606. SELWOOD, P.W., *Chemisorption and Magnetization* (Academic Press, New York, 1975). This book is a complete revision of SELWOOD, P.W., *Adsorption and Collective Paramagnetism* (Academic Press, New York, 1962)
607. SHEVCHIK, N.J., TEJEDA, J., CARDONA, M. and LANGER, D.W., *J. Physique*, **34**, C6 (1973)
608. SHKLYAREVSKII, I.N., EL-SHAZLY, A.F.A. and KOSTYNK, V.P., *Solid State Commun.*, **10**, 1045 (1972)
609. SHOPOV, D., ANDREEV, A. and PETKOV, D., *J. Catalysis*, **13**, 123 (1969)
610. SIDDIQI, M.M. and TOMPKINS, F.C., *Proc. Roy. Soc. (London)*, A **268**, 452 (1962)
611. SILVENT, J.A. and SELWOOD, P.W., *J. Amer. Chem. Soc.*, **83**, 1034 (1961)
612. SIMON, F.N., LICHTMAN, D. and KIRST, T.R., *Surface Sci.*, **12**, 299 (1968)
613. SIMON, H. and SUHRMANN, R., *Der lichtelektrische Effekt und seine Anwendungen*, 2nd edn (Springer-Verlag, Berlin, 1958)
614. SIVUKHIN, D.V., *Zh. Eksper. Teor. Fiz. SSSR*, **18**, 976 (1948)
615. SIVUKHIN, D.V., *Zh. Eksper. Teor. Fiz. SSSR*, **21**, 367 (1951)
616. SIVUKHIN, D.V., *Soviet Phys. - J.E.T.P.*, **3**, 269 (1956)
617. SLICHTER, C.P., *Principles of Magnetic Resonance* (Harper and Row, New York, 1963)
618. SMITH, A.W. and QUETS, J.M., *J. Catalysis*, **4**, 163 (1965)
619. SMITH, D.P., *Surface Sci.*, **25**, 171 (1971)
620. SMITH, G.F., *Phys. Rev.*, **94**, 295 (1954)

621. SMITH, W.H., ECKSTROM, H.C. and BÄR, F., *J. Phys. Chem.*, **72**, 369 (1968)
622. SMUTEK, M., *Vacuum*, **24**, 173 (1974)
623. SOMMER, H., THOMAS, H.A. and HIPPLE, J.A., *Phys. Rev.*, **82**, 697 (1951)
624. SOMORJAI, G.A., *Surface Sci.*, **34**, 156 (1973)
625. SONDHEIMER, E.H., *Advan. Physics*, **1**, 1 (1952)
626. SOSZKA, W., *Surface Sci.*, **36**, 48 (1973)
627. SOSZKA, W., *Surface Sci.*, **36**, 714 (1973)
628. SPARNAAY, M.J., VAN BOMMEL, A.J. and VAN TOOREN, A., *Surface Sci.*, **39**, 251 (1973)
629. SPIEGEL, K., *Surface Sci.*, **7**, 125 (1967)
630. SQUIRES, R.G. and PARRAVANO, G., *J. Catalysis*, **2**, 324 (1963)
631. SROUBEK, Z., *Surface Sci.*, **44**, 47 (1974)
632. STEELE, W.A., in *The Solid-Gas Interface* (ed. E.A. Flood), Vol.1, p.307 (Marcel Dekker, New York, 1967)
633. STEFFEN, H. and MAYER, H., *Z. Physik*, **254**, 250 (1972)
634. STEIGER, R.F., MORABITO, J.M., SOMORJAI, G.A. and MULLER, R.H., *Surface Sci.*, **14**, 279 (1969)
635. STEVENSON, D.P., *J. Chem. Phys.*, **23**, 203 (1955)
636. STRACHAN, C.S., *Proc. Cambridge Phil. Soc.*, **29**, 116 (1933)
637. STREHLOW, H., *Magnetische Kernresonanz und Chemische Struktur* (Steinkopff, Darmstadt, 1962)
638. STROTHENK, H., Diplomarbeit, Technische Universität Hannover (1961)
639. SUHRMANN, R., *Z. Elektrochem., Ber. Bunsenges. Physik. Chem.*, **60**, 804 (1956)
640. SUHRMANN, R., BUSSE, H.J. and WEDLER, G., *Z. Physik. Chem. (Frankfurt/M.)*, **47**, 1 (1965)
641. SUHRMANN, R., BUSSE, H.J. and WEDLER, G., *Z. Physik. Chem. (Leipzig)*, **229**, 10 (1965)
642. SUHRMANN, R., GERDES, R. and WEDLER, G., *Z. Naturforsch.*, **18a**, 1208 (1963)
643. SUHRMANN, R., HAHN, B. and WEDLER, G., *Naturwissenschaften*, **44**, 60 (1957)
644. SUHRMANN, R., HERAS, J.M., VISCIDO DE HERAS, L. and WEDLER, G., *Ber. Bunsenges. Physik. Chem.*, **68**, 511 (1964)
645. SUHRMANN, R., HERAS, J.M., VISCIDO DE HERAS, L. and WEDLER, G., *Ber. Bunsenges. Physik. Chem.*, **68**, 990 (1964)
646. SUHRMANN, R., HERMANN, A. and WEDLER, G., *Z. Physik. Chem. (Frankfurt/M.)*, **35**, 155 (1962)
647. SUHRMANN, R., HEYNE, H.J. and WEDLER, G., *J. Catalysis*, **1**, 208 (1962)
648. SUHRMANN, R., KERN, D. and WEDLER, G., *Z. Physik. Chem. (Frankfurt/M.)*, **36**, 165 (1963)
649. SUHRMANN, R., KRÜGER, G. and WEDLER, G., *Z. Physik. Chem. (Frankfurt/M.)*, **30**, 1 (1961)
650. SUHRMANN, R., MIZUSHIMA, Y., HERMANN, A. and WEDLER, G., *Z. Physik. Chem. (Frankfurt/M.)*, **20**, 332 (1959)

651. SUHRMANN, R., OBER, H. and WEDLER, G., *Z. Physik. Chem. (Frankfurt/M.)*, **29**, 305 (1961)

652. SUHRMANN, R., SCHUMICKI, G. and WEDLER, G., *Z. Physik. Chem. (Frankfurt/M.)*, **42**, 187 (1964)

653. SUHRMANN, R. and WEDLER, G., *Z. Physik. Chem. (Frankfurt/M.)*, **10**, 184 (1957)

654. SUHRMANN, R. and WEDLER, G., *Z. Elektrochem., Ber. Bunsenges. Physik. Chem.*, **63**, 748 (1959)

655. SUHRMANN, R., WEDLER, G. and SCHUMICKI, G., in *Structure and Properties of Thin Films* (ed. C.A. Neugebauer, J.B. Newkirk and D.A. Vermilyea), p.268 (Wiley, New York, 1959)

656. SUURMEIJER, E.P.Th.M. and BOERS, A.L., *J. Phys. E, Sci. Instrum.*, **4**, 663 (1971)

657. SUURMEIJER, E.P.Th.M. and BOERS, A.L., *Surface Sci.*, **43**, 309 (1973)

658. TAMM, P.W. and SCHMIDT, L.D., *J. Chem. Phys.*, **52**, 1150 (1970)

659. TAYLOR, N. and CREASY, R., in *Adsorption-Desorption Phenomena* (ed. F. Ricca), p.297 (Academic Press, London, 1972)

660. TEMKIN, M.J. and PUZHEV, V., *Acta Physicochim. URSS*, **12**, 327 (1940)

661. TERENIN, A. and ROEV, L., *Spectrochim. Acta (London)*, **15**, 946 (1959)

662. THOMAS, J.M. and THOMAS, W.J., *Introduction to the Principles of Heterogeneous Catalysis* (Academic Press, London, 1967)

663. THORPE, B.J., *Surface Sci.*, **33**, 306 (1972)

664. TOMLIN, S.G., *J. Phys. D, Appl. Phys.*, **1**, 1667 (1968)

665. TOMPKINS, H.G. and GREENLER, R.G., *Surface Sci.*, **28**, 194 (1971)

666. TOYA, T., *J. Res. Inst. Catalysis, Hokkaido Univ.*, **9**, 134 (1961)

667. TRACY, J.C., *J. Chem. Phys.*, **56**, 2736 (1972)

668. TRACY, J.C., *J. Chem. Phys.*, **56**, 2748 (1972)

669. TUCKER, C.W., *J. Appl. Phys.*, **35**, 1897 (1964)

670. VAN LAAR, J. and SCHEER, J.J., *Philips Res. Rep.*, **17**, 101 (1962)

671. VAN OOSTROM, A.G.J., *Philips Res. Rep. Suppl. No.1* (1966)

672. VAN OOSTROM, A., *J. Chem. Phys.*, **47**, 761 (1967)

673. VAŠICEK, A., *Optics of Thin Films* (North-Holland, Amsterdam, 1960)

674. VILESOV, F. and TERENIN, A., *Naturwissenschaften*, **46**, 167 (1959)

675. VÖLTER, J. and PROCOP, M., *Z. Physik. Chem. (Leipzig)*, **249**, 344 (1972)

676. VOOK, R.W. and WITT, F., *J. Appl. Phys.*, **36**, 2169 (1965)

677. VOOK, R.W. and WITT, F., *J. Vacuum Sci. Technol.*, **2**, 49 (1965)

678. VOOK, R.W. and WITT, F., *J. Vacuum Sci. Technol.*, **2**, 243 (1965)

679. WACLAWSKI, B.J. and PLUMMER, E.W., *Phys. Rev. Lett.*, **29**, 783 (1972)

680. WACLAWSKI, B.J. and PLUMMER, E.W., *J. Vacuum Sci. Technol.*, **10**, 292 (1973)

681. WAHBA, M. and KEMBALL, C., *Trans. Faraday Soc.*, **49**, 1351 (1953)

682. WARD, L., NAG, A. and DIXON, L.C.W., *J. Phys. D, Appl. Phys.*, **2**, 301 (1969)

683. WATANABE, K. and YAMASHINA, T., *J. Catalysis,* **17,** 272 (1970)
684. WEDLER, G., *Z. Physik. Chem. (Frankfurt/M.),* **24,** 73 (1960)
685. WEDLER, G., *Z. Physik. Chem. (Frankfurt/M.),* **27,** 388 (1961)
686. WEDLER, G., *Disc. Faraday Soc.,* **41,** 104 (1966)
687. WEDLER, G., *Disc. Faraday Soc.,* **41,** 108 (1966)
688. WEDLER, G. and BORGMANN, D., *Ber. Bunsenges. Physik. Chem.,* **78,** 67 (1974)
689. WEDLER, G. and BORGMANN, D., *J. Catalysis,* in press
690. WEDLER, G., BORGMANN, D. and GEUSS, H.P., *Surface Sci.,* **47,** 592 (1975)
691. WEDLER, G. and BRÖCKER, F.J., *Surface Sci.,* **26,** 454 (1971)
692. WEDLER, G. and FISCH, G., *Ber. Bunsenges. Physik. Chem.,* **76,** 1160 (1972)
693. WEDLER, G., FISCH, G. and PAPP, H., *Ber. Bunsenges. Physik. Chem.,* **74,** 187 (1970)
694. WEDLER, G. and FOUAD, M., *Z. Physik. Chem. (Frankfurt/M.),* **40,** 1 (1964)
695. WEDLER, G. and FOUAD, M., *Z. Physik. Chem. (Frankfurt/M.),* **40,** 12 (1964)
696. WEDLER, G. and GEUSS, H.P. (in preparation)
697. WEDLER, G. and PAPP, H., *Z. Physik. Chem. (Frankfurt/M.),* **82,** 195 (1972)
698. WEDLER, G., PAPP, H. and SCHROLL, G., *Surface Sci.,* **44,** 463 (1974)
699. WEDLER, G., PAPP, H. and SCHROLL, G., *J. Catalysis,* **38,** 153 (1975)
700. WEDLER, G., REICHENBERGER, H. and WENZEL, H., *Z. Naturforsch.,* **26a,** 1452 (1971)
701. WEDLER, G. and SANTELMANN, G., *Ber. Bunsenges. Physik. Chem.,* **75,** 1026 (1971)
702. WEDLER, G. and SCHROLL, G., *Z. Physik. Chem. (Frankfurt/M.),* **85,** 216 (1973)
703. WEDLER, G. and STROTHENK, H., *Ber. Bunsenges. Physik. Chem.,* **70,** 214 (1966)
704. WEDLER, G., WENZEL, H., REICHENBERGER, H., WISSMANN, P. and WÖLFING, C., *Ber. Bunsenges. Physik. Chem.,* **75,** 1033 (1971)
705. WEDLER, G. and WIEBAUER, W., *Thin Solid Films,* **28,** 65 (1975)
706. WEDLER, G. and WISSMANN, P., *Thin Solid Films,* **2,** 391 (1968)
707. WEDLER, G. and WISSMANN, P., *Z. Naturforsch.,* **23a,** 1537 (1968)
708. WEDLER, G. and WISSMANN, P., *Z. Naturforsch.,* **23a,** 1544 (1968)
709. WEDLER, G. and WISSMANN, P., *Surface Sci.,* **26,** 389 (1971)
710. WEINBERG, W.H. and MERRILL, R.P., *Surface Sci.,* **33,** 493 (1972)
711. WEINBERG, W.H. and MERRILL, R.P., *Surface Sci.,* **39,** 206 (1973)
712. WEISS, P. and FORRER, R., *Ann. Physik,* **5,** 153 (1926)
713. WERNER, H.W. and DE GREFTE, H.A.M., *Surface Sci.,* **35,** 458 (1973)
714. WHALLEY, L., DAVIS, B.J. and MOSS, R.L., *Trans. Faraday Soc.,* **66,** 3143 (1970)
715. WHEATLEY, G.H. and CALDWELL, C.W. Jr., *Rev. Sci. Instrum.,* **44,** 744 (1973)

716. WHITE, C.W., SIMMS, D.L. and TOLK, N.H., *Science (N.Y.)*, **177**, 481 (1972)
717. WIEBAUER, W., Dissertation, Universität Erlangen-Nürnberg (1974)
718. WINTER, E.R.S., *Advan. Catal.*, **10**, 196 (1958)
719. WISSMANN, P., *Thin Solid Films*, **5**, 329 (1970)
720. WISSMANN, P., *Thin Solid Films*, **6**, R 67 (1970)
721. WISSMANN, P., *Z. Physik. Chem. (Frankfurt/M.)*, **71**, 294 (1970)
722. WISSMANN, P. and SUMMA, Y., *Vakuum-Technik*, **22**, 116 (1973)
723. WOJCIECHOWSKI, K.F., in *Progress in Surface Science* (ed. S.G. Davison), Vol.1, p.65 (Pergamon Press, Oxford, 1972)
724. WOJCIECHOWSKI, K.F., *Surface Sci.*, **36**, 689 (1973)
725. WOOD, E.A., *J. Appl. Phys.*, **35**, 1306 (1964)
726. WORTMANN, R., GOMER, R. and LUNDY, R., *J. Chem. Phys.*, **27**, 1099 (1957)
727. YAMAGUCHI, T., YOSHIDA, S. and KINBARA, A., *J. Opt. Soc. Amer.*, **62**, 634 (1972)
728. YAMAGUCHI, T., YOSHIDA, S. and KINBARA, A., *Thin Solid Films*, **18**, 63 (1973)
729. YANG, A.C. and GARLAND, C.W., *J. Phys. Chem.*, **61**, 1504 (1957)
730. YATES, D.J.C. and JUCCHESI, P.J., *J. Phys. Chem.*, **67**, 1197 (1963)
731. YATES, J.T. Jr., *Surface Sci.*, **38**, 114 (1973)
732. YATES, J.T. Jr., GREENLER, R.G., RATAJCZYKOWA, J. and KING, D.A., *Surface Sci.*, **36**, 739 (1973)
733. YATES, J.T. and KING, D.A., *Surface Sci.*, **30**, 601 (1972)
734. YATES, J.T. and MADEY, T.E., *J. Chem. Phys.*, **43**, 1055 (1965)
735. YATES, J.T. Jr., MADEY, T.E. and ERICKSON, N.E., *Surface Sci.*, **43**, 257 (1974)
736. YATES, J.T., MADEY, T.E. and PAYN, J.K., *Nuovo Cimento Suppl.*, **5**, 558 (1967)
737. YOUNG, D.M. and CROWELL, A.D., *Physical Adsorption of Gases* (Butterworths, London, 1962)
738. ZECCHINA, A., VERSINO, C., APPIANO, A. and OCCHIENA, G., *J. Phys. Chem.*, **72**, 1471 (1968)
739. ZELDOVICH, J., *Acta Physicochim. SSSR*, **1**, 961 (1934)
740. ZIMAN, J.M., *Electrons and Phonons* (Clarendon Press, Oxford, 1960)
741. ZIMAN, J.M., *Phys. Rev.*, **121**, 1320 (1961)
742. ZIMAN, J.M., *Principles of the Theory of Solids* (Cambridge University Press, Cambridge, 1971)
743. ZUEHLKE, R.W., SKIBBA, M. and GOTTLIEB, C., *J. Phys. Chem.*, **72**, 1425 (1968)
744. ZWIETERING, P., KOKS, H.L.T. and VAN HEERDEN, C., *J. Phys. Chem. Solids*, **11**, 18 (1959)

INDEX OF ADSORPTION SYSTEMS ACCORDING TO ADSORBATE

N.B.   A/B denotes an adsorption system; A-B denotes a mixed phase.

INDEX OF ADSORPTION SYSTEMS ACCORDING TO ADSORBENT

N.B. A/B denotes an adsorption system; A-B denotes a mixed phase.

SUBJECT INDEX

249755

249725

LIBRARY OF THE UNIVERSITY OF CALIFORNIA • BERKELEY